Sandra Vaisicca

Henry Van Engen
Maurice L. Hartung
Harold C. Trimble
Emil J. Berger
Ray W. Cleveland
A. B. Evenson

Seeing through mathematics

Book 1, part 1

W. J. Gage Limited
Toronto

This is Part 1 of the seventh book of
The Basic Mathematics Program, published
by Scott, Foresman and Company,
and edited for use in Canadian schools
by W. J. Gage Limited.

The authors of this book are:
Henry Van Engen, Professor of Education and
Mathematics, University of Wisconsin;
Maurice L. Hartung, Professor of Education,
University of Chicago;
Harold C. Trimble, Head of the Department of
Mathematics, State College of Iowa;
Emil J. Berger, Coordinator of Mathematics,
St. Paul Public Schools, St. Paul, Minnesota;
Ray W. Cleveland, Supervisor of Elementary and
Secondary Mathematics, Rahway Public Schools,
Rahway, New Jersey;
A. B. Evenson, General Supervisor, Senior High
Schools, Edmonton Public Schools,
Edmonton, Alberta.

The following persons served as consultants
in preparing this book:
E. Glenadine Gibb, Professor of Mathematics,
State College of Iowa;
Nick Lovdjieff, Teacher of Mathematics, Susan B.
Anthony Junior High School, Minneapolis, Minnesota;
Warren A. Parnell, Mathematics Instructor, Northeast
Intermediate School, Midland, Michigan;
Wayne H. Peterson, Head of the Department of
Mathematics, Marcus Whitman Junior High School,
Seattle, Washington;
James E. Stochl, Instructor, College of Education,
University of Minnesota;
Ray Walch, Director of Mathematics, K-12, Public
Schools, Westport, Connecticut;
Willa Catherine Ware, Mathematics Teacher, Louisville
Board of Education, Louisville, Kentucky.

This book was prepared by the editorial staff under
the direction of George E. Russell, Directing
Editor of The Basic Mathematics Program, and
Clarence E. Olander, Associate Mathematics Editor.
This book was designed by William Nicoll
and illustrated by Paul Hazelrigg.

Printed and bound in Canada.

Contents of Book 1

The work in *Seeing Through Mathematics, Book 1*, is organized in eight units. Units 1 through 5 are contained in Part 1. Units 6, 7, and 8 are contained in Part 2. The eight units are:

Contents of Book 1 part 1

The organization of the work included in each unit is shown in a panel on the first page of each unit.

We live in a world of change. Every day the newspapers and news commentators report new developments in this breath-taking space age. New products, new methods of communication, new ways of travelling, and new scientific discoveries are being developed daily. Many of these modern miracles have been made possible because of new applications for mathematics in electronic computation, nuclear energy, rocketry, and space travel.

Not all of mathematics, however, is immediately concerned with such applications. Many mathematicians are interested in the way mathematics is constructed; they find beauty in the patterns they discover, much as the musician finds beauty in the patterns of music and the artist finds beauty in the patterns of art.

To give you the skills you need for applied mathematics is, of course, one of the purposes of this book. But an equally important purpose is to introduce you to the world of mathematical ideas and patterns.

In Part 1 of *Seeing Through Mathematics, Book 1*, you will learn about special words and symbols that are used to communicate in mathematics; about new uses for numbers; about points, lines, and planes and the ways in which they are related; about patterns and reasoning in mathematics. The ideas presented in many of the lessons will be new and different to you, but they are exciting and they are not difficult. We have planned the book so that you can discover many of these ideas for yourself.

You will use only the natural numbers—that is, 0, 1, 2, and so on—as you examine ideas and solve problems in Part 1. The geometry in Part 1 gives you an introduction to some of the properties of geometric figures.

In Part 2, you will consider some of the ideas and problems from Part 1 again, but in Part 2 you will use rational numbers as well as the natural numbers. You will also learn a great deal more about geometry in Part 2.

We enjoyed planning this book. Often we argued for hours about one idea. Sometimes we ended a day tired and still not sure of the best way to present the idea we had in mind.

We wanted to pass along some of the ideas of mathematicians to you. And so we were tempted just to tell you about mathematics. But then we remembered that it is more fun to do mathematics than to read about it or listen while someone else explains it. Since we enjoyed the arguments we had while we were planning this book, we felt that we should make the book in such a way that you could have the same fun with mathematics as we had. That is why we decided to ask you questions rather than to tell you answers. We think that by answering questions for yourself, you will learn more mathematics—and learn it better—than by studying answers to questions.

We hope that you will find the lessons in Part 1 stimulating and thought-provoking. We know that your understanding of the mathematical ideas will give you a sound introduction to the entire field of mathematics. For we have planned this part of the book as the first stage in your career as a student of mathematics. It is our wish that this career will be a long and fruitful one.

THE AUTHORS

Unit 1

Sets, conditions, and variables

1 1 Exploring ideas

Sentences and placeholders

Throughout your work in mathematics, you will find that certain important ideas are used over and over again. Some of these ideas are explained in this lesson.

Examine the information card shown in D1. ("D1" means "display 1.") Each semester the mathematics teachers in Logan School ask each of their students to fill out a card like the one shown in D1.

A Each blank on the card calls for a special kind of information. Would it make sense for Steve Jones to write "Steve Jones" on the blank following "Age"?

B On which blanks is it correct to write the names of persons?

C The names of persons in one group are written on the blank following "Name." The names of persons in another group are written on the blank following "Mathematics teacher." How are these groups of persons different? Which group has more persons in it?

D Steve wrote "7" on his card after "Grade." Joe wrote "VII." How do you know that Steve and Joe are in the same grade? "7" and "VII" are names of the same number. Do you know any other names for the number seven?

The names of numbers are *numerals*.

nu mer al (nü′mər əl or nū′mər əl). A name of a number. The names 1, 15, 265, three, and V are examples of numerals.

In mathematics it is always important to know exactly what is being talked about. For example, it is important to know whether a number or a numeral is being talked about. Remember that a numeral is a name of a number. A number is an idea. A numeral is a name.

E Logan School has seven class periods a day. Joe wrote the numeral 8 on the blank after "Study period number" on his card. Why did his teacher, Miss Howe, ask him to correct his card?

F Suppose your teacher were to ask the students in your class to fill out a card like the card in D1. What numerals might they write on the blank following "Study period number"?

G Logan School has grades seven, eight, and nine only. What numerals would you expect to see on the blank following "Grade"?

H When you see "Name" on the card, you think of the sentence "My name is ~~~." What sentence do you think of when you see "Age" on the card?

I What sentence do you think of when you see "Favorite subject" on the card? What words might be written on the blank following "Favorite subject"?

Information card

LOGAN SCHOOL MATHEMATICS DEPARTMENT

Name.................................Age........

Birthday.......................................

Mathematics teacher............................

Mathematics period number......................

Study period number............................

Grade..

Favorite subject...............................

D1

Informal treatment of sentence, statement, placeholder, universe, and solution set

Now look at D2. This information came from twelve of the cards that Miss Howe's class turned in. You will need this information to explore some of the ideas in the exercises that follow.

J Read the sentence in D3. If you replace the letter x by the name Richard from D2, will you have sentence A in D4?

K Does sentence A in D4 express a true idea? Could you answer this question if you were unable to look at D2?

L When you replace the letter x by the name of each student listed in D2, you get the sentences in D4. Which sentences express true ideas? Which sentences express false ideas?

M In the sentence "x has a birthday in September," replace the letter x by your name. Does the sentence you obtain express a true idea? Does it express a false idea?

N Imagine that each student in your class has replaced the letter x in "x has a birthday in September" by his name. Will some sentences express true ideas? Will other sentences express false ideas?

Certain exercises in this book are labeled with a large question mark. Exercise O below is such an exercise. Try to answer these exercises without help. When you think you know the answer (or answers), turn to the answer section in the back of the book. The answers in this section will show you whether or not your thinking is correct. Do not turn to this section until you have tried to answer the question without help.

O ? In exercises K through N you have been deciding whether or not sentences express true ideas. Look again at the sentence in D3. Is it possible to decide whether the idea expressed by this sentence is true or false? How does the sentence in D3 differ from sentence A in D4?

Birthday Months
of
Some Students in Miss Howe's
Class

Richard	June
Mary	September
Louise	January
David	November
Susan	September
Joanne	July
Bill	August
Joe	May
Dale	February
Ellen	September
Sandra	April
Debra	December

D2

x has a birthday in September.

D3

A Richard has a birthday in September.
B Mary has a birthday in September.
C Louise has a birthday in September.
D David has a birthday in September.
E Susan has a birthday in September.
F Joanne has a birthday in September.
G Bill has a birthday in September.
H Joe has a birthday in September.
I Dale has a birthday in September.
J Ellen has a birthday in September.
K Sandra has a birthday in September.
L Debra has a birthday in September.

D4

P Look at D5. Is it possible to decide whether the idea expressed by this sentence is true or false? Explain your answer.

Q Suppose you replace the star symbol by each letter of the alphabet, in turn. Which of these replacements make sentences that express true ideas?

R How many replacements make sentences that express false ideas?

S Is it sensible to make any other replacements in the sentence besides the letters of the alphabet?

Now you will begin to use numerals as replacements in sentences. In this lesson and in many of the lessons that follow, the numerals that you use will be the names of the numbers 0, 1, 2, 3, 4, and so on.

A Read the sentence in D6. Is it possible to decide whether the idea expressed by this sentence is true or false? Explain your answer.

B Write the sentences you obtain when you replace the letter *n* in the sentence by a name for each of the first nine numbers. Be sure to include zero.

When you replace the letter *n* in the sentence "*n* is a number greater than 6," you replace it by a numeral. For example, you may use the numeral 5 as a replacement for the letter *n*.

C Examine each sentence you wrote for exercise B. Label it with "T" if it expresses a true idea. Label it with "F" if it expresses a false idea.

D Look at D7. Is it possible to decide whether the idea expressed by the sentence is true or false?

E In the sentence in D7, replace the letter *y* by the numeral 8. Does the sentence you obtain express a true idea? Now replace the letter *y* by the numeral VIII. Does the sentence you obtain express a true idea?

☆ is a letter in the word "mathematics."

D5

n is a number greater than 6.

D6

y is less than 1.

D7

s is greater than 6 and less than 10.

D8

F Does using a different name for the number ? change the idea expressed by the sentence from a false idea to a true idea?

G Suppose you replace the letter *y* by the numerals 1, 2, 3, and so on. Will you obtain any sentences that express true ideas?

H Now replace the letter *y* by the numeral 0. Does the sentence express a true idea?

I Do the replacements you use make a difference in the number of sentences you can make that express true ideas?

J Read the sentence in D8. Then make ten sentences by replacing the letter *s* by the numerals 1, 2, 3, 4, 5, 6, 7, 8, 9, and 10. Which of the numerals that you used made sentences that express true ideas?

K Suppose you replace the letter *s* by fraction numerals like $\frac{1}{2}$, $\frac{1}{3}$, $\frac{9}{8}$, $\frac{5}{4}$, and so on. Are there any fraction numerals that will make sentences that express true ideas?

L The sentence in D8 uses the letter *s* as a symbol in a special way. What other symbols have been used in this way in the sentences you have

> n is a number between 15 and 65.
>
> D9

place hold er (plās′hōl′dər). A symbol that holds the place for numerals or the names of things that are being talked about. ☆, x, n, and many other symbols may be used as placeholders.

been working with? Symbols used in this way in sentences are *placeholders*. What is the placeholder in the sentence "w is less than 14"?

M Read the sentence in D9. Is it possible to decide whether the idea expressed by the sentence is true or false?

N What is the placeholder in the sentence?

O Replace the placeholder in the sentence "n is a number between 15 and 65" by each of the following numerals: 10, 20, 30, 40, 50, 60, 70, 80, 90, and 100.

P Which of the numerals that you used in exercise O made sentences that express true ideas?

Q Which of the numerals that you used in exercise O made sentences that express false ideas?

Now you know that some sentences contain placeholders. You also know that when placeholders are replaced by names, you obtain sentences that express ideas that are either true or false, but not both true and false.

On your own

1 What symbol is used as a placeholder in the sentence below?

∗ writes with the left hand.

2 Choose the names of six students in your class. Then use each of these names in turn as a replacement for the placeholder in the sentence "∗ writes with the left hand." Write the six sentences you obtain.

3 Mark with a "T" each of your sentences that expresses a true idea.

4 Mark with an "F" each of your sentences that expresses a false idea.

5 If any of your sentences express true ideas, list the names of the students you used in these sentences.

For each sentence in exercises 6 through 9, follow the instructions you used for exercises 1 through 5.

6 z is a boy who wears glasses.

7 n is less than 17 years old.

8 ☆ plays an instrument in the school band.

9 x is more than 5 years old.

10 In the sentence "n is less than 5," replace the placeholder by each of the following numerals: 1, 2, 3, 4, 5, 6, 7, and 8.

11 Mark with a "T" each of your sentences that expresses a true idea.

12 Mark with an "F" each of your sentences that expresses a false idea.

13 List the numerals you used in the sentences that express true ideas.

For each sentence in exercises 14 through 19, follow the instructions you used in exercises 10 through 13.

14 x is an even number.

15 y is the number of days in the week.

16 w is greater than 7.

17 ~~~ is less than 12.

18 y is a number less than 8 or equal to 8.

19 z is an odd number.

20 In the sentence "x is the number of months in a year," replace the placeholder by each of the numerals 0, 1, 2, 3, 4, 5, 6, 7, and 8.

21 Do any of the sentences you made for exercise 20 express true ideas?

22 Suppose you replace the placeholder in the sentence "x is the number of months in a year" by the numeral 12. Does the sentence you obtain express a true idea?

1 2 **Exploring ideas**

Sets and subsets

The idea of a collection is very important in mathematics. In this lesson you will begin to see how this idea is used.

The picture shows several collections of objects. The plants make up one collection of objects. The books between book ends make up another collection. A collection of books, a collection of persons, or even a collection of numbers is a *set* of objects.

A What sets of objects besides the sets of plants and books do you see in the picture?

B How many pencils are in the set of writing instruments? How many pens are in the set of writing instruments?

C Are the books between book ends the only books in the picture? What other books belong to the set of books?

Think for a minute about the Logan School information card. Collections, or sets of objects, were discussed in connection with this card. The teachers in Logan School, the students in a mathematics class, the subjects taught, and the numerals used to identify the class periods make up sets of objects.

D D1 shows a sentence that you have worked with before. What set of objects did you use to get replacements for the placeholder in this sentence? If you do not remember, look again at page 6.

D1 x has a birthday in September.

E When you replaced the letter x by each of the names Mary, Susan, and Ellen, you made sentences that express true ideas. Do the names Mary, Susan, and Ellen form a set of names?

The set of objects whose names are used as replacements for the letter x in "x has a birthday in September" is a set of persons. In mathematics you will frequently use sets of numbers, sets of lines, sets of triangles, and so on. Such sets are sets of mathematical objects.

F What sets of objects do you see below?

G What objects belong to the set of baseball equipment? When an object belongs to a set, it is a *member* of the set.

H Is the football a member of the set of balls? Is the bowling ball a member of this set?

> **set** (set). A definite collection of objects. The students in your school, the numbers from 0 through 100, and the books in your classroom are examples of sets.

I How many members are in the set of objects that are used as a kind of club in games?

J How many members are in the set of gloves? How many members are in the set of boxing gloves? Is each member of the set of boxing gloves also a member of the set of gloves?

K How many members are in the set of objects used on ice or on snow? Are the ice skates members of this set? Is each member of the set of ice skates also a member of the set of

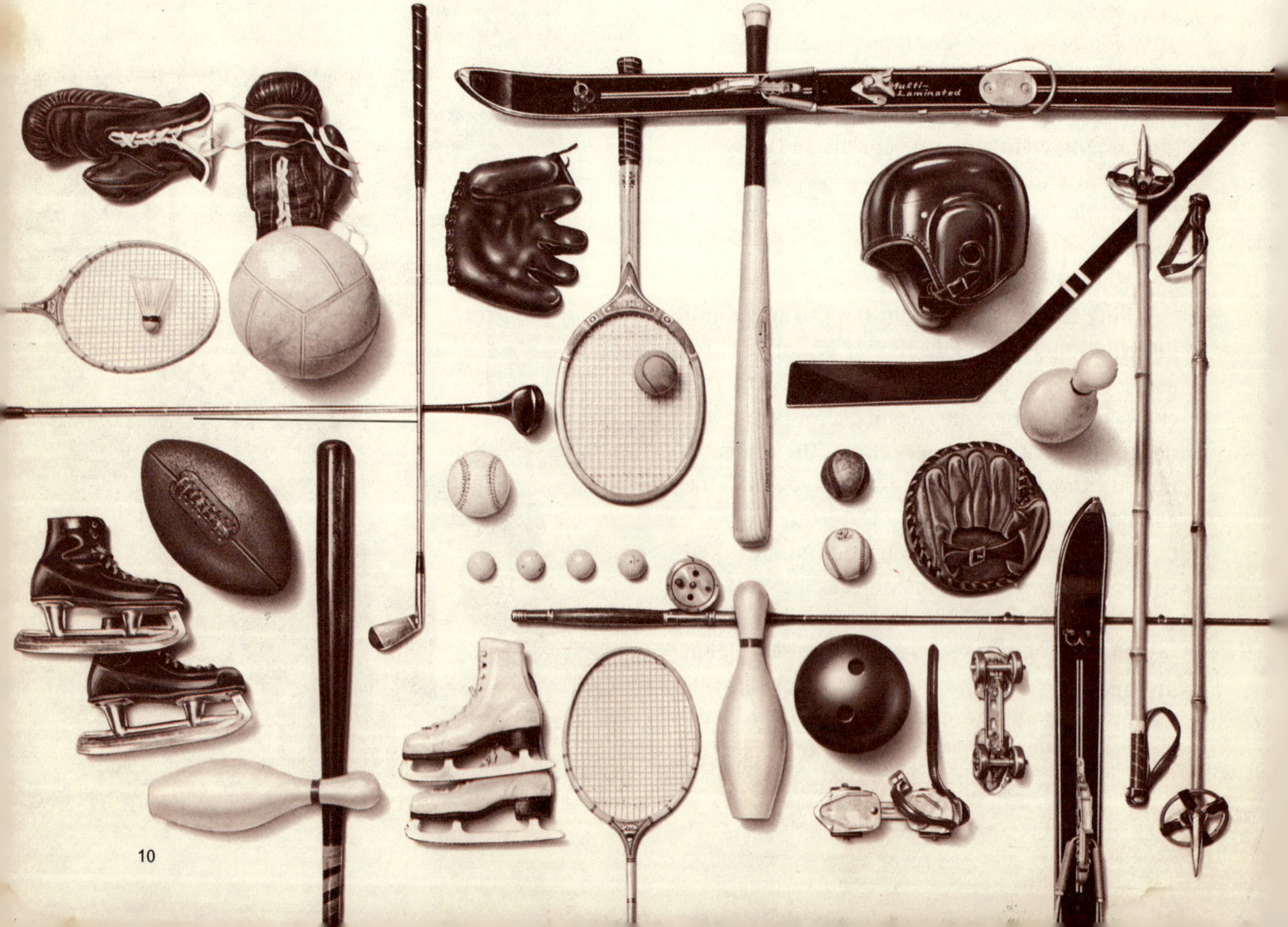

sub set (sub′set′). If each member of one set is also a member of a second set, then the first set is a subset of the second set. The set of cats is a subset of the set of animals; the set of numbers from 2 through 5 is a subset of the set of numbers from 0 through 10.

objects used on ice or on snow? The set of ice skates is a *subset* of the set of objects used on ice or on snow.

L Is each member of the set of numbers from 2 through 4 also a member of the set of numbers from 0 through 6? Is the set of numbers from 2 through 4 a subset of the set of numbers from 0 through 6?

M Is the set whose members are 2, 4, 6, and 8 a subset of the set of numbers from 1 through 10? Is the set whose members are 3, 5, 7, 9, and 11 a subset of the set of numbers from 1 through 10?

N Use the numerals from 1 through 10 as replacements for the letter *n* in the sentence "*n* is greater than 5 and less than 9." Which numerals make sentences that express true ideas?

O What are the members of the set of numbers that are greater than 5 and less than 9?

Suppose you want to talk about a set. You will need some way of making clear exactly what set you are talking about. One way would be to *describe* the set. You could describe one set by saying, "The set of students who have birthdays in September." You could describe another set by saying, "The set of numbers used in counting from 1 through 10." A description of a set must be so clear and definite that the listener or reader can tell exactly what objects belong to the set.

A Think about the set whose members are Mars, Venus, Earth, Jupiter, Saturn, Uranus, Pluto, Mercury, and Neptune. You can describe this set as "The set of known planets in our solar system." Now describe the set whose members are Sunday, Monday, Tuesday, Wednesday, Thursday, Friday, and Saturday.

B ? How would you describe the set whose members are 1, 3, 5, 7, and 9?

Another way to tell about a set is to list the names of its members. The members of the set described as "The set of Great Lakes" can be listed as shown in D2.

Notice that the names of the members of the set are listed between braces like those shown at the right. Listing the names of the members of a set between braces is called *tabulating* the set. The tabulation of a set can be spoken or written. From a tabulation you can decide what objects are members of the set.

{ }

C D2 shows how to read the tabulation of a set. Now read the tabulation that follows: {2, 4, 6, 8, 10}.

D Look at the tabulation of a set in D3. How would you describe the set tabulated in this display?

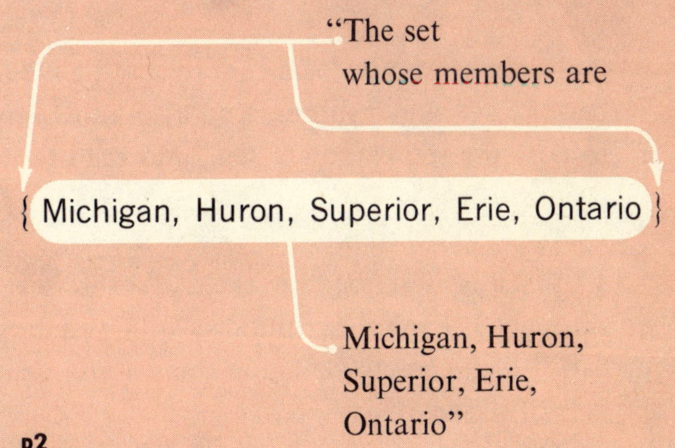

D2

{Huron, Superior, Michigan, Ontario, Erie}

D3

E Look at D4. Is the same set tabulated in three different ways? Explain your answer.

F Does changing the order in which you list the names of the members of a set change the membership of the set?

G D5 shows two tabulations. Are they tabulations of the same set? Read each tabulation.

H Now read each tabulation in exercises I through P.

I {June, January, July}

J {Tom, Bill, Jack, Ed, Ken}

K {w, x, y, z}

L {book, chair, desk}

M {1, 3, 5, 7, 9}

N {10, 20, 30, 40, 50}

O {99, 75, 16, 102, 115, 176}

P {11, 101, 1001, 10001}

Q Tabulate the set of students who sit in your row, or at your table.

R Tabulate the set of numbers from 50 through 60.

S Tabulate the set of even numbers from 50 through 60.

T Use the numerals from 1 through 12 as replacements for the letter *n* in the sentence "*n* is greater than 3 and less than 12." Tabulate the set of numbers greater than 3 and less than 12.

Now you know what is meant by a set, a member of a set, and a subset. You also know how to describe sets, tabulate sets, and read tabulations.

On your own

A set is described in each of exercises 1 through 5. Each description is followed by a list. Which objects named in the list are members of the set described?

1 The set of months of the year.

January	July	Halloween
Sunday	December	October
Autumn	May	Thursday

{John, Mary, Joe}

{Mary, Joe, John}

{Joe, John, Mary}

D4

{1, 2, 3, 4, 5, 6, 7, 8, 9, 10}

{3, 5, 6, 9, 10, 7, 8, 1, 2, 4}

D5

2 The set of Prime Ministers of Canada.

Sir John A. Macdonald	Mackenzie King
Thomas Edison	Maurice Richard
Louis St. Laurent	John Diefenbaker

3 The set of Canadian coins, each of which has a value that is less than one dollar.

nickel	franc	silver dollar
half dollar	dime	cent

4 The set of letters of the alphabet.

a b ☆ q 7 r

5 The set of even numbers from 0 through 10.

8 5 12 3 4 15

Describe each of the sets tabulated in exercises 6 through 13.

6 {North America, South America, Asia, Africa, Europe, Antarctica, Australia}

7 {September, April, June, November}

8 {British Columbia, Alberta, Saskatchewan, Manitoba}

9 {Halifax, Fredericton, Charlottetown}

10 {0, 1, 2, 3}

11 {1, 3, 5, 7, 9}

12 {21, 22, 23, 24, 25, 26, 27, 28, 29}

13 {52, 54, 56, 58}

14 Tabulate the set of measuring instruments shown in the picture on page 9.

15 Tabulate the set of football equipment shown in the picture on page 10.

16 Tabulate the set of fishing equipment shown in the picture on page 10.

1 3 Exploring ideas

Sentences, statements, and conditions

In this lesson you are going to learn about two kinds of sentences. You will learn that these sentences express ideas. You will see that there is a difference between ideas and the sentences that express ideas.

A Read each sentence in D1.

B Each sentence in D1 is made up of symbols. Do all the sentences use the same symbols? How do the four sentences differ?

C These four sentences are alike in one way. Each sentence expresses an idea. Sentence A expresses the idea that the number three is less than the number four. What idea does each of the other sentences express?

D Do all the sentences in D1 express the same idea? Does each of these sentences express a true idea?

E Write a sentence different from those in D1 ? but expressing the same idea as each of the sentences in D1.

F Now read each sentence in D2.

G Do all the sentences in D2 express the same idea? Does each sentence express a true idea? Does each sentence express a false idea?

Look again at D1. This display shows different sentences, all of which express the same true idea. Now look again at D2. This display shows different sentences, all of which express the same false idea. Sentences that express ideas, whether true or false, are *closed sentences*. Ideas that are expressed by closed sentences are *statements*.

Distinction between closed sentence and statement; between open sentence and condition; between placeholder and variable

D1

A 3 is less than 4.
B 3 is less than four.
C Three is less than four.
D III is less than IV.

D2

E 8 is greater than 12.
F Eight is greater than 12.
G Eight is greater than twelve.

D3

H 15 is less than 20.
I Fifteen is less than twenty.

D4

J 5 is greater than 9.
K V is greater than IX.

H Look at D3. Are two different closed sentences shown in D3? Explain your answer.

I Do both sentences in D3 express the same idea? Is the idea true?

A true idea that is expressed by a closed sentence is a *true statement*.

J Write a sentence different from those in D3 but expressing the same true statement as each of the sentences in D3.

K Now look at D4. Are two different closed sentences shown in the display? Explain your answer.

L Do both sentences in D4 express the same idea? Is the idea false?

A false idea that is expressed by a closed sentence is a *false statement*.

M Write a sentence different from those in D4 but expressing the same false statement as each of the sentences in D4.

N Now look at D5. Which of the sentences in D5 express the following statement: "The number nine is less than the number twenty"? Does each of these sentences express a true statement?

O What statement is expressed by each of the other sentences? Do these sentences express the same statement? Does each of these sentences express a true statement?

You have learned that closed sentences express either true ideas or false ideas. The ideas expressed by such sentences are statements. Now you will learn about other sentences and the ideas they express.

A Read sentence A in D6. Is it possible to decide whether the idea expressed by sentence A is a true idea or a false idea? Is sentence A a closed sentence? Explain your answer.

B Is sentence B a closed sentence? Explain your answer.

C Are there two different sentences in D6? What is the placeholder in sentence A? In sentence B?

L	9 is less than 1.
M	9 is less than 20.
N	IX is less than 20.
O	Nine is less than one.

D5

A	n is less than 8.
B	x is less than eight.

D6

The sum of 3 and n is less than 20.

D7

D Each sentence in D6 expresses an idea about numbers. In each sentence the idea expressed is a requirement. Sentence A expresses the requirement that each number you are to find must be less than eight. What requirement does sentence B express?

E Do both sentences in D6 express the same requirement? Does the sentence "y is less than $5 + 3$" also express this requirement? Sentences that express requirements about objects are *open sentences*.

F Write a sentence that expresses the same requirement as each of the sentences in D6. Is the sentence that you wrote an open sentence?

G You have learned about closed sentences and open sentences. Each kind of sentence expresses an idea. The idea expressed by a closed sentence is different from the idea expressed by an open sentence. Explain how these ideas differ.

H Now look at D7. Is the sentence in D7 an open sentence, or is it a closed sentence? The requirement expressed is that the sum of 3 and each replacement for n must be less than what number?

I Does the open sentence "$3 + n$ is less than twenty" express the same requirement as the sentence in D7?

When you see an open sentence like the one in D7, think of the requirement that the symbols express, and not of the symbols themselves. The requirement expressed by an open sentence is a *condition*.

J Now look at D8. Which sentences express the condition that each number you are to find must be less than eighteen?

K What condition does each of the other sentences in D8 express?

L Write an open sentence that expresses this condition: The number you are to find must be less than the sum of five and eleven.

C x is less than 18.

D y is greater than seventeen.

E n is greater than 17.

F r is less than eighteen.

D8

When you think about the condition expressed by an open sentence or the statement expressed by a closed sentence, you are not thinking about symbols on a page. You are thinking about ideas. When you read the sentence "3 is less than x," think about the condition that the sentence expresses and not about the symbols on the page. When you read the sentence "3 is less than 4," think about the statement about numbers and not about the symbols on the page.

In the condition "3 is less than x," the x is a *variable*. When a variable is mentioned in this book, remember that you are to think about an idea and not about the symbol that expresses the idea.

M The condition "y is less than 3" requires that each replacement for y be less than three. Should you think of y as a placeholder or as a variable?

In this lesson you have learned that the ideas expressed by closed sentences are statements. Statements may be true or they may be false. You also have learned that the ideas expressed by open sentences are conditions. Open sentences contain placeholders. Conditions involve variables.

On your own

In exercises 1 through 10, tell whether each closed sentence expresses a true statement or a false statement.

1 Lake Erie is one of the Great Lakes.

2 April is the first month of the year.

3 32 is less than 23.

4 $26 = 17 + 9$.

5 3×6 is greater than 5×3.

6 $45 \div 9 = 5$.

7 $4 + 7$ is less than $14 - 5$.

8 8×5 is greater than $42 \div 6$.

9 $7 \times 1 = 7$.

10 $14 + 0$ is greater than 7×2.

In exercises 11 through 25, tell whether each sentence is an open sentence or a closed sentence.

11 $n = 3 + 17$.

12 9 is less than fifteen.

13 3×20 is greater than 3×19.

14 $4 = 3 + 2$.

15 $5 \times m$ is greater than 24.

16 $28 \div 14 = w$.

17 $2 = 28 \div 14$.

18 $4 + 25$ is less than $35 - 12$.

19 19×32 equals x.

20 n is greater than $45 \div 9$.

21 Fourteen equals $13 + 1$.

22 $9 + 12 = 12 + 9$.

23 4×6 is less than $7 \times m$.

24 The sum of 19 and 8 equals 8×3.

25 $x + x$ is greater than 2.

26 Which sentences in exercises 11 through 25 express true statements? Which express false statements?

27 Which sentences in exercises 11 through 25 express conditions?

In exercises 28 through 35, tell what condition is expressed by each open sentence.

28 $4 + x$ equals 6.

29 n is less than 36.

30 $y - 17$ is greater than 5.

31 $10 + 5$ is less than y.

32 $3 + x$ equals 3.

33 25 is less than $x + 7$.

34 $8 \times 7 = 7 \times m$.

35 16 is greater than $18 - y$.

1 | 4 **Exploring ideas**

Sets, conditions, and equations

You have already learned about sets, conditions, and statements. In this lesson you will learn how members of sets are used to obtain statements from conditions.

A Look at the open sentence in D1. This display also shows how to read the sentence.

Now you will use the condition $x + 6 = 9$ to obtain statements. The condition is about numbers. Before you can obtain statements from the condition, you must have a set of numbers to use.

B A set of numbers is tabulated in D2. Read the tabulation. Describe this set.

$x + 6 = 9.$ — "x plus six equals nine."

D1

$\{1, 3, 5, 7, 9\}$

D2

$x + 6 = 9.$

A $1 + 6 = 9.$
B $3 + 6 = 9.$
C $5 + 6 = 9.$
D $7 + 6 = 9.$
E $9 + 6 = 9.$

D3

C Use each number in the set tabulated in D2 as a replacement for x in $x + 6 = 9$. How many statements do you obtain? Look at D3. Do the closed sentences in the display express these statements?

D Which statements expressed in D3 are true statements?

In the open sentence $x + 6 = 9$, the letter x is a placeholder. In lessons 1 and 2 you learned that placeholders in mathematical sentences are replaced by numerals. However, in the condition $x + 6 = 9$, you think of x as a variable. Variables are mentally replaced by numbers.

When a number is used as a replacement for a variable in a condition and a true statement is obtained, we say that the number *satisfies* the condition. If a false statement is obtained, the number does not satisfy the condition.

E Does the number 3 satisfy $x + 6 = 9$? How do you know?

F How do you know that each of the numbers 1, 5, 7, and 9 does not satisfy $x + 6 = 9$?

G Now think about what you have learned so far. What set did you use when you made replacements for the variable x in $x + 6 = 9$? The set whose members are used as replacements for the variable is the *universe* for the variable.

H Did you use $\{1, 3, 5, 7, 9\}$ as the universe for x in $x + 6 = 9$? How do you know?

I After you replaced x by each member of the universe, statements were obtained. How did you use the statements to find the number that satisfies the condition $x + 6 = 9$?

u ni verse (ū′nə vėrs). The set consisting of all the objects that can be used as replacements for the variable in a condition. $\{1, 3, 5, 7, 9\}$ and $\{0, 1, 2, 3, 4, 5, 6, 7, 8, 9, 10\}$ are sets that may be used as universes.

J Read the tabulation and the open sentence in D4.

K The set tabulated in D4 is the universe for n. Think of the statements expressed by the closed sentences in the display. How were these statements obtained from $12 - n = 8$? Which statements are true? Which are false?

L How many members of the universe satisfy $12 - n = 8$? How do you know?

M Read the tabulation of the universe and the open sentence in D5.

N Replace y by each member of the universe. Write the sentences that express the statements you obtain from $3 + y = 14$.

O How many members of the universe satisfy the condition? How do you know?

P Suppose that 11 is also a member of the universe for y. Does 11 satisfy the condition? How many members of the universe satisfy the condition now?

The symbols you use in mathematics are a short way of expressing ideas. To express the idea of equality, you write the symbol for equality (=). To express the number 3, you write the numeral 3.

To express the idea of "y multiplied by 3," or "3 times y," you write the symbol "$3y$." The symbol $3y$ is read "three y." $3y$ means that the number 3 and the number that replaces y have been multiplied.

When 5 is used to replace y, you can express the product by writing the symbol 3(5). The parentheses help to prevent confusion between the symbol 3(5) and the numeral 35. The symbol 3(5) expresses 3 times 5, or 15. The numeral 35 expresses the number 35. You can also use the times sign and write the symbol 3×5 instead of 3(5).

A Read each sentence in D6. Which sentences express conditions? How do you know?

$\{0, 1, 2, 3, 4\}$

$12 - n = 8.$

A $12 - 0 = 8.$
B $12 - 1 = 8.$
C $12 - 2 = 8.$
D $12 - 3 = 8.$
E $12 - 4 = 8.$

D4

$\{0, 2, 4, 6, 8\}$

$3 + y = 14.$

D5

A $3y = 12.$
B $6 - 2 = 4.$
C $x - 20 = 90.$
D $5(6) = 30.$
E $0 + 5 = 0.$
F $3 + n = 15.$

D6

e qua tion (i kwā′zhən). A true statement that includes the idea of equality. The statement $5(6) = 30$ is an equation. The statement $7 - 4 = 2$ is not an equation.

B Which sentences in D6 express statements?

C Does each of the statements include the idea of equality?

D The statement $5(6) = 30$ means that $5(6)$ is the same number as 30. Is $5(6) = 30$ a true statement?

E The statement $0 + 5 = 0$ means that $0 + 5$ is the same number as 0. Is $0 + 5 = 0$ a true statement?

True statements such as $5(6) = 30$ and $6 - 2 = 4$ are *equations*. False statements such as $0 + 5 = 0$ and $6 \div 3 = 3$ are not equations.

F Is $9 + 6 = 15$ an equation? Is $3(9) = 39$ an equation?

G Look again at D4. How many of the statements expressed in D4 are equations?

H Is $3y = 12$ an equation? Is $3(4) = 12$ an ? equation? Explain your answers.

I Read the tabulation of the universe and the open sentence in D7. Replace x by each member of the universe. Write the sentences that express the statements you obtain.

J Which statements are equations?

K Is $x + 5 = 8$ an equation? Did you use $x + 5 = 8$ in obtaining an equation?

A condition like $x + 5 = 8$ is a *condition for equality*. A condition that includes the idea of equality is a condition for equality. You obtain a statement from a condition for equality by replacing the variable by a member of the universe. If the statement is true, it is an equation.

L Tabulate the set of numbers that satisfy $x + 5 = 8$. Is the set you tabulated a subset of the universe?

M The universe is a set. The members of the universe that satisfy a condition also form a set. This set is the *solution set* of the condition. Is {3} the solution set of $x + 5 = 8$? How do you know?

N Now look at D8. Which sentence expresses a condition for equality? Which sentences express statements obtained from the condition?

O Tabulate the solution set of $2x + 1 = 7$. Is the set you tabulated a subset of the universe?

P Is the solution set of a condition always a ? subset of the universe? How do you know?

Now you know how to use the members of a universe to obtain statements from conditions for equality. You know that the members of the solution set are the replacements that make equations from conditions for equality.

> **solution set of a condition** (sə lü′shən). The set consisting of all members of the universe that satisfy the condition. If the universe is {0, 1, 2, 3, 4, 5}, then the solution set of $x + 2 = 2$ is {0}.

{0, 1, 2, 3, 4, 5}

$x + 5 = 8.$

D7

{0, 1, 2, 3, 4, 5}

$2x + 1 = 7.$

A $2(0) + 1 = 7.$	**D** $2(3) + 1 = 7.$
B $2(1) + 1 = 7.$	**E** $2(4) + 1 = 7.$
C $2(2) + 1 = 7.$	**F** $2(5) + 1 = 7.$

D8

On your own

Which of the sentences in exercises 1 through 14 express equations? Which express conditions for equality?

1 $0 + 3 = 3.$	**8** $25 = 5n.$
2 $14 - x = 9.$	**9** $2n = 6.$
3 $y - 7 = 8.$	**10** $3(7) = 20 + 1.$
4 $2(9) = 18.$	**11** $z - 4 = 13.$
5 $4n = 8.$	**12** $n + 2 = 9.$
6 $13 + x = 24.$	**13** $7(11) = 70 + 7.$
7 $5 = 9 - 4.$	**14** $54 = 9x.$

15 Use {1, 3, 5, 7, 9} as the universe for x in $3 + x = 10$. Write the sentences that express the statements you obtain. Write "T" after each sentence that expresses an equation.

16 Is $3 + x = 10$ a condition for equality? How do you know?

17 How do you know that {7} is the solution set of $3 + x = 10$?

For each condition expressed below, use {0, 5, 10, 15, 20} as the universe for the variable. Tabulate the solution set of each condition.

18 $2 + x = 12.$	**22** $5(4) = x.$
19 $16 = y + 6.$	**23** $y + 9 = 9.$
20 $3n = 15.$	**24** $20 - 10 = x.$
21 $31 - x = 16.$	**25** $60 = 4n.$

1 | 5 **Exploring ideas**

Sets, conditions, and inequalities

In this lesson you will learn about conditions that include ideas different from the idea of equality. You will obtain solution sets of this new kind of condition.

A The tabulation in D1 is one way to name a set. Think of the braces and the numerals together as a symbol for a set. Read the symbol in D1. Describe the set tabulated in the display.

After a set has been described or tabulated, it can be identified as set A, or set B, or set K, or set Y. This makes it unnecessary to use the description or the tabulation when you talk about the set. You may use any capital letter as a short name for a set. When a short name like A or B is used, it is important, of course, to keep the description or tabulation of the set in mind.

B The set tabulated in D2 is set K. Study D2.

C Now look at D3. Can the set tabulated here be called set A? The symbol for equality tells you that A and {10, 20, 30, 40, 50} are the same set. How do you read the sentence in D3?

D If M = {1, 2, 3}, and N = {1, 2, 3}, are M and N the same set?

We use the symbol for equality between names for the same object or idea. If M and N are the same set, we say M = N. Notice that equal sets have the same members.

E R = {7, 9, 11}. T = {9, 11, 7}. Is {7, 9, 11} **?** the same set as {9, 11, 7}? Does R = T?

F S = {13, 14, 15}, and T = {13, 14, 15, 13}. **?** Does S = T? Explain your answer.

G Look at D4. The set tabulated has been chosen as the universe for x in the condition "3 + x is greater than 6." What letter is used as a name of this universe?

The letter U is often used as a name of the universe.

H What numbers will you use as replacements for the variable in "3 + x is greater than 6"? Can you use any other numbers? Explain your answer.

I Does 3 satisfy the condition expressed in D4? Is 4 the only member of the universe that satisfies the condition? Explain your answers.

J Tabulate the solution set of the condition 3 + x is greater than 6. The solution set is a subset of what set?

You will learn many new symbols as you study mathematics. You have often used the symbol for equality. In this lesson you will use

{5, 6, 7, 8, 9, 10}

D1

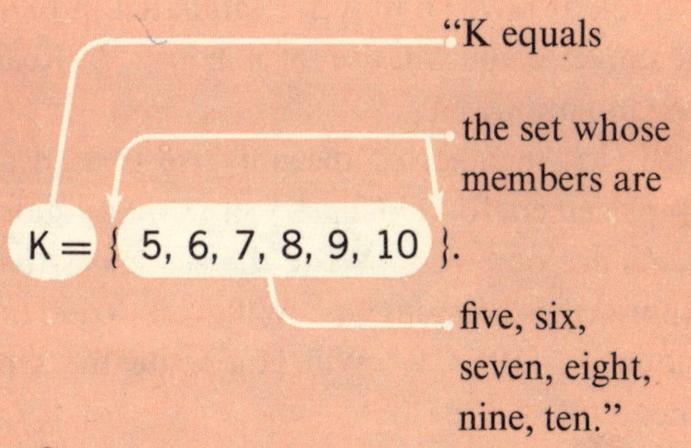

D2

A = {10, 20, 30, 40, 50}.

D3

U = {0, 1, 2, 3, 4, 5}.
3 + x is greater than 6.

D4

Using capital letters to name sets; conditions for inequality; inequalities; solution sets of conditions for inequality three new symbols. These symbols express ideas different from the idea of equality.

Mathematicians use the symbol at the right to express the idea of "greater than." Study D5. $>$

A Look at D6. Use the members of U as replacements for x in $x+2>6$. How many statements can you obtain from this condition? Do the sentences in D6 express all of these statements?

B How can you use the statements expressed in D6 to find the members of the universe that satisfy $x+2>6$?

C What is the name of the set of numbers that satisfy a condition? Tabulate this set for $x+2>6$.

D Can you use the condition $x+2>6$ to obtain an equation? Is $x+2>6$ a condition for equality?

The symbol at the right below resembles the symbol for "greater than," but it points in the opposite direction. This symbol is used to express the idea of "less than." Study D7. $<$

E Look at D8. The universe tabulated in D8 is the universe you will use for n in $2n<9$. Read the tabulation.

F If each member of the universe is used as a replacement for n in $2n<9$, how many statements are obtained? Write the sentences that express these statements. Will you write the sentence $2(10)<9$? Will you write the sentence $2(0)<9$?

G How many of the sentences that you wrote for exercise F express true statements? How can you use the statements expressed by the sentences you wrote to find the members of the universe that satisfy $2n<9$?

H Tabulate the solution set of the condition $2n<9$. How is the solution set related to the universe?

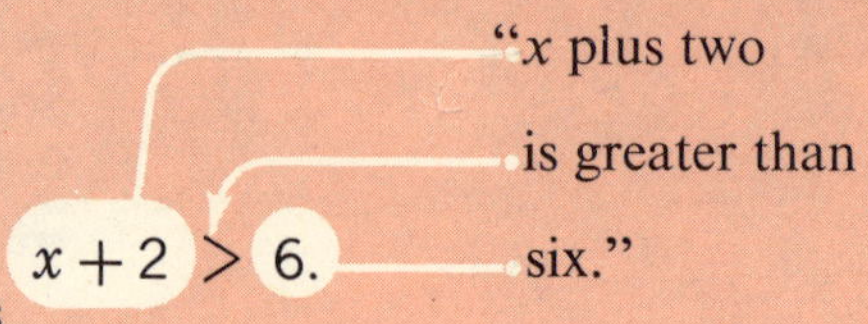

D5

$U = \{0, 1, 2, 3, 4, 5, 6\}.$

$x+2>6.$

A $0+2>6.$
B $1+2>6.$
C $2+2>6.$
D $3+2>6.$
E $4+2>6.$
F $5+2>6.$
G $6+2>6.$

D6

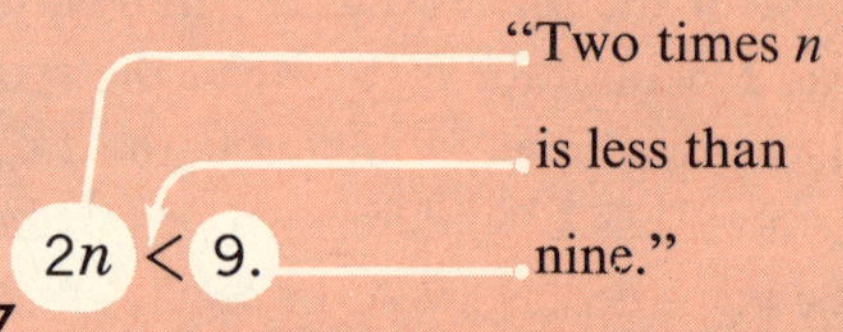

D7

$U = \{0, 1, 2, 3, 4, 5, 6, 7, 8, 9, 10\}.$

$2n<9.$

D8

$U = \{0, 1, 2, 3, 4, 5, 6, 7, 8\}.$

$y \neq 5.$

D9

I Can you use the condition $2n<9$ to obtain an equation? Is $2n<9$ a condition for equality?

J Now look at the open sentence in D9. Notice the symbol between the placeholder y and the numeral 5. How is this symbol different from the symbol for equality?

K The symbol used in D9 and shown at the right is used to express the idea of "not equal to." $\neq$
The condition expressed in D9 requires that each replacement for y be not equal to what number?

A $11 + 5 = 16$.
B $3 + 8 < 12$.
C $19 + 6 > 16$.
D $12 \neq 9$.
E $4 + 3 < 9$.
F $2(4) \neq 7$.
G $9 - 2 = 7$.
H $9(3) > 20$.

D10

$U = \{0, 1, 2, 3, 4, 5, 6, 7, 8, 9\}$.

$n + n < 15$.

D11

$U = \{0, 1, 2, 3, 4, 5, 6, 7, 8, 9\}$.

$n + n < 15$.

A $0 + 0 < 15$.
B $1 + 1 < 15$.
C $2 + 2 < 15$.
D $3 + 3 < 15$.
E $4 + 4 < 15$.
F $5 + 5 < 15$.
G $6 + 6 < 15$.
H $7 + 7 < 15$.
I $8 + 8 < 15$.
J $9 + 9 < 15$.

D12

L The universe that you are to use for y is tabulated in D9. What letter is used as a name of the universe?

M Using this universe, how many statements ? can you obtain from the condition $y \neq 5$? Are any of the statements equations? Is $y \neq 5$ a condition for equality?

N Is 5 a member of the solution set of $y \neq 5$? Explain your answer.

O Tabulate the solution set of $y \neq 5$.

P Now look at D10. Read each sentence. Does each sentence express a statement? How do you know? Which statements are true?

Q You have learned that an equation is a true statement that includes the idea of equality. Which sentences in D10 express equations?

R Look at sentence B in D10. Does the statement expressed by the sentence include the idea of "greater than," or "less than," or "not equal to," or equality? Is the statement true?

S Which of the ideas named in exercise R is used in the statement expressed by sentence C? Is the statement true?

A true statement that includes the idea of "greater than," or "less than," or "not equal to" is an *inequality*. A false statement that includes one of these three ideas is not an inequality.

T Which of the sentences in D10 express inequalities?

U Now you know that equations and inequalities are true statements. Is $3 + 5 = 8$ an inequality? Is $2 < 5$ an equation? Explain your answers.

V Look at D11. The universe for the variable n is tabulated in the display.

W How many times does the variable n occur in $n + n < 15$? When the same variable is used more than once in a condition, the same number must be used to replace the variable each time that the variable occurs.

X Look at D12. Do the sentences express the statements that result when the variable in $n + n < 15$ is replaced by each member of the universe?

Y Tabulate the solution set of $n + n < 15$.

Z Which sentences in D12 express inequalities?

Conditions like $n + n < 15$ and $n + 2 > 9$ are *conditions for inequality*. Conditions for inequality usually include the idea of "greater than," or "less than," or "not equal to." A

in e qual i ty (in′i kwol′ə ti). A true statement that includes the idea of "greater than," "less than," or "not equal to." The statements $3 < 5$, $5 > 3$, and $3 \neq 5$ are inequalities. The statements $3 > 5$, $5 + 2 = 7$, $9 < 6$, and $5 \neq 5$ are not inequalities.

statement is obtained from a condition for inequality by replacing the variable by a member of the universe. The statement that results, if true, is an inequality.

Now you know about the symbols that express inequalities. You know how to find the solution set of a condition for inequality. You know that the members of the solution set make inequalities from a condition for inequality.

On your own

Which of the following sentences express inequalities?

1 $3 < 7.$ **4** $9 > 7.$
2 $4(2) = 8.$ **5** $10 \neq 11.$
3 $3n < 10.$ **6** $17 < 15.$

Which of the following sentences express equations? Which express inequalities?

7 $20 + 5 = 25.$ **10** $14 = 16 - 2.$
8 $7 < 11 + 2.$ **11** $2(10) > 15.$
9 $14 \neq 2(8).$ **12** $10 - 9 < 3.$

In exercises 13 through 18, replace each wavy line by the symbol =, >, or < to make a sentence that expresses a true statement.

13 $5 + 2 \sim 7.$ **16** $3 \sim 8 - 5.$
14 $4 \sim 8 - 6.$ **17** $3 \times 5 \sim 14.$
15 $16 + 3 \sim 20.$ **18** $12 \sim 4(6).$

For each condition expressed in exercises 19 through 36, use {10, 9, 0, 6} as the universe for the variable. Tabulate the solution set of the condition.

19 $x + 3 > 5.$ **28** $x + 6 > 1.$
20 $4 + n = 10.$ **29** $4n = 40.$
21 $5y < 7.$ **30** $16 - x = 10.$
22 $z \neq 6.$ **31** $x < 6.$
23 $x < 16.$ **32** $15 - x = 15.$
24 $z + 1 = 11.$ **33** $7z + 5 < 30.$
25 $17 - y < 8.$ **34** $21 - n = 21.$
26 $3n > 19.$ **35** $n + 8 = 8.$
27 $y + 2 \neq 12.$ **36** $x > 5 + 2.$

1 6 **Exploring ideas**

Finite sets and infinite sets

In this lesson you will learn how to tabulate sets that have many members. You will learn about two kinds of sets. You will learn how to use a condition for equality to help find the solution set of a condition for inequality.

You are already familiar with the numbers 0, 1, 2, 3, 4, 5, and so on. In this book we will call these numbers the *natural numbers.*

A The natural numbers from 0 through 1000 make up a set of numbers. Which is easier, to describe this set or to tabulate it?

There is an easy way to tabulate sets that have many members. This easy way of tabulating the set of natural numbers from 0 through 1000 is shown in D1. First write the numerals 0, 1, 2. Then make three dots. Finally, write the numeral 1000 for the last number in the set. The next display, D2, shows how to read the tabulation of this set.

B In the symbol {0, 1, 2, . . ., 1000}, the three dots are used instead of what numerals?

D1

{0, 1, 2, . . ., 1000}

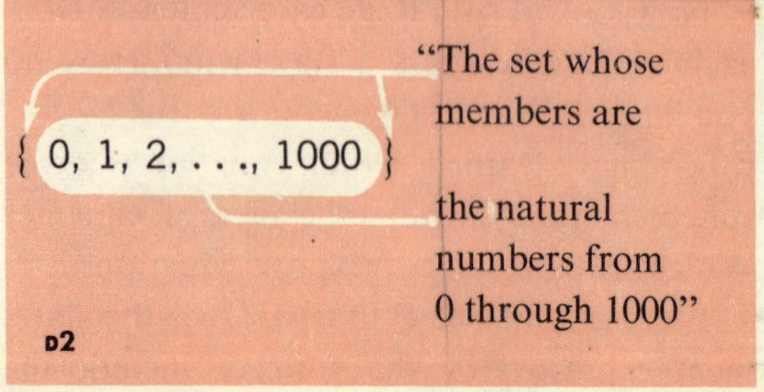

D2

Introduction to finite and infinite sets; use of infinite sets as universes and solution sets

{50, 51, 52, . . ., 100}

D3

{0, 1, 2, . . .}

D4

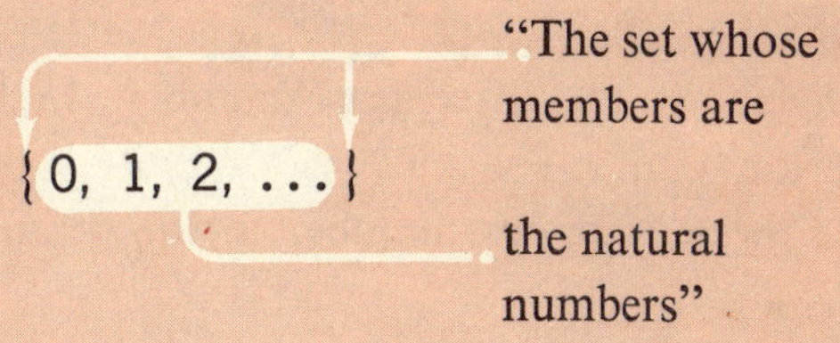

D5

C How many members are in the set of natural numbers from 0 through 1000? Remember to include 0.

D How do you read the symbol in D3?

E In D3 the three dots are used instead of what numerals?

F How many members are in the set tabulated in D3?

So far you have worked only with sets in which you can determine the number of members. When the number of members in a set is a natural number, the set is a *finite* set.

G Can you count the members in {5, 10, 15, 20}? Can you count the members in {5, 10, 15, . . ., 10,000,000}? Explain your answers.

H Why are the three dots used in the symbol {5, 10, 15, . . ., 10,000,000}?

I How many members are there in this set: {5, 10, 15, . . ., 10,000,000}?

J Is {5, 10, 15, . . ., 10,000,000} a finite set? How do you know?

K Is {0, 1, 2, . . ., 100,000,000} a finite set? How do you know?

Now you will learn about sets that are not finite. The set of natural numbers includes all the numbers from 0 through 1000. It also includes 1001, 1002, 10,000, 3,999,999, and many, many more.

L Is there a natural number that is greater than every other natural number? Why is it impossible to list the names of all the members in the set of natural numbers?

Since it is impossible to list the names of all the members in the set of natural numbers, it is necessary to find some other way to express this set. D4 shows how to do this. D5 shows how to read the new symbol.

M What do the three dots tell you? Why is no last member named in the tabulation?

N What natural number immediately follows 36? How do you find this number?

O For each natural number, is there a next greater natural number? How do you find this number?

P Can you use a natural number to tell how many members are in the set of natural numbers? Explain your answer.

Q Is the set of natural numbers a finite set? Explain your answer.

A set that is not finite is an *infinite* set. You cannot tell how many members are in an infinite set by using a natural number. There is no end to the members in an infinite set.

R Is the set of even numbers an infinite set? Use braces, numerals, and three dots to express the set of even numbers.

S Is the set of odd numbers an infinite set? Use braces, numerals, and three dots to express the set of odd numbers.

T Is the set of natural numbers less than 5 a finite set? An infinite set?

U Is the set of natural numbers greater than 5 a finite set? An infinite set?

V Is there a natural number that is less than every other natural number?

Because the set of natural numbers is used very often, it is convenient to name this set by a letter. The letter N is often used as a name of the set of natural numbers.

A Look at D6. What is the universe for x? Is the universe an infinite set?

B Is 5 a member of the solution set of $x+4>9$? Is any number less than 5 a member of the solution set?

C What are the three least numbers in the solution set of $x+4>9$?

D Is there a greatest number in the solution set?

Look again at D4 (repeated on this page), which shows how to indicate the tabulation of an infinite set. When you tabulate an infinite set, list the names of the first few members and then use three dots to show that the list goes on and on. You must list at least three names so that it is clear how the list continues.

E Tabulate the solution set of $x+4>9$. If necessary, use three dots in your tabulation.

F Describe the solution set of $x+4>9$. Is the solution set of $x+4>9$ an infinite set?

G Look again at D6. Is 5 a member of the solution set of $x+4<9$? Is any number greater than 5 a member of the solution set?

H Tabulate the solution set of $x+4<9$. Is the solution set an infinite set? A finite set?

You know that 0, 1, 2, 3, and 4 are the members of the solution set of $x+4<9$. The numbers 0, 1, 2, 3, and 4 are *solutions* of $x+4<9$. The members of the solution set of a condition are solutions of the condition.

I Look again at D6. Is any number less than 5 a solution of $x+4=9$? Is any number greater than 5 a solution?

J Tabulate the solution set of $x+4=9$. How many members does this solution set have? Is the solution set a finite set?

$\{0, 1, 2, \ldots\}$

D4

$U = N.$

$x+4>9.$

$x+4<9.$

$x+4=9.$

D6

$U = N.$

$x+4>9.$	$\{6, 7, 8, \ldots\}$
$x+4=9.$	$\{5\}$
$x+4<9.$	$\{0, 1, 2, 3, 4\}$

D7

$U = N.$

$7+m=10.$

$7+m>10.$

$7+m<10.$

D8

solution of a condition. Each member of a solution set of a condition. If the universe is the set of natural numbers, then each member of $\{0, 1, 2, 3, 4\}$ is a solution of $x<5$.

K Which sentences in D7 express conditions for inequality? Which express conditions for equality?

L Look at the tabulation of the solution set of $x+4>9$. Is each solution greater than the solution of $x+4=9$?

M Look at the tabulation of the solution set of $x+4<9$. Is each solution less than the solution of $x+4=9$?

When you know the solution of a condition like $x+4=9$, you can use this information to help you find the solutions of conditions like $x + 4 > 9$ and $x + 4 < 9$. In the exercises that follow, notice how you can use a condition for equality to help find the solution set of a condition for inequality.

N Look at D8. What is the solution of $7 + m = 10$?

O Is each solution of $7 + m > 10$ greater than the solution of $7 + m = 10$?

P Is each solution of $7 + m < 10$ less than the solution of $7 + m = 10$?

Q Tabulate the solution set of $7 + m > 10$. Tabulate the solution set of $7 + m < 10$.

You know now that some solution sets are finite sets and some are infinite sets. Some finite sets have many members, some have a few members, and some have only one member.

A Look at D9. Read the sentence that expresses a condition. Now replace s in the condition by each member of the universe. Tabulate the solution set of the condition.

B $11 + 2 < 15$ and $12 + 2 < 15$ are true statements. Why are 11 and 12 not solutions of the condition expressed in D9?

C Look again at D9. How many members are in the universe for the variable? How many members are in the solution set of the condition?

D Is each member of the solution set also a member of the universe? Is the solution set a subset of the universe?

E Is each member of the universe a member of the solution set? Is the universe a subset of the solution set? Is the solution set of $s + 2 < 15$ the same set as the universe?

F Look at D10. Replace x by 2. Do you obtain a true statement?

G Now replace x by 5,999,999. Do you obtain a true statement?

H What is the solution set of $x + 3 = 3 + x$?

$$U = \{0, 1, 2, 3, 4, 5, 6, 7, 8, 9, 10\}.$$
$$s + 2 < 15.$$

D9

$$U = N.$$
$$x + 3 = 3 + x.$$

D10

$$U = \{0, 1, 2, 3, 4, 5, 6, 7, 8, 9, 10\}.$$
$$x + 5 = 110.$$

D11

empty set (emp′ti). A set that has no members. Two descriptions of the empty set are: the set of women who have been Prime Minister of Canada and the set of natural numbers less than 0.

I Is the solution set of $x + 3 = 3 + x$ an infinite set?

J Are all the members of the universe solutions of $x + 3 = 3 + x$?

K Now look at D11. Replace x in the condition by each member of the universe. How many true statements do you obtain? How many members of the universe are in the solution set?

A set that has no members is the *empty set*.

The symbol at the right shows how to express the set that has no members. This symbol is read "the empty set."

$$\{\ \}$$

Since it is possible to use a natural number to tell how many members there are in the empty set, the empty set is a finite set.

L Is the solution set of the condition expressed in D11 the empty set?

M Think of the set consisting of students in your class who are younger than five years of age. Tabulate this set.

$U = N.$

$1 + x = x.$

D12

N Look at D12. What is the universe for x? Replace x by 2. Do you obtain a true statement? Now replace x by 10,000. Do you obtain a true statement?

O Is there any member of the universe that satisfies the condition? How can you express the solution set? How do you know that the solution set is a finite set?

Now you know what finite sets and infinite sets are. You know that solution sets may be either finite or infinite sets. You also know how to use a condition for equality to help find the solutions of a condition for inequality.

On your own

Tabulate each set described in exercises 1, 2, and 3.

1 The set of odd numbers from 1 through 40

2 The set of natural numbers greater than 10

3 The set of odd numbers from 3 through 7

Describe each set tabulated below.

4 {0, 1, 2, . . ., 34}

5 {3, 6, 9, . . ., 30}

6 {11, 13, 15, . . .}

In each condition expressed in exercises 7 through 18, the universe for x is N. Tabulate the solution set of each condition. If a solution set has no members, use the symbol for the empty set. Tell whether each solution set is a finite or an infinite set.

7 $x + 7 > 21.$	13 $x + 4 < x.$
8 $x + 3 = 8.$	14 $x + 4 > x.$
9 $15 + x = 20.$	15 $x + 3 < 3.$
10 $20 < 15 + x.$	16 $x + 4 \neq 4.$
11 $2x + x = 3x.$	17 $24 < x + 2x.$
12 $x + 4 = x.$	18 $15 > 3x + 1.$

1 7 **Exploring ideas**

Standard description of sets

For several lessons now you have been finding solution sets of conditions. You have expressed these solution sets by tabulation. Now you will learn to express solution sets in a different way.

A You have learned to name sets in two ways, by tabulation and by description. Read this tabulation: {0, 1, 2, 3, 4, 5}. Can you describe the set just tabulated by writing "the set whose members are the natural numbers less than six"?

B When you tabulate a set, you use braces instead of what words? You also may use braces when you describe a set. For example, you can write {the natural numbers less than six} for the set that is described in exercise A.

C Now read the open sentence in D1. Also read the description of the solution set of the condition $x < 6$. The universe for x is N. The braces are used instead of what words?

There is a way of writing the description of a solution set that is shorter and more convenient than the description given in D1. We will work out this new description step by step.

First you use the symbol x instead of the words "natural numbers." You use the symbol x again instead of the word "number."

D Read the description of the solution set given in D2.

E Next you use the symbol < for the words "is less than" and use the numeral 6 instead of the word "six." Notice how these symbols are

$x < 6$.

{all natural numbers that satisfy the condition that each number is less than six}

D1

{all x that satisfy the condition that each x is less than six}

D2

{all x that satisfy the condition that each $x < 6$}

D3

$\{\text{all } x \mid \text{each } x < 6\}$

D4

$\{x \mid x < 6\}$

D5

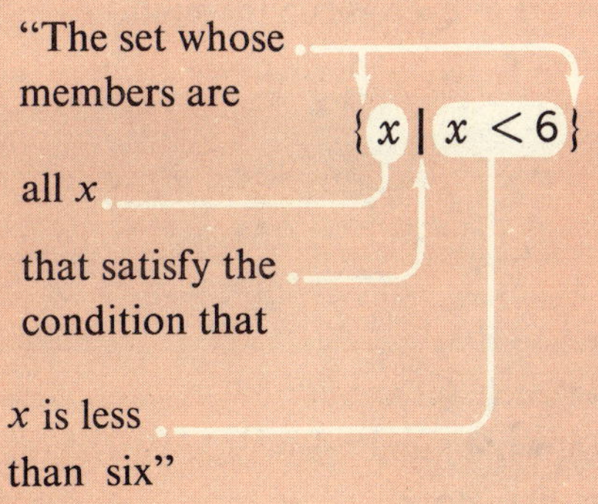

D6

U = N.

$x + 4 < 20$.

{0, 1, 2, . . ., 15}

D7

used in D3. Read the description of the solution set given in D3.

F Finally you use a symbol instead of the words "that satisfy the condition that." This symbol is a picture of a vertical line. Notice how this new symbol is used in D4. Read the description of the solution set given in D4.

It usually is not necessary to write the words "all" and "each." You may write the description of the solution set as shown in D5. D6 shows how to read the description of the solution set given in D5.

When braces and an open sentence are used to describe a solution set, such a description is a *standard description*.

G If you want to, you may use the words "such that" instead of the words "that satisfy the condition that." Reread the standard description of the solution set given in D5. This time use the words "such that."

Write a standard description of each of the solution sets described in exercises H, I, and J. U = N.

H {all x such that each $x + 4 < 7$}

I {all numbers that satisfy the condition that each number is less than ten}

J The set whose members are all numbers that satisfy the condition that each number is greater than 100

A standard description is a convenient way of describing a solution set that has many members or that is an infinite set.

K Look at D7. Is each member of the tabulated set a solution of the condition? Is this set the solution set of $x + 4 < 20$?

L The solution set may be described in this way: $\{x \mid x + 4 < 20\}$. Is $\{x \mid x + 4 < 20\}$ the same set as {0, 1, 2, . . ., 15}?

M Does the sentence below express a true statement? Explain your answer. U = N.

$\{x \mid x + 4 < 20\} = \{0, 1, 2, \ldots, 15\}$.

$U = N.$

$5 + x > 7.$

$\{3, 4, 5, \ldots\}$

D8

N Look at D8. Is $\{x | 5 + x > 7\}$ a standard description of the solution set of $5 + x > 7$? Is $\{x | 5 + x > 7\}$ the same set as $\{3, 4, 5, \ldots\}$?

Now you know that you can express a solution set by using a standard description.

On your own

Write a standard description of each set described in exercises 1 through 9. U=N.

1 {all x such that each $x < 50$}

2 {all n that satisfy the condition that each n is not equal to three}

3 {all y such that each $y + 3 > 9$}

4 {all numbers that satisfy the condition that two times each number is less than twenty}

5 {all z such that each $z + 1 \neq 4$}

6 {all numbers such that each number < 7}

7 {all r that satisfy the condition that each r is equal to nine}

8 {all x | each $x + 3 > 8$}

9 The set whose members are all numbers that satisfy the condition that each number added to itself is greater than ten

Write in words each standard description given in exercises 10 through 13. U = N.

10 $\{x | x > 2\}$

11 $\{n | n + 3 \neq 10\}$

12 $\{x | x + x < 17\}$

13 $\{z | 6z = 18\}$

For each condition expressed in exercises 14 through 17, write a standard description of the solution set. U = N.

14 $x + 3 > 20.$

15 $y + 6 = 14.$

16 $m + 3 < 10.$

17 $r + 2 \neq 2.$

18 For each condition expressed in exercises 14 through 17 above, tabulate the solution set. Remember that U = N.

Read each sentence below. Tell which sentences express true statements and which express false statements. U=N.

19 $\{0, 1, 2, 3\} = \{x | x < 3\}.$

20 $\{2, 0, 3, 1\} = \{x | x < 4\}.$

21 $\{x | x > 10\} = \{11, 12, 13, \ldots, 50\}.$

22 $\{x | x + 2 = x\} = \{ \}.$

Tabulate each set described below. U=N.

23 $\{x | x < 7\}$

24 $\{m | m > 9\}$

25 $\{z | z = 10\}$

26 $\{x | x + 1 \neq 1 + x\}$

27 $\{y | 2y > 50\}$

28 $\{w | 2w = w + w\}$

CHECKING UP

Use lessons 1 through 7 if you need to restudy the ideas expressed in these tests.

Test 1

For each condition expressed in exercises 1 through 4, write the sentences that express all the statements that can be obtained by using {0, 1, 5, 10} as the universe for x. Tell which of these sentences express true statements.

1 $10 > 3x.$

2 $5 \neq x.$

3 $8 + x = 17.$

4 $12 - x < 3.$

Tabulate the solution set of each condition expressed in exercises 5 through 12.
$U = \{0, 1, 2, 3, 4, 5\}.$

5 $x > 4.$

6 $2 < x.$

7 $3 \neq x.$

8 $6 - x < 3.$

9 $x + 1 > 4.$

10 $2 \neq x + x.$

11 $3 + 3 = x.$

12 $x + 2 < 5.$

Test 2

For each set tabulated in exercises 13, 14, and 15, what numerals would you write instead of the three dots?

13 $\{5, 6, 7, \ldots, 12\}$

14 $\{0, 2, 4, \ldots, 14\}$

15 $\{7, 9, 11, \ldots, 19\}$

Which of the sets tabulated in exercises 16 through 19 are subsets of $\{1, 9, 7, 12, 5\}$?

16 $\{1, 7, 12, 5\}$

17 $\{5, 7, 9, \ldots\}$

18 $\{1, 3, 5, \ldots\}$

19 $\{12\}$

D1

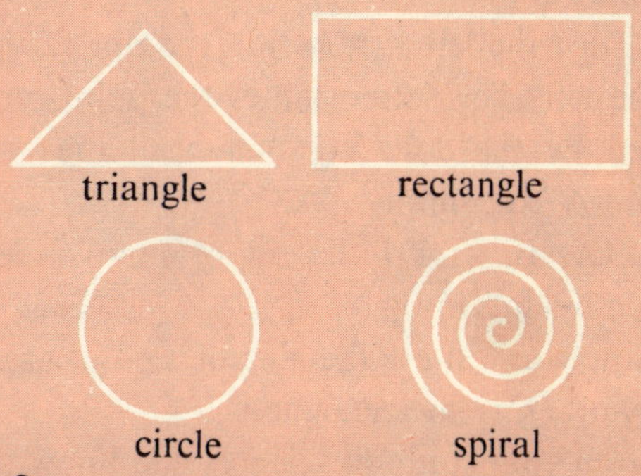

D2

ge o met ric fig ure (jē′ə met′rik fig′yər). A set of points. Triangles, rectangles, circles, and spirals are geometric figures.

1 8 Exploring ideas

Sets of points

You know that mathematics is concerned with numbers and with sets of numbers. Mathematics also deals with such objects as points, lines, planes, and space. The part of mathematics that deals with these objects is called *geometry*. Some of these geometric objects are represented in D1 and D2.

A Look at D1. The dot in picture A represents a *point*. The dots in picture B represent several points. These points form a set of points. Picture C was obtained by first reproducing the dots in picture B and then placing another dot between each two dots. Do the points that are represented in picture C also form a set of points?

B Explain how picture D was obtained from picture C. Do the points represented in picture D also form a set of points?

C ? Suppose that you have a pencil with the sharpest tip possible. Imagine that with this pencil you place a dot between each two dots in picture D and that you continue placing dots in this way. Do you think there are many points between any two points represented by dots?

D ? Picture E represents the set of points indicated in picture D and all points between these points. Do you think that picture E represents an infinite set of points?

Look at the pictures of geometric objects in D2. The triangle is made up of three sides. Each side is a set of points like the set represented by picture E in D1. The triangle itself is the set of points that contains all the points in its three sides.

E The rectangle is made up of four sides. Is each side of the rectangle a set of points? Is the rectangle a set of points?

F Do you think that the circle is a set of points? Do you think that the spiral is a set of points?

Each geometric object represented in D2 is a set of points. A set of points is a *geometric figure*. As you continue to study geometry, you will learn more about some of these geometric figures.

G Think of two geometric figures that are different from those represented in D2. Make sketches of these two figures.

H Now look at D3. Notice that several dots have been drawn to show how a dot would look if it were shrinking. If the dot continues to shrink, will it finally disappear?

Even when there is no dot, there is a point. You can only imagine the point. A point is a mathematical idea.

I Look at D4. How many dots are there in the display? How many points are represented by dots?

Notice the letter A beside the dot farthest to the left. This letter names the point represented by the dot. You may call the point "point A" or, simply, "A."

J Is {A, B, C, D} the set of points represented by dots in D4?

Now you will use the idea of a point as you study other geometric figures.

K From your study of science, you know that the earth's atmosphere contains particles of dust. Are there many particles of dust in the earth's atmosphere?

L Each dust particle suggests a point. Do all the dust particles in the earth's atmosphere suggest many points?

M Imagine that more and more particles of dust are released into the atmosphere. Do these dust particles suggest more and more points?

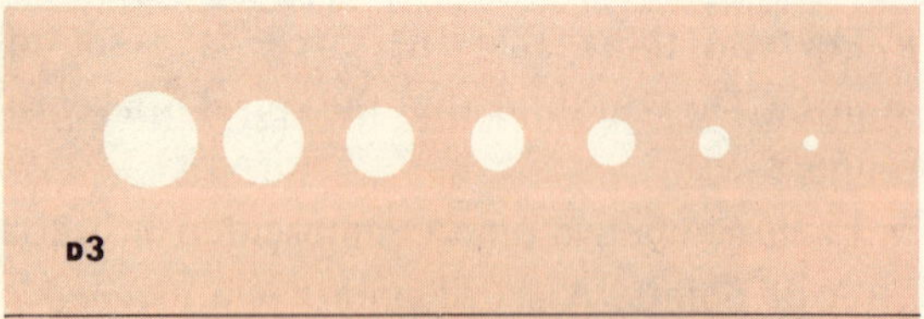

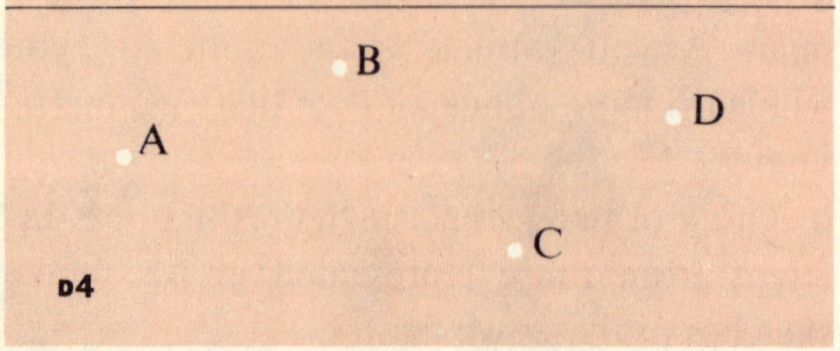

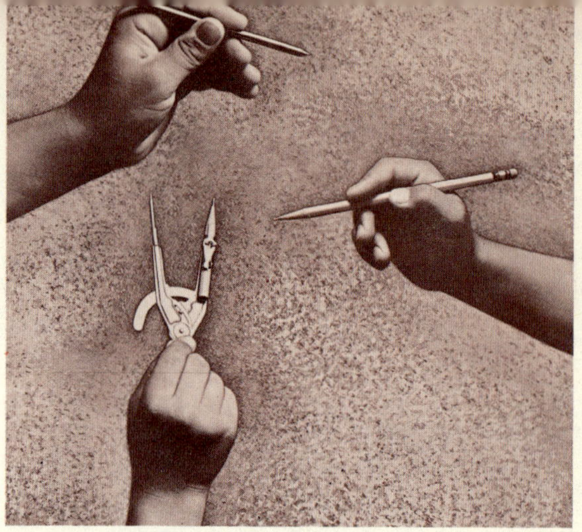

N Imagine the earth's atmosphere completely filled with dust particles. These particles still do not suggest all possible points. The set of all points is called *space*. Do you think that space is an infinite set of points?

O Look at the photograph above. Can you think of the tip of the pencil as suggesting a point in space? For each of the other objects pictured, what part best suggests a point?

Now you will learn about some special subsets of space.

A Imagine an unlighted room filled with dust particles. Light is being directed into the room through an extremely small pinhole in the door. The dust particles illuminated by the light form a set of dust particles. Is this set a subset of the set of dust particles in the room?

REMINDER

If each member of one set is also
a member of a second set, then
the first set is a subset of the second set.

See lesson 2, page 11.

B Since each dust particle suggests a point, the set of illuminated particles suggests a set of points. Is this set of points a subset of space?

The set of points suggested by the set of illuminated particles is a *line*. Since a line is a set of points, a line is a subset of space. You can only imagine a line. A line is a mathematical idea.

C Is a line a geometric figure? How do you know?

D Can you think of a tightly stretched wire as suggesting a line? Name two objects in your classroom that suggest lines.

In geometry, a line is understood to be a "straight line." In this unit, when we say "line," we will mean "straight line."

E Look at D5. The display shows two ways to represent a line. One picture has arrows to remind you that a line goes on and on in opposite directions. The other picture does not have arrows. When you look at a picture of a line without arrows, remember that the line goes on endlessly in opposite directions. Each picture in D5 is an incomplete picture of a line.

F Is each line represented in D5 an infinite set of points? Is any line an infinite set of points?

G Notice the letter b beside one picture in D5. One way to name a line is to use a letter. You may call this line "line b" or, simply, "b."

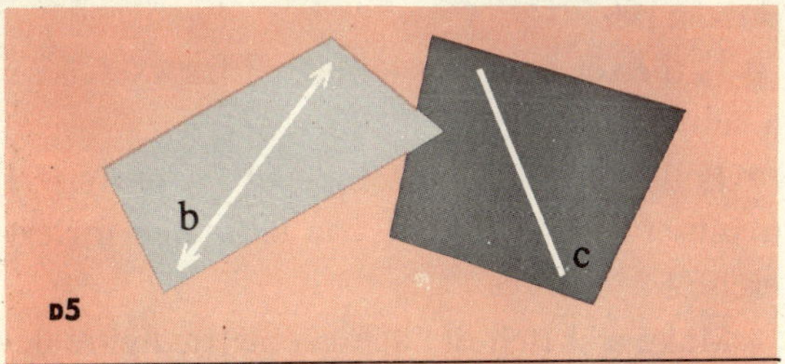

D5

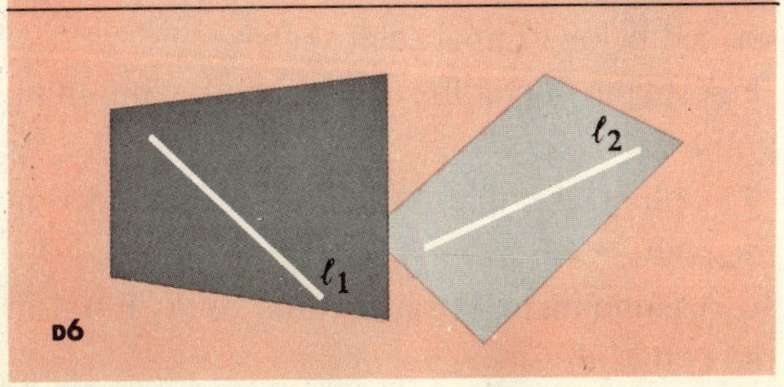

D6

What is the name of the other line represented in D5?

H Is it sensible to ask if line b is longer than ? line c? Explain your answer. How does line b differ from line c?

I D6 shows another way to name lines. The picture of one line is labelled with the letter ℓ and a small numeral 1. This numeral 1 is called a *subscript*. It is written at the right and below the letter. This name of the line is read "ℓ subscript one," "ℓ sub one," or, simply, "ℓ one." What is the name of the other line represented in D6?

J Does ℓ_1 extend endlessly in opposite directions? Does ℓ_2 extend endlessly in opposite directions?

Now you will learn about another subset of space.

A Again imagine an unlighted room filled with dust particles. Light is being directed into the room through a door that is opened slightly. The dust particles illuminated by the light form a set of dust particles. Is this set a subset of the set of dust particles in the room?

B Since each dust particle suggests a point, the set of illuminated dust particles suggests a set of points. Is this set of points a subset of space?

The set of points suggested by the set of illuminated particles is a *plane*. Since a plane is a set of points, it is a subset of space. A plane is unlimited in extent; that is, it has no boundaries. A plane, like a point or a line, can only be imagined. A plane is a mathematical idea.

C Is a plane a geometric figure? How do you know?

D Can you think of the surface of a mirror as suggesting a plane? Name two other objects that suggest a plane.

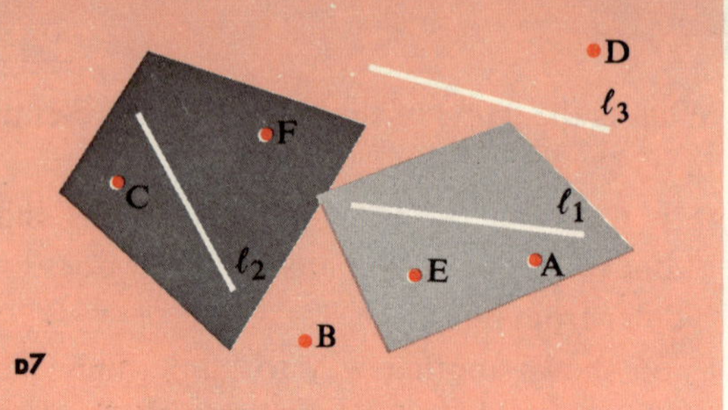

D7

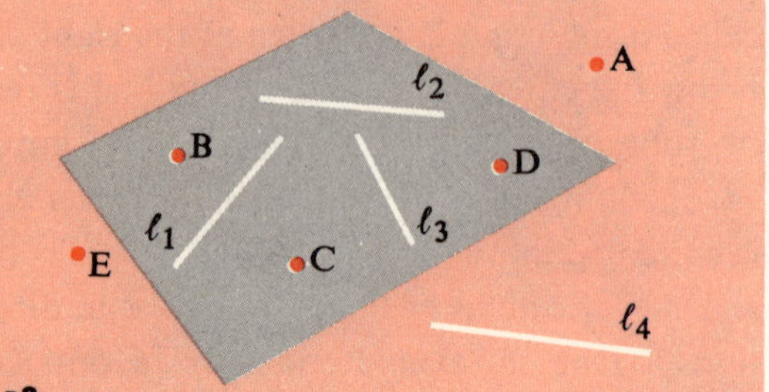

D8

E Look at D7. It includes pictures of points, lines, and planes. When you look at the pictures, remember that planes extend on and on.

F Is {A, B, C, D, E, F} the set of points that are represented by dots in D7?

G Point A is in a plane represented in D7. What other point in this plane is represented by a dot?

H For each plane represented in D7, tabulate the set of points in the plane that are represented by dots.

I Do the planes contain any points besides the points represented by dots? Is a plane an infinite set of points? Explain your answers.

J Point B is a member of space. Is point B in a plane that is represented in D7?

K Is D a member of space? Is D in a plane that is represented in D7?

L Is $\{\ell_1, \ell_2, \ell_3\}$ the set of lines represented in D7? For each plane represented, you can find a line that is a subset of the plane. For example, ℓ_1 is a subset of one plane represented in D7. What other line named in D7 is a subset of a plane represented in the display?

When we say that a line is "*included* in a plane," we mean that the line is a subset of the plane.

M ? Are any lines other than ℓ_1 and ℓ_2 included in the planes represented in D7? Explain your answer.

N ? Is the set of lines that are included in a plane an infinite set?

Now you know that points, lines, planes, and space are mathematical ideas. Although no one has ever seen a point, a line, a plane, or space, you can use drawings and objects to represent or suggest these mathematical ideas.

On your own

Use D8 to help you with exercises 1 through 7. The plane referred to is the plane represented in D8.

1 Tabulate the set of points in the plane that are represented by dots.

2 Tabulate the set of points not in the plane that are represented by dots.

3 Is ℓ_1 a subset of the plane? What other lines named in D8 are included in the plane?

4 Tabulate the set of lines that are not included in the plane.

5 Tabulate the set of all points represented by dots in D8.

6 Is the set that you tabulated for exercise 5 a subset of space?

7 Is the set that you tabulated for exercise 1 a subset of the set that you tabulated for exercise 5?

Make a sketch of each geometric figure described below. Label each sketch.

8 A plane including line b and containing point F

9 A plane and lines ℓ_1 and ℓ_2 not included in the plane

10 A plane including line c and point E not in the plane

1 9 **Exploring ideas**

Relating points, lines, and planes

In this lesson you will learn how points, lines, and planes are related.

A Look at D1. What points are represented by dots? Line ℓ_1 contains A and B.

B Is ℓ_1 a set of points? Is {A, B} a subset of ℓ_1? How do you know?

C What lines are represented in D2? Is C contained in each of these lines?

D Is the set of lines, each of which contains C, **?** an infinite set? Explain your answer.

E Are all lines that contain C included in the **?** same plane?

F How many lines represented in D2 contain both C and D?

G How many lines are represented in D3? Does more than one line contain both E and F?

H Is the set of geometric figures, each of which **?** contains both E and F, an infinite set?

Exercises F, G, and H have helped you discover that there is only one line that contains two different points. This idea is common to, or characteristic of, any two different points. This idea is a *property* that relates points and lines. The property is expressed below.

For any two different points there is exactly one line that contains both of these points.

From now on, when we say "two points," we will mean "two *different* points." In the same way, when we refer to two lines or to two planes, we mean two different figures.

I Look at D4. What line contains R and S? What line contains T and U?

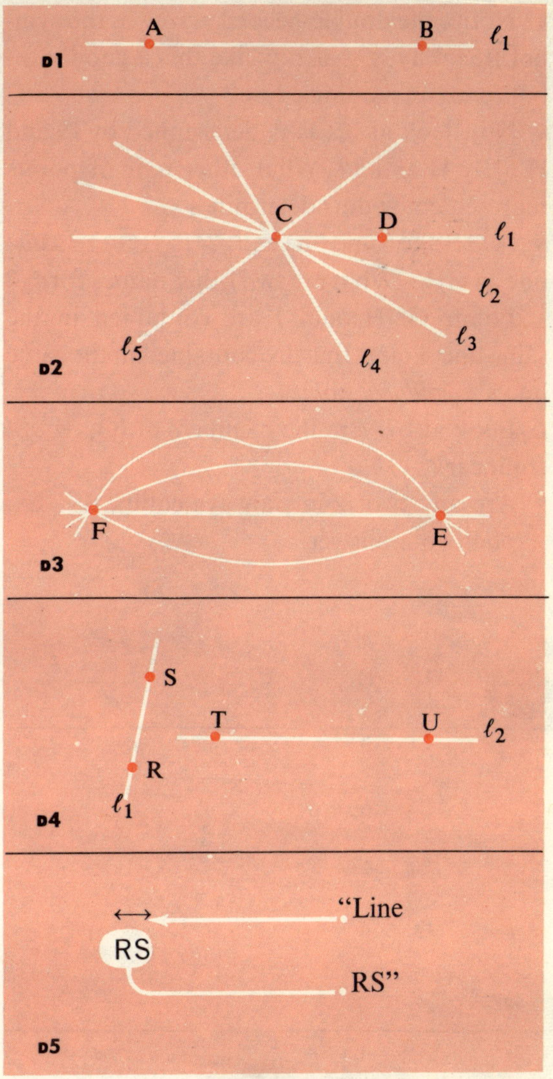

J Since there is exactly one line that contains both R and S, points R and S *determine* ℓ_1. What line is determined by T and U? Do U and T determine the same line as T and U?

K How many lines are determined by any two points?

Since any two points determine exactly one line, you can use the names of the two points in naming the line. D5 shows another way to name ℓ_1, represented in D4. The words in D5 tell how to read this name.

L Notice the double-headed arrow in the symbol $\overleftrightarrow{RS}$. Why is an arrow like this a good symbol to use in naming a line?

M Now look at D6. Is ℓ_6 determined by G and H? By H and J? What other pair of points represented by dots determines ℓ_6?

N Is $\overleftrightarrow{GH}$ the same line as ℓ_6? Is $\overleftrightarrow{HG}$ the same line as $\overleftrightarrow{GH}$? What are two other names for ℓ_6?

Points G, H, and J are contained in the same line. Points that are contained in the same line are *collinear points.*

O Look at D7. Are the members of {Q, R, S} collinear?

P Are any two points always collinear? Explain your answer.

D6

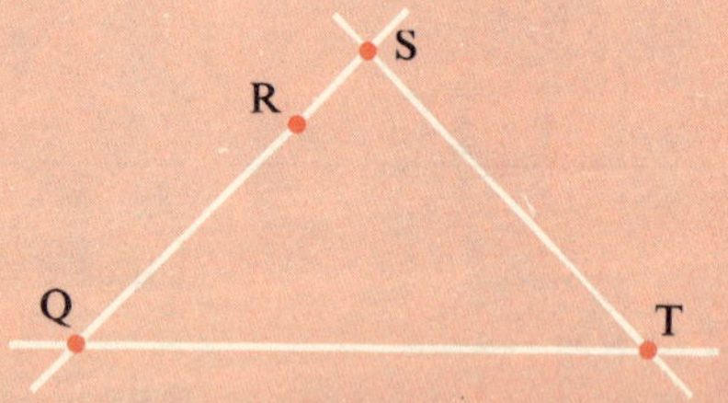

D7

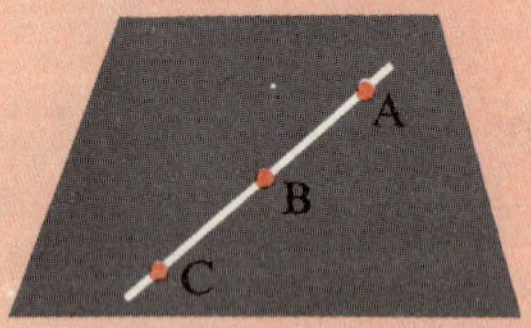

D8

col lin e ar points (kə lin′ē ər). Points that are contained in the same line. Points A, B, C, and D, represented below, are collinear points.

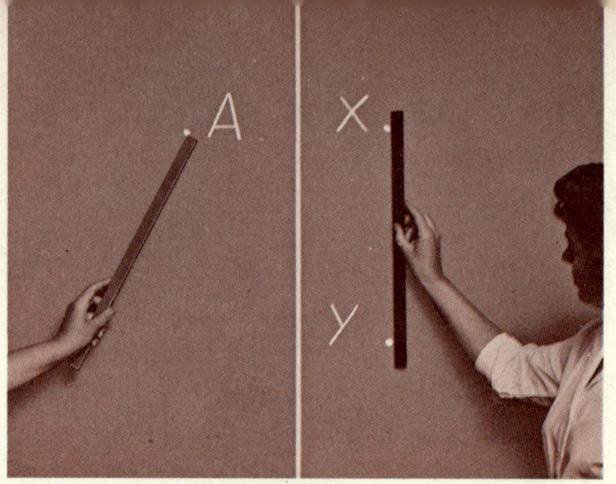

Q Look again at D7. How do you know that Q, R, and T are not collinear?

Points Q, R, and T are *not* contained in the same line. They are *noncollinear points.*

Next you will study a property that relates lines and planes.

A Look at the photographs. Does the surface of the chalkboard in each photograph suggest a plane? Does each stick suggest a line?

B Think of the stick in the photograph at the left as touching the board at dot A. Does this stick touch the board at any other place?

C Think of the other stick as touching the board at dots X and Y. Does this stick touch the board at any other place?

D If a stick touches a board at two places, does it touch the board at more than two places?

E Look at the picture of a plane in D8. A, B, and C are collinear points. A and B are in the plane. Is C in the plane?

F Is $\overleftrightarrow{AC}$ included in the plane? Is $\overleftrightarrow{CB}$ included in the plane?

Now you have learned about a property that relates lines and planes. This property is expressed below.

If a line contains two points of a plane, the line is included in the plane.

G Points E, F, and G are in the plane represented in D9. Point H is not in the plane. Is $\overleftrightarrow{EF}$ included in the plane? Name two other

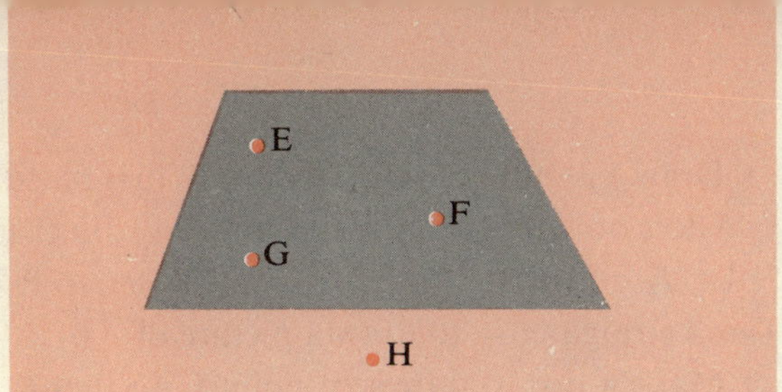

D9

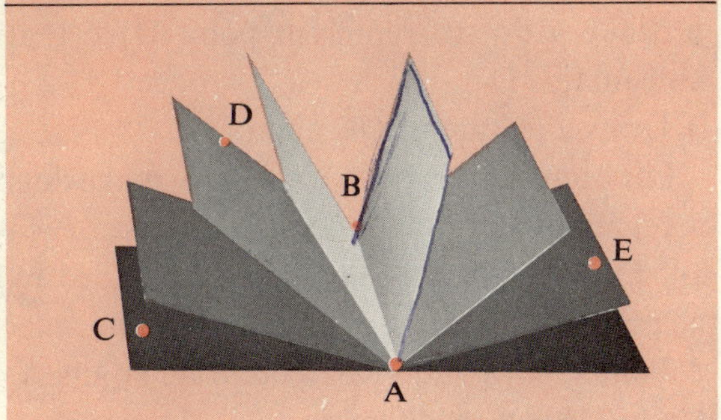

D10

lines that are included in the plane. Name three lines that are not included in the plane.

In the following exercises you will learn more about the properties that relate points, lines, and planes.

A Look at D10. Point A and point B determine how many lines? How do you know?

B Is $\overleftrightarrow{AB}$ included in the plane suggested by **?** the surface of the book cover? How do you know?

C The surface of the book cover suggests a plane. Each leaf of the book also suggests a plane. Is $\overleftrightarrow{AB}$ included in each of these planes?

D Is every plane that includes $\overleftrightarrow{AB}$ represented **?** in D10? Explain your answer.

E Is the set of planes, each of which includes **?** $\overleftrightarrow{AB}$, an infinite set? Explain your answer.

When we say that the set of planes, each of which includes $\overleftrightarrow{AB}$, is an infinite set, we mean that infinitely many planes include $\overleftrightarrow{AB}$.

You have learned about another property that relates lines and planes. This property is expressed as follows:

A given line is included in infinitely many planes.

F Look again at D10. Name the points that are represented by dots. Which of these points are not contained in $\overleftrightarrow{AB}$?

G Point C is in the plane suggested by the surface of the book cover. How many planes that contain C also include $\overleftrightarrow{AB}$?

H How many planes that contain D also include $\overleftrightarrow{AB}$? How many planes that contain E also include $\overleftrightarrow{AB}$?

In exercises F, G, and H you have seen how a line and a point not in the line are related to a plane. The following sentence expresses this property.

There is exactly one plane that includes a given line and contains a point not in the line.

We say that point C and $\overleftrightarrow{AB}$ determine the plane that contains C and includes $\overleftrightarrow{AB}$.

I Do point D and $\overleftrightarrow{AB}$ determine a plane? Explain your answer.

J Look again at D10. You know that point A and point B determine $\overleftrightarrow{AB}$. You also know that $\overleftrightarrow{AB}$ and point D determine the plane suggested by a leaf of the book. Are A, B, and D noncollinear points? How do you know?

K Are A, B, and D contained in just one **?** plane? Are A, B, and E contained in just one plane? Explain your answers.

L Are A, D, and E contained in just one **?** plane? How do you know? Is the plane that contains A, D, and E suggested by a leaf of the book?

Now you know how three noncollinear points are related to a plane. This property is expressed by the sentence below.

There is exactly one plane that contains three noncollinear points.

M How many planes represented in D10 are determined by A, B, and C? Explain your answer.

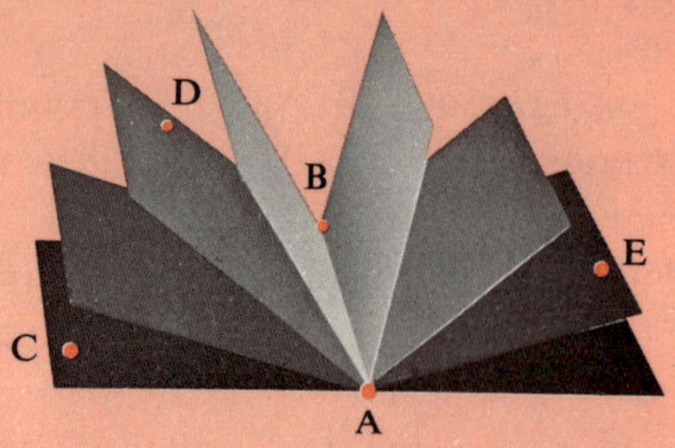

D10

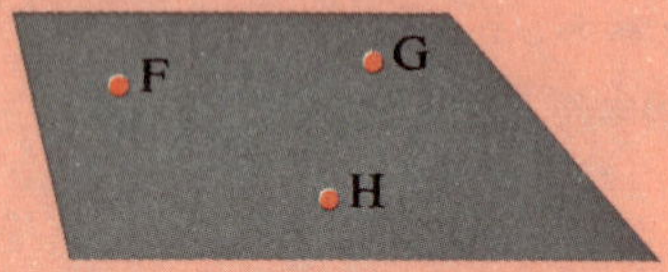

D11

Since three noncollinear points are contained in exactly one plane, you can use the names of these points to name the plane.

N Look at D11. The dots represent three noncollinear points. Are F, G, and H in the same plane? You may call the plane represented in D11 "plane FGH."

O Look again at D10. Is plane ADB represented? Name two other planes represented in D10.

P Look again at D11. Imagine that D is in plane FGH but is not in $\overleftrightarrow{GH}$. Is plane DGH the same plane as FGH? Explain your answer.

Q Can you name a plane by using the names of any three noncollinear points in that plane?

Now you know certain properties that relate points, lines, and planes.

On your own

For some of the following exercises, you will use a *straightedge* to draw pictures of lines. A ruler can be used as a straightedge. Make only one drawing for exercises 1 through 4.

1 Draw a picture of $\overleftrightarrow{AB}$. To do this, first place two dots on your paper. Label one dot with the letter A and the other dot with the letter B. Use a straightedge to draw a picture of $\overleftrightarrow{AB}$.

2 Make a dot to represent point C so that C is not contained in $\overleftrightarrow{AB}$. Draw a picture of $\overleftrightarrow{BC}$.

3 Make a dot to represent point D so that $\overleftrightarrow{AB}$ contains D.

4 Draw a picture of $\overleftrightarrow{DC}$ and of $\overleftrightarrow{AC}$.

For each of exercises 5 through 8, make dots to represent the points described. Label each dot. Draw pictures of the lines determined by the points and write a name for each line.

5 Points A, B, and C are collinear. Points A, B, and D are noncollinear.

6 Points A, B, and C are noncollinear. Points B, C, and D are noncollinear. Points A, B, and D are noncollinear. Points A, D, and C are collinear.

7 Points A, B, and C are collinear. Points B, D, and E are collinear. Points A, B, and D are noncollinear.

8 No three of points A, B, C, and D are collinear.

9 How many lines are determined by four points, no three of which are collinear?

10 Represent five points, no three of which are collinear. How many lines are determined by these points? Draw a picture of each line.

11 How many lines can contain a given point?

12 How many lines can contain two points?

13 How many planes can contain a given point?

14 How many planes can include a given line?

15 If $\overleftrightarrow{AB}$ and $\overleftrightarrow{AC}$ are two lines, what do you know about points A, B, and C?

16 How many planes are determined by four points that are not all in the same plane, and no three of which are collinear?

17 If A, B, and C are in more than one plane, what do you know about A, B, and C?

1 | 10 **Exploring ideas**

Segments and congruent segments

You have studied some of the properties that relate points, lines, and planes. Now you will study subsets of lines and learn how these subsets are related to each other.

A Look at D1. Point E is between point D and point F. Point E is also between D and G. Is E between D and H?

B Is F between D and H? Is G between D and H? Are points D, E, F, G, and H collinear points?

C Look again at D1. Are points D, J, and H collinear?

Since D, J, and H are not collinear, it is not sensible to discuss whether or not J is between D and H. *Betweenness* applies only to collinear points. You have been studying one of the properties of betweenness. This property is expressed below.

If one point is between two other points, then the three points are collinear.

D Think of the three points A, B, and D. Point D is between B and A. Are A, B, and D collinear? Explain your answer.

E Tabulate the set of points named in D1 that are between D and H. Is I a member of this set? Explain your answer.

F Since E is between D and H, can you also say that E is between H and D?

G Now look at D2. Four collinear points are named in the display.

H Is N between O and P? Is P between O and N? Is O between P and N?

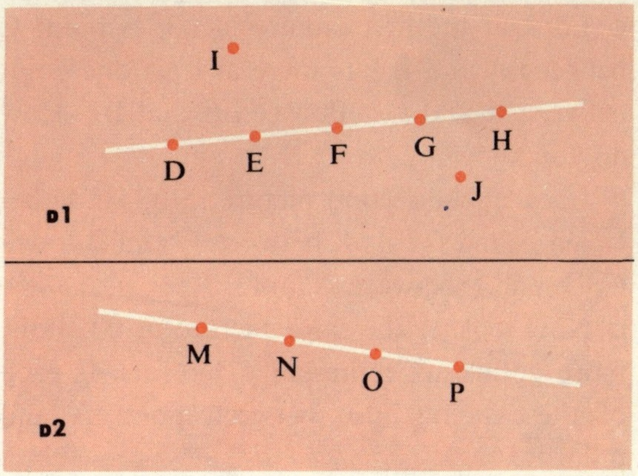

I When three points are collinear, is one of the points between the other two?

J When three points are collinear, is it possible for more than one of these points to be between the other two?

Now you know another property of betweenness. This property is expressed below.

For every three collinear points, just one of the points is between the other two.

K If you know that A is between B and C, then is it possible for B to be between A and C? For C to be between A and B? Explain your answers.

L S, V, and W are three collinear points. S is not between V and W. V is not between S and W. What can you decide about the position of the points S, V, and W?

M Look again at D2. Could you locate a point between M and N? Between N and O? Between O and P?

N Imagine that M and N are represented as "closer together" than they are in D2. Could you locate a point between M and N? Explain your answer. Remember that a point is an idea. A point does not have size.

You have learned another property of betweenness. This property is expressed below.

For any two points, there is at least one point between them.

O Look at the first picture in D3. Is point C between A and B? Is there at least one point between A and C? Between C and B? How do you know?

P Look at the second picture in D3. Is D between A and C? Is E between C and B? Are C, D, and E between A and B?

Q Now look at the third picture in D3. Four more points are represented by dots. Is each of these points also between point A and point B?

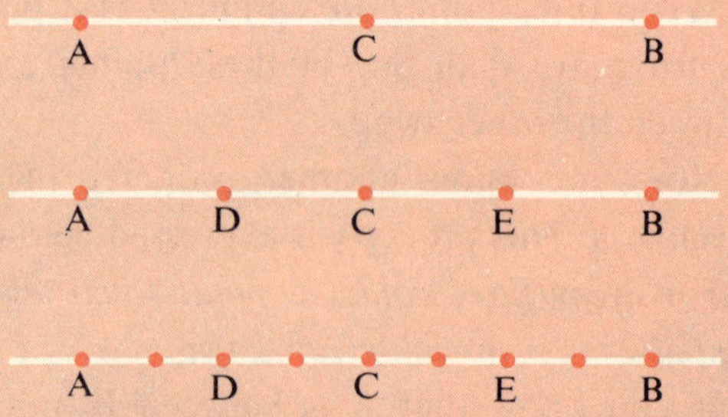

D3

D4

D5

seg ment (seg′mənt). A set of points whose members are two given points and all points between these two. The set whose members are A and B and all points between A and B is a segment. Points A and B are the **endpoints** of the segment.

R Could 10 points be located between A and B? Could 100 points be located between A and B?

S Are there infinitely many points between A and B?

T Which property of betweenness can you use ? to explain that there are infinitely many points between two given points?

You know now what it means to say that a point is between two other points. Next you will learn about a set of points whose members are two given points and all points between these two.

A Look at D4. You will work with the set of points whose members are X and Z and all points between X and Z. Is Y between X and Z? Is Y a member of the set you are working with?

B Is W between X and Z? Is W a member of the set you are working with?

The set of points whose members are X and Z and all points between X and Z is a *segment*. Points X and Z are the *endpoints* of the segment. Point Y is a member of the segment.

D5 shows how to write a name of the segment whose endpoints are X and Z. It also shows how to read the name of the segment.

C Is $\overline{ZX}$ the same segment as $\overline{XZ}$? Explain your answer.

Sometimes a segment is called a "line segment." If you wanted to, you could say "line segment XZ" instead of "segment XZ." You would be naming the same set of points in a slightly different way. In this book we will use the name "segment."

D Three segments are represented in D6. Name each segment.

Notice the three different ways in which we have represented segments in D6. The endpoints of $\overline{AB}$ are not represented by dots. The

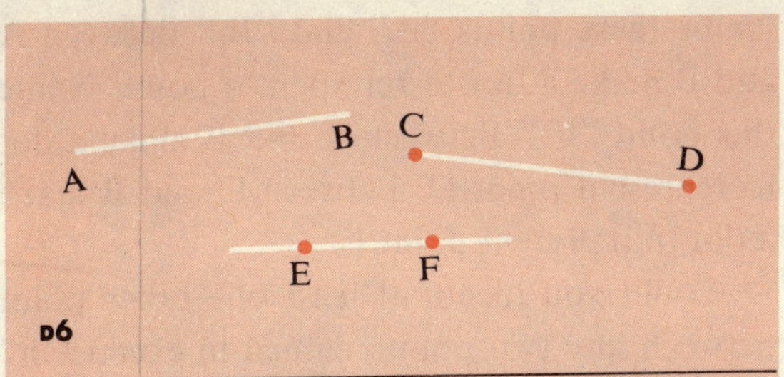

D6

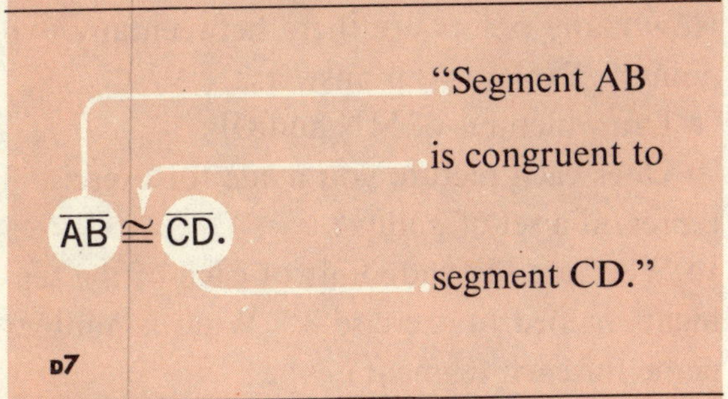

D7

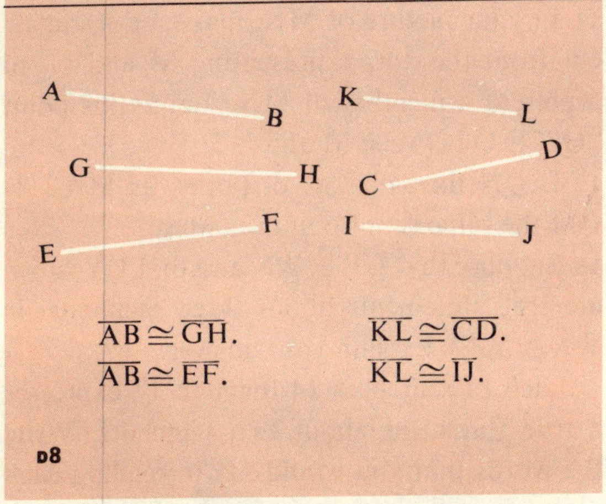

D8

endpoints of $\overline{CD}$ and $\overline{EF}$ are represented by dots. In this book we will use all three ways to represent segments.

Since two given points are the endpoints of exactly one segment, we say that two points determine a segment.

E Look again at D4. What segment is determined by X and Z? Is Y a member of this segment? Is W a member of this segment? Is Z a member of this segment?

F Can you draw a complete picture of a line? Can you draw a complete picture of a segment? Explain your answers.

G Look again at D4. Is $\overline{XW}$ a subset of $\overleftrightarrow{XW}$? ? Explain your answer.

Now you will learn about segments that are the same size. Such segments are *congruent* segments. When you are comparing segments, congruent means "the same size." Mathematicians use the symbol below to express the idea of congruence. Study D7, which shows how to read a sentence that includes this new symbol. $\overline{AB} \cong \overline{CD}$ is a true statement about two line segments. You will learn later that, for other geometric figures, congruence means "the same size *and* shape."

$\cong$

A Six segments are represented in D8. Name each segment.

B Now read each sentence in D8. Each sentence expresses a true statement about two of the segments represented.

Notice that the statements expressed in D8 use the idea of congruence and not the idea of equality. Remember that, in this book, equality means "the same as" or "identical."

C Is $\overline{AB}$ the same segment as $\overline{GH}$? Is $\overline{AB} = \overline{GH}$ a true statement? Explain your answer. ?

D Think about the statements expressed in D8. Since $\overline{KL} \cong \overline{CD}$ is a true statement, do you think that $\overline{CD} \cong \overline{KL}$ is also a true statement?

E Is $\overline{IJ} \cong \overline{KL}$ a true statement? Is $\overline{EF} \cong \overline{AB}$ a true statement? Is $\overline{GH} \cong \overline{AB}$ a true statement?

F In exercise E you accepted $\overline{GH} \cong \overline{AB}$ as a true statement. In other words, you *assumed* that this statement is true. You know that $\overline{AB} \cong \overline{EF}$ is a true statement. Do you think that $\overline{GH} \cong \overline{EF}$ is also a true statement?

$\overline{GH} \cong \overline{EF}$ is a true statement because of a property of congruence. This property, expressed below, applies to any three segments.

If $\overline{AB} \cong \overline{CD}$ and $\overline{CD} \cong \overline{EF}$ are true statements, then $\overline{AB} \cong \overline{EF}$ is a true statement.

This property can also be expressed in the shorter way shown below:

If $\overline{AB} \cong \overline{CD}$ *and* $\overline{CD} \cong \overline{EF}$, *then* $\overline{AB} \cong \overline{EF}$.

Reread the two ways of expressing the property. Notice that in the shorter way the phrases "are true statements" and "is a true statement" are omitted. From now on, when you see a sentence like $\overline{AB} \cong \overline{CD}$, assume that the sentence expresses a true statement unless you are told otherwise.

G You know that $\overline{CD} \cong \overline{KL}$ and $\overline{KL} \cong \overline{IJ}$. Is $\overline{CD} \cong \overline{IJ}$?

H Do you think that $\overline{AB} \cong \overline{KL}$ is a true statement? Explain your answer.

Now you know that segments are sets of points. You know what it means to say that two segments are congruent. You also know a property of congruent segments.

On your own

1 Draw a picture of a line. Then make six dots to represent six points in the line. Name these points, in order, with the letters H, I, J, K, L, and M. Now make two dots to represent two points not in the line. Name these points "N" and "O." Use your drawing to help you answer the questions in exercises 2 through 5.

2 Tabulate the set of points named in your drawing that are between H and M. The set of points that are between I and L. The set of points that are between J and K.

3 Tabulate the set of points named in your drawing that are between H and L. That are between L and H.

4 Did you tabulate two different sets for exercise 3?

5 Explain why neither point N nor point O is a member of the sets you tabulated for exercises 2 and 3.

6 Now draw another picture of a line. Make two dots to represent two points in the line. Name these points "A" and "B." Between A and B make a dot to represent a point. Name this point "C." Between C and B make a dot to represent point D. Between D and B make a dot to represent point E.

7 Could you locate at least one other point between any two points named in exercise 6? How many points are there between any two points? Explain your answers.

8 Draw pictures of $\overline{MN}$ and $\overline{OP}$.

9 Does each picture you made for exercise 8 represent a set of points?

10 What are the endpoints of each of the segments named in exercise 8? What is another name for each segment?

11 In your picture of $\overline{MN}$, make a dot, different from the dots representing M and N, to represent a member of $\overline{MN}$. Name this point "Q." Is Q between M and N?

12 Is $\overline{QN}$ the same set of points as $\overline{MN}$? Is $\overline{QM}$ the same set of points as $\overline{MN}$?

13 Suppose that $\overline{UV} \cong \overline{WX}$ and that $\overline{UV} \cong \overline{YZ}$ are true statements about three segments. Is $\overline{WX} \cong \overline{YZ}$? Explain your answer.

Each of sentences 14 through 17 expresses a true statement about two segments. Write the words that you would say in reading each sentence.

14 $\overline{AB} \cong \overline{CD}$.

15 $\overline{AB} \cong \overline{EF}$.

16 $\overline{GH} \cong \overline{IJ}$.

17 $\overline{KL} \cong \overline{MN}$.

$\overline{AB} \cong \overline{GH}$ is also a true statement. $\overline{AB} \cong \overline{KL}$ is a false statement. Use this information and the statements expressed in exercises 14 through 17 to decide which of the following sentences express true statements and which express false statements. You may use pictures to help you decide.

18 $\overline{EF} \cong \overline{CD}$.

19 $\overline{AB} \cong \overline{IJ}$.

20 $\overline{KL} \cong \overline{CD}$.

21 $\overline{GH} \cong \overline{EF}$.

22 $\overline{AB} \cong \overline{MN}$.

23 $\overline{GH} \cong \overline{MN}$.

24 $\overline{CD} \cong \overline{GH}$.

25 $\overline{MN} \cong \overline{EF}$.

1 | 11 **Exploring ideas**

Comparing segments

In this lesson you will use the idea of betweenness to help you understand a new idea, the idea of *separation*. Then you will learn to compare line segments without measuring them.

A Look at the picture of a plane in D1. Since the plane extends endlessly, it separates space into two sets of points. The two sets are called *half-spaces*. Is each half-space an infinite set of points?

B Tabulate the set of points that are named in D1.

Now you will decide whether or not all the members of the set that you have just tabulated are in the same half-space.

C Look again at D1. How many points between A and B are in the plane?

Since no point between A and B is in the plane, point A and point B are in the same half-space.

D How many points between B and C are in the plane?

Since there is one point between B and C that is in the plane, point B and point C are not in the same half-space.

E Are A and C in the same half-space? How do you know?

A plane that separates space into two half-spaces is the *boundary* of each half-space. The points in the boundary are not in either half-space.

F Does every plane separate space into two **?** half-spaces?

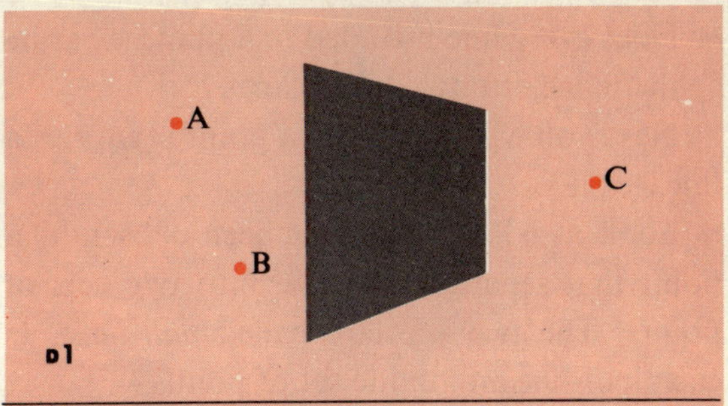

Next you will learn that a line separates a plane.

G Look at D2. The picture represents a line included in plane EFG. Does ℓ_1 extend endlessly in opposite directions?

H Line ℓ_1, represented in D2, separates the plane into two sets of points. The two sets are called *half-planes*. Is each half-plane an infinite set of points?

I Tabulate the set of points in the plane that are named in D2.

Now you will decide whether or not all the members of the set that you have just tabulated are in the same half-plane.

J Look again at D2. How many points between E and F are in line ℓ_1?

Since no point between E and F is in ℓ_1, point E and point F are in the same half-plane.

K How many points between E and G are in line ℓ_1?

Since there is one point between E and G that is in ℓ_1, point E and point G are not in the same half-plane.

L Are F and G in the same half-plane?

A line that separates a plane is the boundary of each half-plane. The points in the boundary are not in either half-plane.

M ? Does every line included in a plane separate the plane into two half-planes?

Next you will learn that a point separates a line.

N Look at D3. Point R has been chosen as a point that separates the line into two sets of points. The two sets are called *half-lines*. Is each half-line an infinite set of points?

O Tabulate the set whose members are the points H, I, and J.

Now you will decide whether or not the members of the set that you have just tabulated are in the same half-line.

P Look again at D3. Remember that you are thinking about R as the point that separates the line. Is R between H and I?

Since R is not between H and I, point H and point I are in the same half-line.

Q Now think about H and J. Is point R between H and J?

Since R is between H and J, point H and point J are not in the same half-line.

R Are points I and J in the same half-line?

A point that separates a line is the boundary of each half-line. The boundary is not in either half-line.

S ? Does H separate the line? Does J separate the line? Does I separate the line? Does every point in a line separate the line into two half-lines?

T ? Suppose that H is the boundary of two half-lines. Are points I and J in the same half-line? How do you know?

You know that a point separates a line into two half-lines. You will use this idea of separation and the idea of congruence to compare segments. You have already used the ideas of "less than" and "greater than" with numbers. You can also use these ideas to compare segments without measuring them.

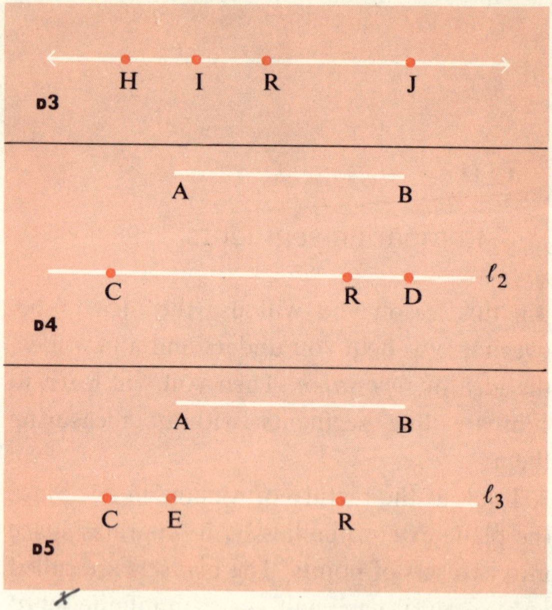

A Look at D4. You are going to compare $\overline{AB}$ and $\overline{CD}$.

In the pictures of the two segments, $\overline{AB}$ appears to be less than $\overline{CD}$. Let us see if there is a way to decide whether or not $\overline{AB} < \overline{CD}$.

B Think about ℓ_2, represented in D4. Point C separates ℓ_2 into two half-lines. There is a point R, in the same half-line as point D, that makes $\overline{AB} \cong \overline{CR}$. In ℓ_2, is R between C and D?

Notice what you have done. You wanted to compare $\overline{AB}$ and $\overline{CD}$. You know that there is a point R, in the same half-line as D, so that $\overline{AB} \cong \overline{CR}$. Since it happens that R is between C and D, you are now sure that $\overline{AB} < \overline{CD}$.

C Now look at D5. You are going to compare $\overline{AB}$ and $\overline{CE}$.

In the pictures of the two segments, $\overline{AB}$ appears to be greater than $\overline{CE}$. Now you will decide whether or not $\overline{AB} > \overline{CE}$.

D Think about ℓ_3, represented in D5. Point C separates ℓ_3 into two half-lines. There is a point R, in the same half-line as point E, that makes $\overline{AB} \cong \overline{CR}$. In ℓ_3, is R between C and E? Is E between C and R?

Notice that you have compared $\overline{AB}$ and $\overline{CE}$ in the same way you compared $\overline{AB}$ and $\overline{CD}$. You know that there is a point R, in the same half-line as E, that makes $\overline{AB} \cong \overline{CR}$. This time it happens that R is *not* between C and E. Instead, E is between C and R. You are therefore sure that $\overline{AB} > \overline{CE}$.

E Look at D6. You cannot tell by looking at the pictures of $\overline{EF}$ and $\overline{GH}$ whether $\overline{EF}$ is less than, congruent to, or greater than $\overline{GH}$. To compare $\overline{EF}$ and $\overline{GH}$, you must use what you have just learned about comparing segments.

F First think about line ℓ_4. Point G separates ℓ_4 into two half-lines. Imagine a point R, in the same half-line as H, so that $\overline{EF} \cong \overline{GR}$.

G If R is between G and H, is $\overline{EF} < \overline{GH}$?

H If H is between G and R, is $\overline{EF} > \overline{GH}$?

I If R is the same point as H, what do you know about $\overline{EF}$ and $\overline{GH}$?

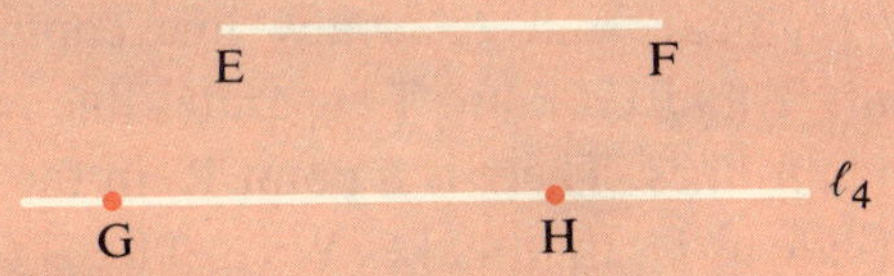

D6

$\overline{IJ} \cong \overline{KL}$. $\overline{IJ} < \overline{OB}$. $\overline{OB} < \overline{RS}$.

D7

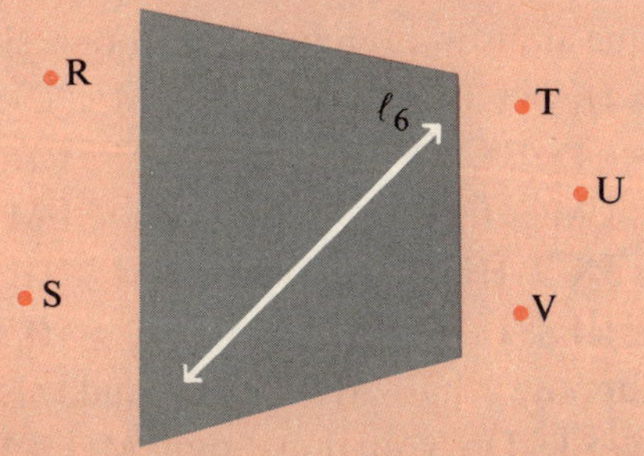

D8

Now you know what it means to compare segments. The exact meanings of "less than" and "greater than" are expressed below. You should make sketches to help you understand these meanings.

Let $\overline{UV}$ be any segment. Let $\overline{XY}$ be any segment included in line ℓ_5. Point X separates ℓ_5 into two half-lines. A point R in line ℓ_5 is in the same half-line as Y, so that $\overline{UV} \cong \overline{XR}$. If R is between X and Y, then $\overline{UV} < \overline{XY}$. If Y is between X and R, then $\overline{UV} > \overline{XY}$.

J Suppose that $\overline{JK} < \overline{LM}$ is a true statement.
? Is $\overline{JK} \cong \overline{LM}$? Is $\overline{JK} > \overline{LM}$? Explain your answers.

K Look at D7. Each sentence expresses a true statement. Do you think that $\overline{OB} < \overline{IJ}$? Do you think that $\overline{OB} > \overline{IJ}$? Explain your answers.

L Do you think that $\overline{KL} < \overline{OB}$? Explain your answer.

M Do you think that $\overline{IJ} < \overline{RS}$? Explain your answer.

$\overline{IJ} < \overline{RS}$ because of a property of "less than" for segments. This property is expressed below.

If $\overline{AB} < \overline{CD}$, and $\overline{CD} < \overline{EF}$, then $\overline{AB} < \overline{EF}$.

From this lesson you have learned that a plane separates space, that a line separates a plane, and that a point separates a line. You also know how the ideas of "less than" and "greater than" are used to compare segments.

On your own

Use D8 as you answer the questions in exercises 1 through 13. Line ℓ_6 is included in the plane represented in D8. Points R, S, T, U, and V are not in this plane.

1 Does the plane separate space into two half-spaces?

2 Is there a point between R and T that is in the plane? Are R and T in the same half-space?

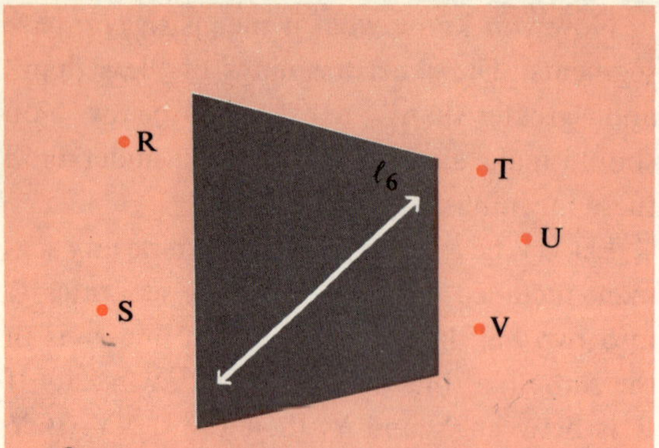

D8

$\overline{CD} \cong \overline{HI}$. $\overline{CD} < \overline{JK}$. $\overline{JK} < \overline{LM}$.

D9

3 Is there a point between R and V that is in the plane? Are R and V in the same half-space?

4 Is there a point between R and S that is in the plane? Are R and S in the same half-space?

5 Is there a point in the plane between R and U? Are R and U in the same half-space?

6 Does line ℓ_6 separate the plane into two half-planes?

7 Points X, Y, and Z are not represented in D8. Suppose that they are in the plane represented, but are not in line ℓ_6. There is a point between X and Y that is in ℓ_6. Are X and Y in the same half-plane?

8 No point between Y and Z is in ℓ_6. Are Y and Z in the same half-plane?

9 There is a point between X and Z that is in line ℓ_6. Are X and Z in the same half-plane?

10 Now think about a point Q in line ℓ_6. Does Q separate ℓ_6 into two half-lines?

11 Point Q separates line ℓ_6. Suppose points M, N, and O are also in line ℓ_6. Point Q is between N and O. Are N and O in the same half-line?

12 Point Q is not between M and N. Are M and N in the same half-line?

13 Point Q is between M and O. Are M and O in the same half-line?

Make sketches to help you answer exercises 14, 15, and 16.

14 Let $\overline{AB}$ be any segment, and let ℓ_7 be any line containing points E and F. Point E separates ℓ_7 into two half-lines. There is a point R, in the same half-line as F, that makes $\overline{AB} \cong \overline{ER}$. Suppose that R is between E and F. Write a sentence that expresses a true statement comparing $\overline{AB}$ and $\overline{EF}$.

15 Suppose that F is between E and R. Write a sentence that expresses a true statement comparing $\overline{AB}$ and $\overline{EF}$.

16 Suppose that R and F are the same point. Write a sentence that expresses a true statement comparing $\overline{AB}$ and $\overline{EF}$.

Use the following information to answer the questions in exercises 17, 18, and 19: $\overline{WS}$ is any segment, and ℓ_8 is any line containing points T and U. Point T separates line ℓ_8 into two half-lines. There is a point R, in the same half-line as U, that makes $\overline{WS} \cong \overline{TR}$.

17 If $\overline{WS} < \overline{TU}$, is R between T and U?

18 If $\overline{WS} > \overline{TU}$, is R between T and U? Is U between T and R?

19 If $\overline{WS} \cong \overline{TU}$, what do you know about points U and R?

Each sentence in D9 expresses a true statement. Use the sentences to help you answer the questions in exercises 20 through 29.

20 Is $\overline{JK} > \overline{CD}$?

21 Is $\overline{CD} < \overline{LM}$?

22 Is $\overline{LM} > \overline{CD}$?

23 Is $\overline{JK} > \overline{HI}$?

24 Is $\overline{HI} < \overline{JK}$?

25 Is $\overline{LM} < \overline{CD}$?

26 Is $\overline{JK} < \overline{CD}$?

27 Is $\overline{HI} < \overline{LM}$?

28 Is $\overline{LM} > \overline{HI}$?

29 Is $\overline{JK} < \overline{HI}$?

30 Suppose that $\overline{MO} > \overline{RQ}$ and also that $\overline{RQ} > \overline{ST}$. Do you think that $\overline{MO} > \overline{ST}$ is a true statement?

Universe for X
is plane ABC.
$\overline{AX} \cong \overline{AB}$.

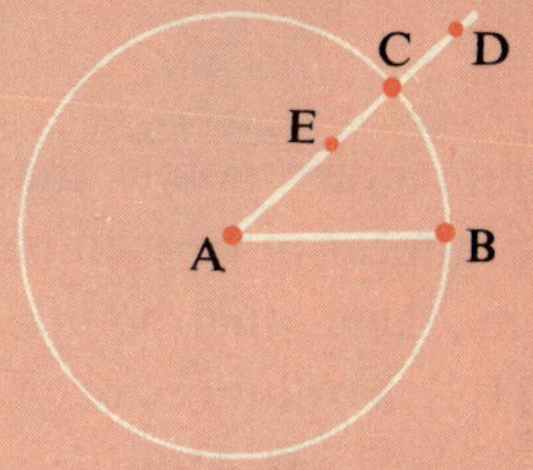

D1

Universe for X is plane ABC.
$\overline{AX} \cong \overline{AB}$.

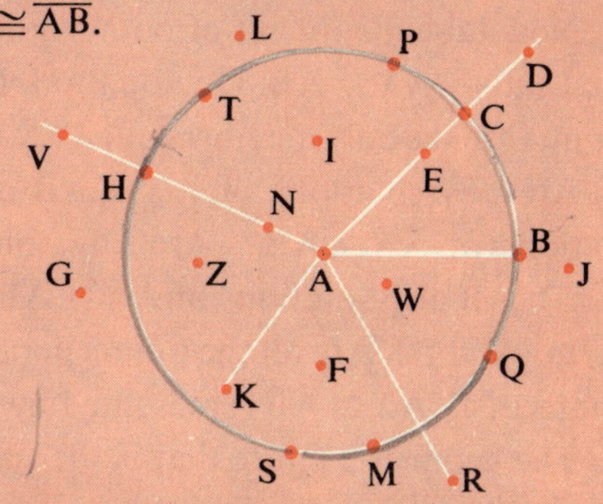

D2

1 | 12 Exploring ideas

The circle

You have studied universes, variables, conditions, and solution sets of conditions. Up to now, the universes and solution sets have been sets of numbers. Variables and conditions are also used with sets of points. Universes and solution sets can be sets of points as well as sets of numbers.

A Study D1. The sentence $\overline{AX} \cong \overline{AB}$ expresses a condition. The variable in the condition is X. What is the universe for X? How do you know that points can be used as replacements for X?

Notice that the letter X, used to express the variable, is a capital letter. This will help you remember that the replacements for X in the condition will be points, not numbers.

You remember that a condition is a requirement that applies to members of the universe. Usually, some members of the universe satisfy the requirement, and some members do not. The condition $\overline{AX} \cong \overline{AB}$ means that each point you are to find must, together with A, determine a segment that is congruent to $\overline{AB}$. Keep in mind that the universe is plane ABC and the points you find must be in the universe.

B Is D in this universe?

When you work with conditions about numbers, you are usually given certain numbers. In $2x = 8$, for example, you are given the numbers 2 and 8. When you work with conditions about points, you will be given certain points. In the condition $\overline{AX} \cong \overline{AB}$, points A and B are given points.

C Look again at D1. Suppose that $\overline{AC} \cong \overline{AB}$. Does C satisfy $\overline{AX} \cong \overline{AB}$? Is C a member of the solution set?

> REMINDER
>
> The solution set of a condition consists of all members of the universe that satisfy the condition.
> A standard description of the solution set of $\overline{AX} \cong \overline{AB}$ is $\{X \mid \overline{AX} \cong \overline{AB}\}$.
> This description is read, "The set of all points X such that segment AX is congruent to segment AB."
> *See lesson 4, page 18. See lesson 7, page 27.*

D Look again at D1. You know that C is a member of $\{X \mid \overline{AX} \cong \overline{AB}\}$. $\overline{AE} < \overline{AC}$, and $\overline{AD} > \overline{AC}$. Is $\overline{AE} < \overline{AB}$? Is $\overline{AD} > \overline{AB}$?

E Are D and E members of $\{X \mid \overline{AX} \cong \overline{AB}\}$?

F Look at D2. You know that B and C are members of $\{X \mid \overline{AX} \cong \overline{AB}\}$. From the display, certain other points that are represented by dots appear to be members of $\{X \mid \overline{AX} \cong \overline{AB}\}$. Name these other points.

G H is a solution of $\overline{AX} \cong \overline{AB}$. $\overline{AN} < \overline{AH}$, and $\overline{AV} > \overline{AH}$. How do you know that neither N nor V is a solution of $\overline{AX} \cong \overline{AB}$?

H Do you think that K satisfies $\overline{AX} \cong \overline{AB}$? Do you think that R satisfies $\overline{AX} \cong \overline{AB}$?

I Now tabulate the set of points named in D2 that satisfy $\overline{AX} \cong \overline{AB}$. Do you think that these points are the only members of $\{X \mid \overline{AX} \cong \overline{AB}\}$?

J Are any solutions of $\overline{AX} < \overline{AB}$ also solutions of $\overline{AX} \cong \overline{AB}$? Are any solutions of $\overline{AX} > \overline{AB}$ also solutions of $\overline{AX} \cong \overline{AB}$?

K Look at D3. Are all the points in plane ABC that satisfy $\overline{AX} \cong \overline{AB}$ represented by dots?

L The geometric figure that is the solution set of $\overline{AX} \cong \overline{AB}$ is a *circle*. Is a circle an infinite set of points?

M Point A is the *centre* of the circle represented in D3. Is A in the solution set of $\overline{AX} \cong \overline{AB}$? Is the centre of the circle a member of the circle?

To name a circle, you may use the name of its centre. The circle represented in D3 is called "circle A."

N Is the centre of the circle an endpoint of $\overline{AB}$? What is the other endpoint of $\overline{AB}$? Is this endpoint in circle A?

A segment one of whose endpoints is the centre of a circle and whose other endpoint is in the circle is a *radius* of the circle.

O Look again at D3. Is $\overline{AB}$ a radius of circle A? Do A and C determine a segment? Is $\overline{AC}$ a radius of circle A? Explain your answers.

You see that a circle can have more than one radius. You use the word *radii* (rā′ dē ī) when you refer to more than one radius.

P Is each point in the circle an endpoint of a radius? For a given circle, how many radii are there?

Universe for X is plane ABC.

$\overline{AX} \cong \overline{AB}$.

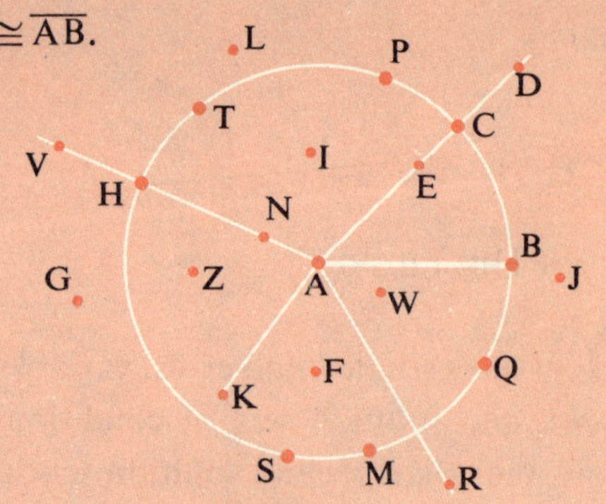

D2

Universe for X is plane ABC.

$\{X \mid \overline{AX} \cong \overline{AB}\}$

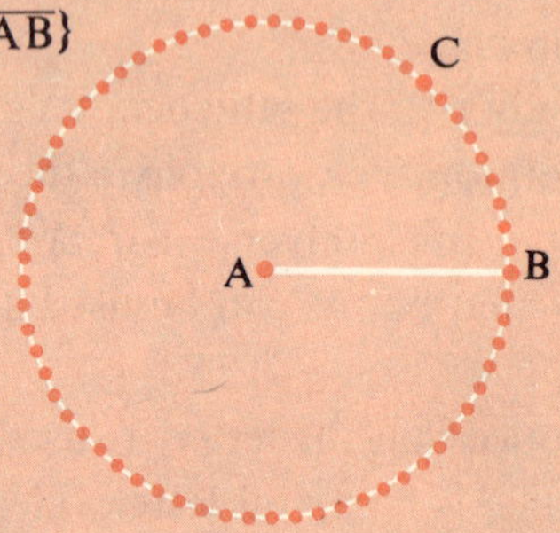

D3

Universe for X is plane AKB.

$\{X \mid \overline{KX} \cong \overline{KC}\}$

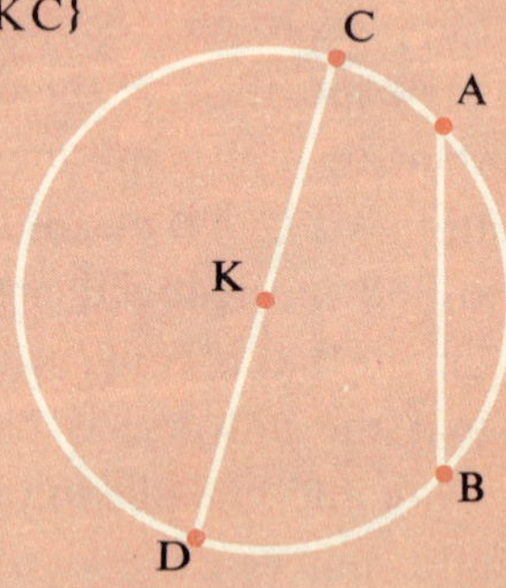

D4

cir cle (sėr′kəl). The set of all points in a plane that satisfy $\overline{RX} \cong \overline{RT}$. The centre of the circle is point R. A segment one of whose endpoints is the centre of the circle and whose other endpoint is in the circle is a **radius** (rā′di əs) of the circle.

Q For a given circle, is each radius congruent to each of the other radii?

R How many centres does a circle have?

If point A is the centre of a circle that has a radius AB, then the circle is the set of all points in a plane that satisfy $\overline{AX} \cong \overline{AB}$. We say that, in a given plane, circle A is determined by point A and radius AB. A circle is determined by a point called the centre and a segment called a radius.

A Name the circle represented in D4. What is the centre of this circle?

B Name the radii represented in D4.

C Is each point in circle K also in plane AKB?

D Is circle K the solution set of $\overline{KX} \cong \overline{KC}$? Is $\{X \mid \overline{KX} \cong \overline{KC}\}$ the same circle as K? Remember that the universe for X is plane AKB.

E Is $\{X \mid \overline{KX} \cong \overline{KD}\}$ also the same circle as K?

F To write a standard description of a circle, what must you know?

G Look again at D4. Are both endpoints of $\overline{AB}$ in circle K? What other segment represented in D4 has both endpoints in circle K?

A segment that has both of its endpoints in a circle is a *chord* of that circle.

H Is $\overline{CD}$ a chord of circle K? Does $\overline{CD}$ contain the centre of circle K?

A chord that contains the centre of a circle is a *diameter* of the circle.

I Is $\overline{CD}$ a diameter of circle K? Is $\overline{AB}$ a diameter of circle K?

J Look at D5. How many radii of circle M are represented? Name them. Name the chords represented. Name the diameters represented.

K How do a radius of a circle and a chord of ? the same circle differ?

L Suppose that E and F are in circle M. Is $\overline{EF}$ a chord of circle M? Do any two points in a circle determine a chord of that circle? Does a circle have infinitely many chords?

Universe for X is plane MCD.

$\{X \mid \overline{MX} \cong \overline{MD}\}$

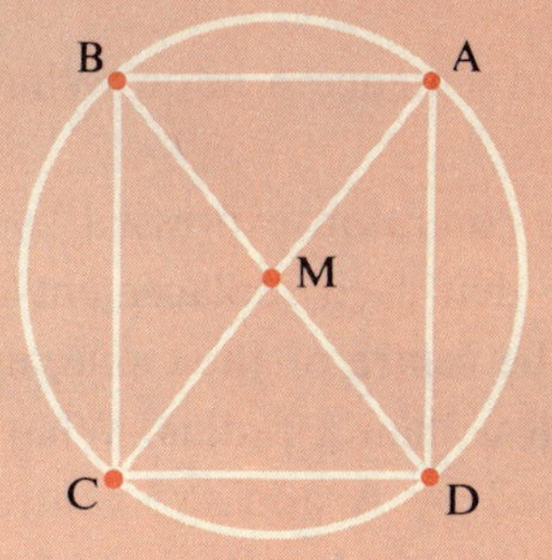

D5

chord of a circle (kôrd). A segment whose endpoints are in a circle. A chord of a circle that contains the centre is a **diameter** (dī am′ə tər) of the circle.

co pla nar points (cō plā′nər). Points that belong to the same plane. A circle is a set of coplanar points.

M Think of any point G in circle M. Is G an endpoint of a diameter of circle M? Is each point in circle M an endpoint of a diameter of circle M? Does a circle have infinitely many diameters?

N Look again at D5. Suppose the universe is ? changed from plane MCD to space. Then what geometric figure is the solution set of $\overline{MX} \cong \overline{MD}$?

You know that all the points in a circle are in the same plane. When all the points of a set belong to the same plane, they are *coplanar points*.

A Are any three given points coplanar? Ex- ? plain your answer.

B Make a sketch to represent four points that ? are not coplanar.

You have been studying the circle. Now you will learn about the interior and the exterior of a circle.

C Look at D6. Is $\overline{RS}$ a radius of circle R? What other radius of circle R is represented in D6?

D Read sentence A in D6. What is the universe for X?

E The condition expressed by sentence A requires that each replacement for X, together with the centre of the circle, determine a segment less than a radius. What segment is determined by A and the centre of the circle? Is this segment less than a radius? Is A a solution of $\overline{RX} < \overline{RS}$?

F $\overline{RT} \cong \overline{RS}$, and $\overline{RG} > \overline{RS}$. Is T a solution of $\overline{RX} < \overline{RS}$? Is G a solution of $\overline{RX} < \overline{RS}$? How do you know?

The solution set of $\overline{RX} < \overline{RS}$ is the *interior* of circle R. The interior of circle R is $\{X \mid \overline{RX} < \overline{RS}\}$.

G What points named in D6 are in the interior of circle R?

H Are there any other points in the interior of circle R? Is the interior of a circle an infinite set of points?

I How do circle R and the interior of circle R ? differ?

J Now read sentence B in D6. Is G a solution of $\overline{RX} > \overline{RS}$? Explain your answer.

K $\overline{RT} \cong \overline{RS}$, and $\overline{RD} < \overline{RS}$. Is T a solution of $\overline{RX} > \overline{RS}$? Is D a solution of $\overline{RX} > \overline{RS}$? How do you know?

The solution set of $\overline{RX} > \overline{RS}$ is the *exterior* of circle R. The exterior of circle R is $\{X \mid \overline{RX} > \overline{RS}\}$.

L What points named in D6 are in the exterior of circle R? Is the exterior of a circle an infinite set of points?

M How do circle R and the exterior of circle R ? differ?

Universe for X is plane RSN.

A $\overline{RX} < \overline{RS}$. **B** $\overline{RX} > \overline{RS}$.

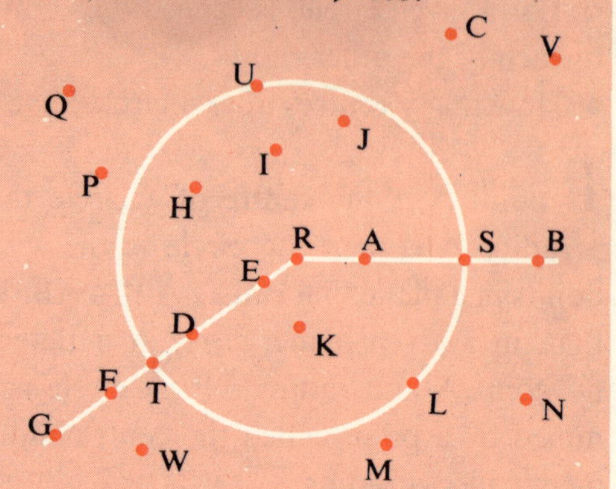

D6

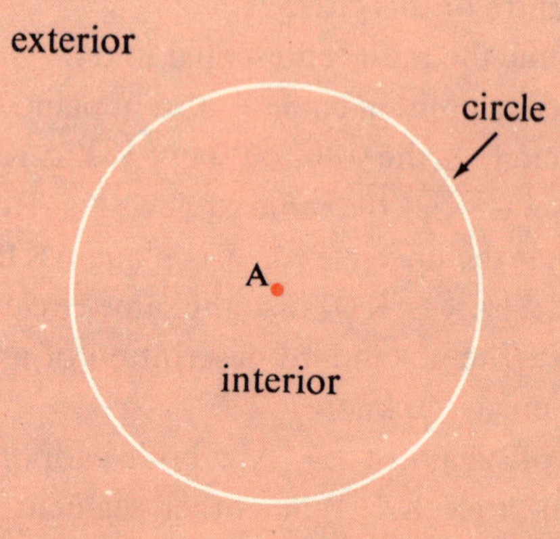

D7

in te ri or of a circle (in tēr′ē ər). The set of all points in a plane that satisfy $\overline{AX} < \overline{AB}$. If $\overline{AB}$ is a radius of circle A, then $\{X \mid \overline{AX} < \overline{AB}\}$ is the interior of circle A. The universe for X is the plane that includes circle A. The points in the interior of a circle and in the circle are coplanar.

ex te ri or of a circle (eks tēr′ē ər). The set of all points in a plane that satisfy $\overline{AX} > \overline{AB}$. If $\overline{AB}$ is a radius of circle A, then $\{X \mid \overline{AX} > \overline{AB}\}$ is the exterior of circle A. The universe for X is the plane that includes circle A. The points in the exterior of a circle and in the circle are coplanar.

You have studied three important geometric figures included in a plane. A geometric figure, all of whose points are coplanar, is called a *plane figure*. The plane figures that you have studied in this lesson are the circle, the interior of a circle, and the exterior of a circle.

N Study D7. Can any point that is in circle A also be in the interior of circle A? Can any point in the exterior of circle A also be in the interior of circle A?

O A circle separates a plane into two *regions*. The circle is the boundary of each region. One region is the interior of the circle. What is the other region? Can you say that each point in the plane is either in one of the regions or in the boundary?

P Suppose that G is in the interior of a circle and H is in the exterior of the same circle. Is there a point in the circle between G and H?

Q Suppose that G and H are in the interior of a circle. Is there a point in the circle between G and H?

In this lesson you have learned about geometric conditions. Now you know that the solution set of a geometric condition is a geometric figure.

On your own

1 Make a sketch of circle A. Now locate B in the exterior of circle A. Use your sketch for exercises 2, 3, and 4.

2 Locate C in the interior of circle A.

3 Locate D in circle A.

4 Make a sketch of radius AE of circle A. Be sure to label the dot that represents E.

5 Now make a sketch of $\overline{FG}$. Use your sketch for exercises 6 through 11.

6 Locate H between F and G.

7 Locate I between H and G.

8 Make a sketch of the circle that has $\overline{FG}$ as a radius and G as a point in the circle.

9 Make a sketch of the circle that has $\overline{FH}$ as a radius and H as a point in the circle.

10 Now make a sketch of the circle that has segment FI as a radius and I as a point in the circle.

11 How many circles can have the same centre?

A standard description of a circle is given in each of exercises 12 through 15. For each exercise, name the circle, the centre, and one radius. The universe is the plane that includes the circle described.

12 $\{X \mid \overline{RX} \cong \overline{RM}\}$

13 $\{X \mid \overline{BC} \cong \overline{CX}\}$

14 $\{X \mid \overline{XL} \cong \overline{KL}\}$

15 $\{X \mid \overline{ED} \cong \overline{XE}\}$

A circle is described in each of exercises 16 through 19. Write a standard description of each circle. The universe is the plane that includes the circle described.

16 Circle with centre at A and a radius AB

17 Circle C with a radius DC

18 Circle E with a radius congruent to $\overline{FG}$

19 Circle with radii HJ and HK

20 What is a standard description of the interior of circle L with a radius LM? The universe is the plane that includes circle L.

21 What is a standard description of the exterior of a circle that has $\overline{NP}$ and $\overline{NQ}$ as two radii? The universe is plane NPQ.

22 The universe for X is the plane that includes circle R. Circle R is $\{X \mid \overline{XR} \cong \overline{TR}\}$. What is a standard description of the interior of circle R?

Make a sketch of circle M. Now locate points E, F, and G in circle M. Use this sketch for exercises 23 through 30.

23 Make a sketch of radius MG.

24 Make a sketch of the radius that has F as an endpoint.

25 Is each radius of a circle congruent to each of the other radii of the circle?

26 Make a sketch of chord EF.

27 Make a sketch of chord EG.

28 Make a sketch of the diameter that has F as an endpoint.

29 Make a sketch of diameter EH. Label the dot that represents H.

30 Is each diameter of a circle congruent to each of the other diameters? Is a diameter congruent to a radius of the same circle?

CHECKING UP

If you have trouble with these two tests, you should restudy lessons 8 through 12.

Test 3

Use D1 for exercises 1 through 8.

1 How many planes include {B, G, D}?

2 How many segments are determined by C and E?

3 What are the endpoints of $\overline{EG}$?

4 What points named are collinear with C and F?

5 What points named are noncollinear with B and G?

6 What points named are between B and F?

7 E separates ℓ_1 into how many half-lines?

8 Think of the half-lines determined by E. What point named is in the same half-line as C? What points named are in ℓ_1 but are not in the same half-line as C?

Test 4

Use D2 for exercises 9 through 16.

9 Name the centre of circle K.

10 Name two radii of circle K.

11 Name two chords of circle K.

12 Name a diameter of circle K.

13 Name 3 points in the interior of circle K.

14 Name 3 points in the exterior of circle K.

15 Name 3 points that are in circle K.

16 Name a pair of congruent segments.

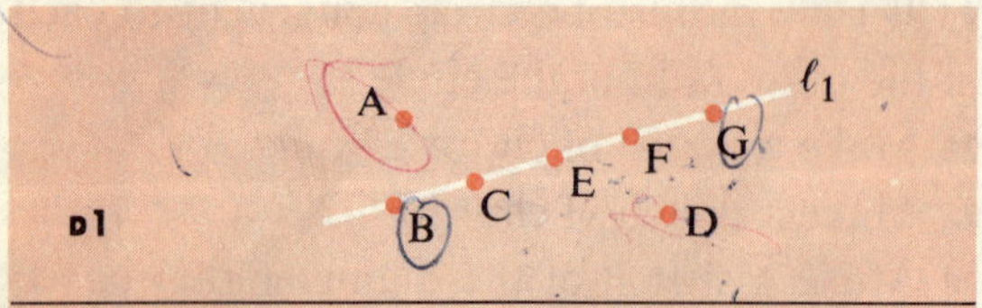

D1

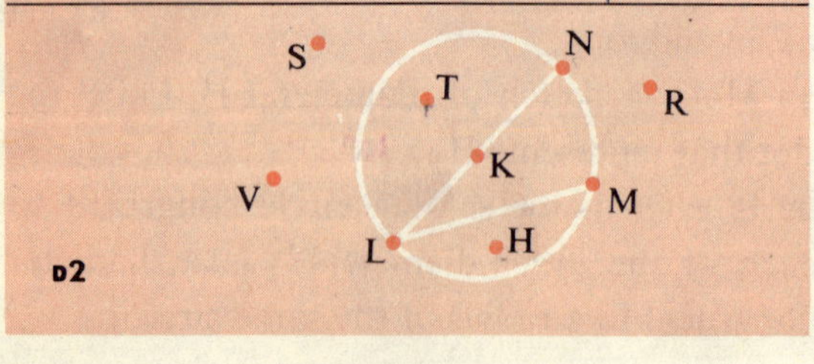

D2

1 | 13 **Exploring ideas**

Number lines and graphs

So far in this book you have been working with sets of objects. First you worked with sets of numbers and with conditions about numbers. Then you worked with sets of points and with conditions about points. In this lesson you first will see how numbers and points are associated. Then you will see how you can use dots to represent a set of numbers.

A Look at the picture of a line in D1 on page 51. How many points in the line are represented by dots?

A natural number can be matched with each point that is represented by a dot. Of course, a line is an infinite set of points, but only those points represented by dots are referred to here. Suppose you match, or assign, the number 0 to the point represented by the dot farthest to the left. You may call this point "point 0."

B What natural number is one more than 0? Assign this number to the point whose dot is immediately to the right of the dot for point 0. Remember that only those points represented by dots are being discussed. Call this point "point 1." D2 shows the numerals for 0 and 1 placed below the first two dots.

C What natural number is one more than 1? What number should be assigned to the point represented by the next dot in D2? What is the name of this point?

So far we have assigned numbers to points. We can also assign points to numbers. In either case, numbers and points are *associated*. When

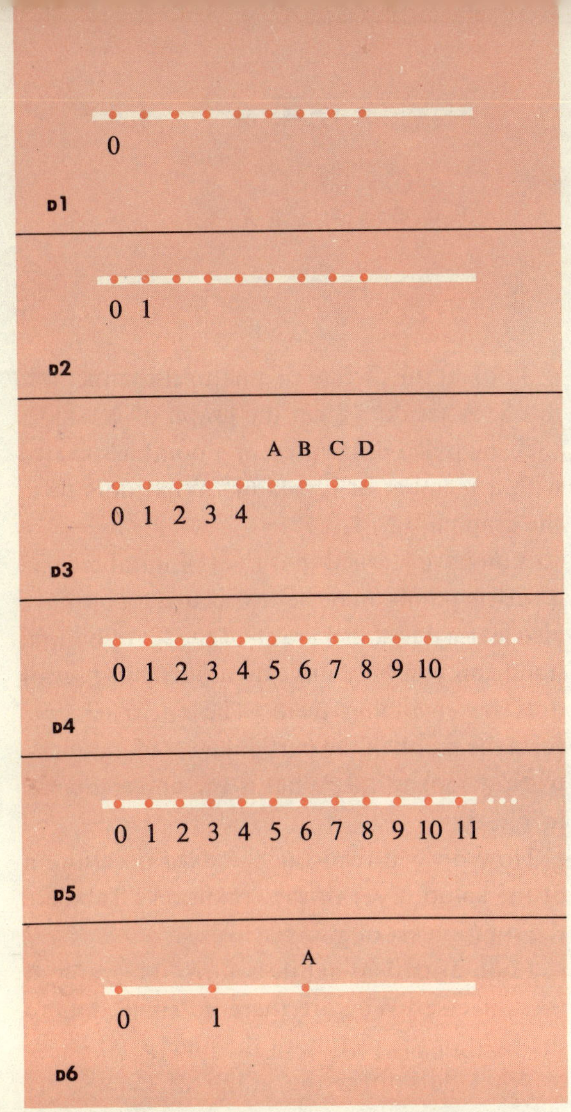

we say "The number 1 is associated with point 1," we mean that the number 1 is assigned to point 1, and that point 1 is assigned to the number 1.

D Look at D3. How many numbers and points have been associated? Why is point 3 to the right of point 2? Why is point 4 to the right of point 3?

E Suppose that you want to locate points to which you can assign natural numbers that are greater than 4. Look again at D3. The points represented by successive dots determine segments. These segments are congruent.

F What numbers should be assigned to points A, B, C, and D represented in D3? Is the segment determined by point 7 and point 8 congruent to the segment determined by point 0 and point 1?

G How would you locate point 9? Point 10?

H Look at D4. You already know that the set of natural numbers is an infinite set. You can think, then, about associating more and more points with the natural numbers. The three small dots to the right of the picture of the line in D4 tell you that the points you can associate with the natural numbers go on and on. Do the points associated with the natural numbers form an infinite set of points?

I A line that has points associated with natural numbers is a *natural-number line*. Is a natural-number line represented in D5?

J In D5, what do the three small dots to the right of the picture of the line represent?

K If more points were located, you could assign a natural number to each of these points. Imagine that you have located all the points to point 50. What points are to the left of point 38?

L What point is represented by the dot immediately to the right of the dot for point 38?

M The universe is the set of natural numbers. Are the points assigned to the members of $\{x \mid x < 26\}$ to the right of point 26 in a natural-number line? To the left of point 26?

N Now look at D6. Is the segment determined by point 0 and point 1 greater than the segment determined by point 0 and point 1 as represented in D5?

O Can you use this new segment to locate points in a natural-number line?

P What number should be assigned to point A represented in D6? How would you locate point 3? Point 4?

Any segment may be selected as the segment determined by point 0 and point 1 in a number line. But once the segment is chosen, it is convenient to use this segment in locating other points.

Point 1 can be located either to the right or to the left of point 0, but it is customary to locate point 1 to the right of point 0, and we have done so in this book.

Now you will see how pictures of natural-number lines are used to help you understand subsets of the set of natural numbers.

Look at D7. The dots in D7 form a picture, or *graph*, of the set of natural numbers. Of course, it is impossible to make a dot for each natural number, but the three small dots to the right of the picture of a line indicate that the dots in the graph of the set of natural numbers form an infinite set.

A Describe the set tabulated in D7.

B In D7 the dot representing point 0 is encircled to show that the number 0 belongs to the set tabulated. Why are the dots representing point 1, point 2, and point 3 also encircled? The four dots that are encircled form a graph of {0, 1, 2, 3}. Is {0, 1, 2, 3} a subset of N?

{0, 1, 2, 3}

D7

graph (graf). The graph of a set of numbers is a set of dots. Each dot in the graph represents a point associated with a member of the set of numbers. Each member of the set of numbers is associated with a point represented by a dot in the graph. The dots below form a graph of the set of natural numbers. The encircled dots form a graph of {3, 4, 5, 6}, a subset of the set of natural numbers.

{2, 4, 6}

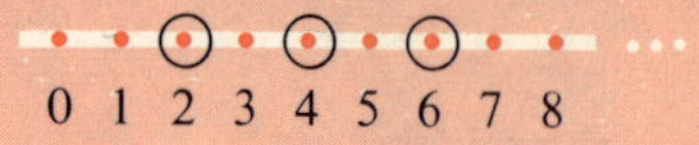

D8

C Look at the picture of a natural-number line in D8. What dots form the graph of N? Does each encircled dot represent a point associated with a member of {2, 4, 6}? What dots form the graph of {2, 4, 6}?

You have learned that a set of numbers and a set of points may be associated. You have also learned that in a graph of the set of natural numbers, you may indicate a particular set of dots by encircling them. The encircled dots form the graph of the particular set of numbers.

D Now look at D9. What is the universe for x in $x < 5$?

E How do you read the standard description of the solution set of the condition? Tabulate the solution set of $x < 5$.

F Look at D10. What dots form the graph of the universe? Why are there no small dots to the right of the picture of the line?

G What dots form the graph of $\{x | x < 5\}$? Why is the dot for point 2 encircled? Why is the dot for point 7 not encircled? Are the dots that form the graph of $\{x | x < 5\}$ a subset of the graph of the universe?

H What is the universe for x in the condition expressed in D11? How is the graph of this universe different from the graph of the universe in D10? What condition is expressed by the sentence $x + 1 < 8$?

I How do you read the standard description of the solution set of $x + 1 < 8$? Tabulate the solution set.

J What dots form the graph of $\{x | x + 1 < 8\}$? Why are certain points in the number line represented by encircled dots? Why is the dot for point 7 not encircled? How is the graph of $\{x \mid x + 1 < 8\}$ related to the graph of the universe?

Remember that to make a graph of a solution set, you first use a picture of a natural-number line to make a graph of the universe. Then you encircle the dots that form the graph of the solution set.

K Look at D12. Tabulate the solution set described.

L Make a graph of the universe and of the solution set described in D12.

M The graph of the solution set of a condition is shown in D13. What is the condition?

Notice that the three small dots to the right of the picture of a line in D13 have been en-

$U = \{0, 1, 2, \ldots, 10\}$.
$x < 5$.
$\{x \mid x < 5\}$

D9

$U = \{0, 1, 2, \ldots, 10\}$.
$\{x \mid x < 5\}$

D10

$U = N$.
$x + 1 < 8$.
$\{x \mid x + 1 < 8\}$

D11

$U = N$.
$\{x \mid x + 3 = 9\}$

D12

$U = N$.
$\{x \mid x + 3 > 9\}$

D13

D14

circled. This tells you that all the dots representing points to the right of point 10 belong to the graph of $\{x \mid x + 3 > 9\}$. The solution set of $x + 3 > 9$ is an infinite set.

N What is the least solution of $x + 3 > 9$? What is the greatest solution?

O Tabulate the solution set of $x + 7 > 12$. $U = N$. Is $\{x \mid x + 7 > 12\}$ an infinite set? Make a graph of this set.

P Tabulate the set of numbers whose graph is shown in D14. Remember that the members of the set are the numbers that are assigned to the points represented by encircled dots.

Q ? The graph of the solution set of a condition is shown in D14. Give a condition whose solution set is shown in the graph. $U = N$.

Now you know how to use a picture of a number line to draw a graph of a set of numbers. You also know that you can use a graph of a set of numbers to make a tabulation of the set.

On your own

For exercises 1 through 8, you are to make a graph of each of the sets tabulated. First make a graph of the set of natural numbers. Extend your picture of the line to contain as many dots as you need for the particular exercise. Then encircle the dots that represent the points associated with the members of each set.

1 {3, 5, 9}
2 {0, 1}
3 {9}
4 {0, 1, 2, . . ., 12}
5 {0, 1, 2, 3, 4}
6 {7, 8, 9, . . .}
7 {5, 6, 4, 7, 0}
8 { }

Tabulate each of the sets of numbers whose graphs are shown in exercises 9 through 13.

9
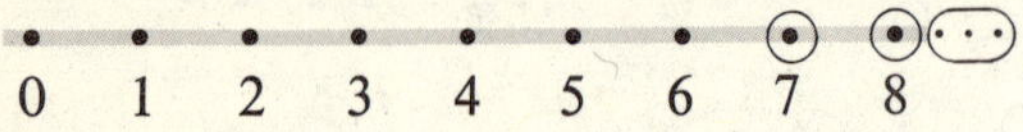

10
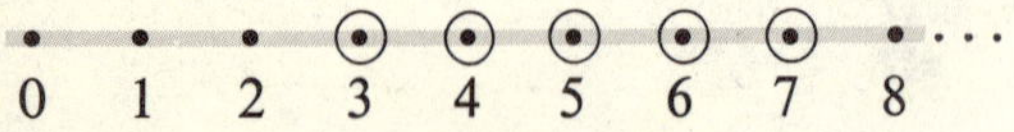

11
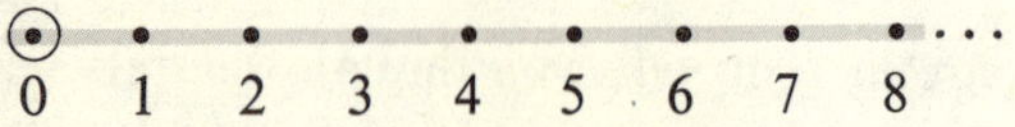

12
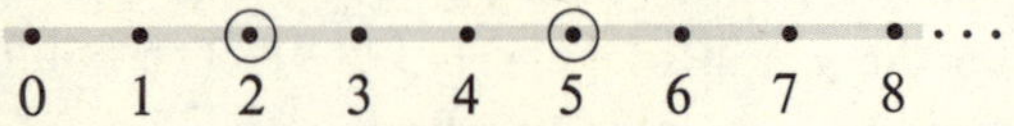

13

Tabulate each solution set described in exercises 14 through 19. Then make a graph of the universe and of the subset described. U = N.

14 $\{x \mid x < 6\}$
15 $\{x \mid x + 3 > 10\}$
16 $\{x \mid x \neq x\}$
17 $\{x \mid 2x < 20\}$
18 $\{x \mid x + 1 = 1 + x\}$
19 $\{x \mid 3x > 2x\}$

For each solution set described in exercises 20 through 23, make a graph of the universe and of the subset described. U = N.

20 $\{x \mid 7 < x\}$
21 $\{x \mid x + 6 > 11\}$
22 $\{x \mid 2x + 1 = 3\}$
23 $\{x \mid 3x + 1 = x\}$

The graphs of two solution sets are shown in exercises 24 and 25. Give a condition for each solution set. U = N.

24
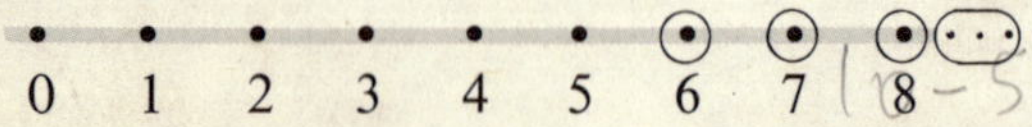

25

CHECKING UP

These tests will help you find out how well you can compute.

Test 5

Add

1 3647, 8492, 6386.
2 7652, 5295, 9821, 1370.
3 4288, 9095, 2927, 4696.
4 1967, 3499, 2028, 356.
5 5026, 428, 7309, 819.
6 9273, 429, 738, 4976.
7 32167, 89450, 89629.
8 14023, 37259, 28435.
9 34276, 8075, 50392.
10 72943, 408, 6661.

Test 6

Subtract

11 54298 from 76032.
12 27292 from 36376.
13 43986 from 72010.
14 385749 from 942617.
15 293872 from 400307.
16 84729 from 620038.
17 96273 from 142968.
18 63672 from 70241.
19 5682 from 12013.
20 7683 from 303452.

Test 7

Multiply

21 48612 by 8.
22 368 by 40.
23 38 by 24.
24 109 by 60.
25 318 by 75.
26 849 by 93.
27 506 by 41.
28 180 by 86.
29 726 by 29.
30 570 by 59.

Test 8

Multiply

31 308 by 900.
32 639 by 796.
33 810 by 593.
34 168 by 321.
35 703 by 327.
36 514 by 548.
37 480 by 307.
38 630 by 180.
39 725 by 905.
40 608 by 305.

Test 9

Divide

41 5184 by 54.
42 1504 by 16.
43 1400 by 40.
44 4450 by 89.
45 2048 by 32.
46 4816 by 43.
47 23850 by 75.
48 13356 by 84.
49 6960 by 29.
50 23923 by 47.

Test 10

Divide

51 7616 by 136.
52 12992 by 224.
53 10791 by 109.
54 29718 by 127.
55 613470 by 726.
56 55480 by 380.
57 37761 by 123.
58 106797 by 367.
59 253495 by 419.
60 150700 by 275.

1 | 14 **Learning computation**

Multiplication

The computation you will use to find solutions of conditions includes multiplication. This lesson will help you review multiplication involving natural numbers.

When you compute, using multiplication, the number you multiply is the *multiplicand*. The number you multiply by is the *multiplier*. The answer you get is the *product*. In $7 \times 4 = 28$, the multiplier is 7; the multiplicand is 4; and the product is 28.

$56 = 50 + 6.$ To multiply 423 by 56, first think of 56 as $50 + 6$.

Imagine that 6 groups of 423 are combined. Multiply 423 by 6.

$$\begin{array}{r} 423 \\ 6 \\ \hline 2538 \end{array} \leftarrow 6 \times 423 = 2538.$$

Now imagine that 50 groups of 423 are combined. Multiply 423 by 50.

$$\begin{array}{r} 423 \\ 50 \\ \hline 21150 \end{array} \leftarrow 50 \times 423 = 21150.$$

You have multiplied 423 by 6 and by 50. Imagine that the 50 groups of 423 are put with the 6 groups of 423. Add 2538 and 21150.

$$\begin{array}{r} 2538 \\ 21150 \\ \hline 23688 \end{array} \leftarrow 56 \times 423 = 23688.$$

You should write all of the work in one place, as shown at the left.

$$\begin{array}{r} 423 \\ 56 \\ \hline 2538 \\ 21150 \\ \hline 23688 \end{array} \begin{array}{l} \\ \\ \leftarrow 6 \times 423 = 2538. \\ \leftarrow 50 \times 423 = 21150. \\ \leftarrow 56 \times 423 = 23688. \end{array}$$

The following exercises will help you multiply 508 by 49.

$49 = 40 + 9.$ First think of 49 as the sum of what two numbers?

$$\begin{array}{r} 508 \\ 49 \\ \hline 4572 \end{array}$$

You first imagine that how many groups of 508 are combined? You multiply 508 by what number? What product do you get?

$$\begin{array}{r} 508 \\ 49 \\ \hline 4572 \\ 20320 \end{array}$$

You next imagine that how many groups of 508 are combined? You multiply 508 by what number? What product do you get?

$$\begin{array}{r} 508 \\ 49 \\ \hline 4572 \\ 20320 \\ \hline 24892 \end{array}$$

Why is the numeral 20320 written under the numeral 4572? Why do you add 4572 and 20320? What product do you obtain when you multiply 508 by 49?

The work that follows will help you multiply 276 by 394. First think of 394 as $300 + 90 + 4$.

$$\begin{array}{r} 276 \\ 394 \\ \hline 1104 \end{array}$$

You first imagine that how many groups of 276 are combined? You multiply 276 by what number? What product do you get?

276 394 1104 24840	You next imagine that how many groups of 276 are combined? You multiply 276 by what number? What product do you get?
276 394 1104 24840 82800	You then imagine that how many groups of 276 are combined? You multiply 276 by what number? What product do you get?
276 394 1104 24840 82800 108744	What product is obtained when you multiply 276 by 394?

For each of exercises A through F, find the product. After you complete your work, compare it with the work given below the exercise.

A Multiply 47092 by 7.

```
 47092
     7
------
329644
```

B Multiply 469 by 80.

```
  469
   80
-----
37520
```

C Multiply 568 by 38.

```
  568
   38
-----
 4544
17040
-----
21584
```

D Multiply 196 by 408.

```
  196
  408
-----
 1568
78400
-----
79968
```

E Multiply 8692 by 24.

```
  8692
    24
------
 34768
173840
------
208608
```

F Multiply 716 by 490.

```
   716
   490
------
 64440
286400
------
350840
```

Now you know how to multiply.

On your own

Multiply

1 95763 by 9.
2 98 by 76.
3 167 by 45.
4 4382 by 78.
5 659 by 52.
6 3759 by 800.
7 302 by 178.
8 412 by 645.
9 382 by 791.
10 107 by 570.
11 902 by 405.
12 780 by 208.

1 15 Learning computation

Preparation for division

This lesson will help you review certain ideas you need to understand when you divide.

In your work in arithmetic, you learned about rounding numbers. 7614 can be rounded to the next greater thousand, 8000, or to the next lesser thousand, 7000. It can be rounded to the next greater hundred, 7700, or to the next lesser hundred, 7600. 7614 can also be rounded to the next greater ten, 7620, or to the next lesser ten, 7610.

A If you round 42,304 to the next greater thousand, do you get 43,000? If you round 42,304 to the next lesser hundred, do you get 42,300?

B Round 217 to the next greater hundred. To the next lesser hundred. To the next lesser ten.

C Round 4568 to the next lesser thousand. To the next greater ten. To the next lesser hundred.

D Round 74 to the next lesser ten. Round 72,468 to the next lesser hundred.

E Round 592 to the next greater hundred. Round 17,009 to the next lesser thousand.

When you compute using division, the number you divide is the *dividend*. The number you divide by is the *divisor*. The answer you get is the *quotient*. In $28 \div 4 = 7$, the dividend is 28; the divisor is 4; and the quotient is 7.

When we say "the quotient of 30 and 5," we mean the number that is obtained when the first number, 30, is divided by the second number, 5. The quotient of 30 and 5 is 6.

F What is the quotient of 24 and 6? Divide both 24 and 6 by 2. What two numbers do you get? What is the quotient of these two numbers?

G When you divide 24 by 6, do you get the same quotient as when you divide 12 by 3?

H The quotient of 270 and 90 is 3. Divide both the dividend and the divisor by 10. What two numbers do you get? What is the quotient of these two numbers?

I Is the quotient of 270 and 90 the same as the quotient of 27 and 9?

J The quotient of 5600 and 700 is 8. Divide both the dividend and the divisor by 100. What two numbers do you get? What is the quotient of these two numbers?

K Is the quotient of 5600 and 700 the same as the quotient of 56 and 7?

To show that you have divided both 270 and 90 by 10, you can write the sentence $27\not{0} \div 9\not{0} = 3$. To show that you have divided both 5600 and 700 by 100, you can write the sentence $56\not{0}\not{0} \div 7\not{0}\not{0} = 8$.

L If you divide both the dividend and the divisor by the same number, is the quotient changed?

M What is the quotient of 15 and 3? Multiply both 15 and 3 by 3. What two numbers do you get? What is the quotient of these two numbers?

N When you divide 15 by 3, do you get the same quotient as when you divide 45 by 9?

O What is the quotient of 24 and 8? Multiply both the dividend and the divisor by 100. What numbers do you get?

P The quotient of 2400 and 800 is 3. When you divide 24 by 8, do you get the same quotient as when 2400 is divided by 800?

Q If you multiply both the dividend and the divisor by the same number (except 0), is the quotient changed?

Now you know how to round numbers. You also know that when you multiply or divide both the dividend and the divisor by the same number (except 0), the quotient remains the same.

On your own

For exercises 1 through 9, round each of the numbers named to the next greater hundred, to the next lesser hundred, and to the next greater ten. For exercise 1, you write the numerals 400, 300, 370.

1 362	**4** 9836	**7** 760
2 815	**5** 3178	**8** 4105
3 427	**6** 19,368	**9** 24,214

For exercises 10 through 18, round each of the numbers named to the next greater thousand, to the next lesser hundred, and to the next lesser ten.

10 2476	**13** 7638	**16** 17,803
11 6911	**14** 53,259	**17** 8910
12 4532	**15** 42,015	**18** 2596

For each of exercises 19 through 32, first tell how the second dividend or divisor was obtained from the first. Then find the missing number. For exercise 19, you could write: "Divide by 100. The missing divisor is 8."

	Dividend	Divisor		Dividend	Divisor
19	2400	800	**21**	360	40
	24	?		?	4
20	4	2	**22**	28	7
	?	8		280	?

	Dividend	Divisor		Dividend	Divisor
23	72	8	**28**	32	8
	?	1		?	2
24	3200	800	**29**	15	3
	32	?		1500	?
25	54	6	**30**	4800	80
	?	600		?	8
26	81,000	90	**31**	21	3
	?	9		?	9
27	24	3	**32**	28,000	400
	240	?		280	?

1 16 Learning computation

Division

When you find the solutions of some conditions, you will need to use division. This lesson will help you review division involving natural numbers.

To find the quotient of 3057 and 39, you can use the ideas you reviewed in the last lesson. It is helpful to round the divisor to a greater number and the dividend to a lesser number. When you round the numbers in this way, you will always get a quotient that you can use. First round the divisor, 39, to the next greater ten, 40. Then round the dividend, 3057, to 2800 because you know that the quotient of 2800 and 40 is 70. Would it be sensible to round the dividend to 2900? To 3000?

```
                 2800 ÷ 40 = 70.
39)3057 | 70 ←—— Use 70 groups of 39.
   2730 | ←————— 70 × 39 = 2730.
    327 | ←————— Subtract 2730 from 3057
                 to find how many are left
                 to divide into groups of
                 39.
```

```
                 Next divide 327 by 39.
                 Round the 39 to 40 and
39)3057 | 70     the 327 to 320.
   2730 |        320 ÷ 40 = 8.
    327 |  8 ←—— Use 8 groups of 39.
    312 | ←————— 8 × 39 = 312.
     15 | ←————— 327 − 312 = 15.
```

```
                 Since 15 is less than 39,
39)3057 | 70     you cannot remove an-
   2730 |        other group of 39.
    327 |  8     Add the groups of 39.
    312 |        70 + 8 = 78.
     15 | 78 ←—— There are 78 groups of 39.
      ↑————————— 15 is left over. 15 is the
                 remainder.
```

The work below will help you find the quotient of 5423 and 78. Will you round 78 to 80? Will you round 5423 to 4800? Explain your answers. Why will you first use 60 groups of 78?

```
78)5423 | 60
   4680 |
    743 |
```

What product do you get when you multiply 78 by 60? Why do you subtract 4680 from 5423?

Next you divide 743 by 78. Round 78 to what number?

```
78)5423 | 60
   4680 |
    743 |  9
    702 |
     41 |
```

Round 743 to what number?

What is the quotient of 720 and 80? Why do you now use 9 groups of 78?

What product do you get when you multiply 78 by 9?

Why do you subtract 702 from 743?

```
78)5423 | 60
   4680 |
    743 |  9
    702 |
     41 | 69
```

How do you know that you cannot remove another group of 78?

How do you find the total number of groups of 78? Is there a remainder?

There are how many groups of 78 in 5423? What is the remainder?

The exercises that follow will help you find the quotient of 38,793 and 193. First round the divisor, 193, to 200. Then round the dividend, 38,793, to 20,000. You use 20,000 because you can easily find the quotient of 20,000 and 200.

What is the quotient of 200~~00~~ and 2~~00~~?

```
193)38793 | 100
    19300 |
    19493 |
```

Why will you first use 100 groups of 193?

What product do you get when you multiply 193 by 100?

Why do you subtract 19,300 from 38,793?

```
193)38793 | 100
    19300 |
    19493 |  90
    17370 |
     2123 |
```

Next you divide 19,493 by 193.

You round 193 to what number?

You round 19,493 to what number?

What is the quotient of 18,000 and 200?

Why do you now use 90 groups of 193?

What product do you get when you multiply 193 by 90?

Why do you subtract 17,370 from 19,493?

```
193)38793 | 100
    19300 |
    19493 |  90
    17370 |
     2123 |  10
     1930 |
      193 |
```

Now you divide 2123 by 193. Round 193 to what number? Round 2123 to what number?

What is the quotient of 2000 and 200? Why do you use 10 groups of 193?

What product do you get when you multiply 193 by 10?

Why do you subtract 1930 from 2123?

Can you remove another group of 193?

```
193)38793 | 100
    19300 |
    19493 |  90
    17370 |
     2123 |  10
     1930 |
      193 |   1
      193 |
        0 | 201
```

What is the quotient of 193 and 193?

How do you find the total number of groups of 193?

Is the remainder 0?

What is the quotient of 38,793 and 193?

The work below shows the first steps you used in finding the quotient of 38,793 and 193.

```
                        200ØØ ÷ 2ØØ = 100.
193)38793 | 100 ←—————— Use 100 groups of 193.
    19300 | ←—————————— 100 × 193 = 19300.
    19493 | ←—————————— 38793 − 19300 = 19493.
```

```
193)38793 | 100
    19300 |
    19493 | 100
    19300 |
      193 |   1
      193 |
        0 | 201
```

Next you divided 19,493 by 193. What product do you get when you multiply 193 by 100?

Can you remove another 100 groups of 193 instead of 90 groups of 193? Explain your answer.

Sometimes it is very helpful to round the divisor and dividend. At other times, it is not necessary to round them. You can decide for yourself when you should round the dividend and divisor.

For each of exercises A through D, find the quotient. Then compare your work with the work shown below the exercises. The groups you used may not be the same as those shown below, but the answer should be the same.

A Divide 3000 by 56.

```
56)3000 | 50
   2800 |
    200 |  3
    168 |
     32 | 53
```

B Divide 2323 by 101.

```
101)2323 | 20
    2020 |
     303 |  3
     303 |
       0 | 23
```

C Divide 15603 by 538.

```
538)15603 | 20
    10760 |
     4843 |  8
     4304 |
      539 |  1
      538 |
        1 | 29
```

D Divide 50025 by 72.

```
72)50025 | 600
   43200 |
    6825 |  80
    5760 |
    1065 |  10
     720 |
     345 |   4
     288 |
      57 | 694
```

Now you know how to divide.

On your own

Divide

1 2840 by 29.
2 6302 by 46.
3 11700 by 38.
4 33040 by 74.
5 49640 by 246.
6 36320 by 89.
7 84384 by 308.
8 96600 by 190.
9 5000 by 19.
10 104000 by 759.
11 343200 by 65.
12 132615 by 315.
13 70000 by 563.
14 29700 by 605.

KEEPING SKILFUL

Find the sum.

1 7985, 856, 114
2 294, 703, 5578
3 7216, 6532, 1187
4 5769, 3014, 83118
5 18568, 88923
6 95410, 588736

Find the difference.

7 5701, 843
8 8563, 8097
9 7275, 5086
10 11345, 7649
11 90357, 89756
12 74001, 63428

Multiply

13 68 by 34.
14 1357 by 7.
15 80 by 54.
16 706 by 89.
17 145 by 86.
18 758 by 900.
19 150 by 408.
20 426 by 534.

Divide

21 4641 by 53.
22 3342 by 68.
23 2809 by 24.
24 16068 by 52.
25 2088 by 124.
26 16929 by 213.
27 31416 by 154.
28 18373 by 123.

For each of exercises 29 through 38, tabulate the solution set. $U = \{0, 2, 4, 6, 8, 10, 12\}$.

29 $x + 5 = 11$.
30 $5(3) > m$.
31 $12 - d = 4$.
32 $14 > 8 + s$.
33 $2v = 8$.
34 $3 < b + 2$.
35 $n + 3 = 6$.
36 $d > 76 \div 19$.
37 $x + 9 = 21$.
38 $s < 15 - s$.

For each of exercises 39 through 48, tabulate the solution set. $U = N$.

39 $27 + n = 41$.
40 $x + 9 < 17$.
41 $m + 21 = 59$.
42 $s + s > 14$.
43 $26 + n = 11$.
44 $f + f = 16$.
45 $6n = 35$.
46 $13 + d > 12$.
47 $2x = x$.
48 $21(8) > v$.

For each solution set described in exercises 49 through 56, make a graph of the universe and of the solution set described. $U = N$.

49 $\{n \mid n < 9\}$
50 $\{s \mid s + 2 > 3\}$
51 $\{b \mid b + b = 8\}$
52 $\{d \mid d + 3 > 2\}$
53 $\{w \mid w + 3 < w + 4\}$
54 $\{f \mid f \neq f\}$
55 $\{x \mid 13 + x < 14\}$
56 $\{m \mid m + 4 > 4\}$

1 | 17 Exploring problems

Problems involving conditions for equality

In this lesson you will learn to write sentences that express conditions for equality for problems. U = N.

When you read a problem, you actually read sentences that express a problem. Before you can answer the question asked, you must think about the condition for the problem. The work below shows how to develop the condition for the problem in D1. The markers represent coins.

You know how many quarters Sue had at first. Because Sue had 15 quarters to begin with, use 15 in the condition.

15

n

Sue spent some quarters, but you do not know how many. You can use n as a variable for the number of quarters she spent.

You can use $15 - n$ in the condition. $15 - n$ refers to the number of quarters Sue had left.

$15 - n$

9

You know that Sue had 9 quarters left. You can also use 9 for the number of quarters she had left.

$15 - n = 9.$ Now you have the condition for the problem.

Sue had 15 quarters. After she spent some of them, she had 9 quarters left. How many quarters did Sue spend?

D1

George collects coins. After Joe gave him 5 coins, he had 39 coins. How many coins did George have before Joe gave him the 5 coins?

D2

Read the problem in D2. The work that follows shows how to develop the condition for the problem.

You do not know how many coins were in George's collection at first. You can use x as a variable for the number of coins he had at first.

x

You know that Joe gave 5 coins to George. You can use $x + 5$ in the condition. $x + 5$ refers to the number of coins George had then.

$x + 5$

39

You know how many coins George had after Joe had given him 5. You can also use 39 for the number of coins George had then.

$x + 5 = 39.$ Now you have the condition for the problem.

In later lessons you will find solution sets of conditions like $15 - n = 9$ and $x + 5 = 39$. The solutions of the conditions will be used to obtain the answers to the problems.

A Reread the problem in D1. Why is $15 - n$, and not $15 + n$, used in the condition for the problem?

B Why is the idea of equality used in the condition?

C Reread the problem in D2. Why is $x + 5$, and not $x - 5$, used in the condition for the problem?

D Why is the idea of equality used in the condition?

E What name is given to such conditions as $15 - n = 9$ and $x + 5 = 39$?

Read the problem in D3. First you will develop the condition for the problem.

F Is 17 the number of model cars Ernie had in May? 17

G Do you know how many model cars he built during the summer? For what is n a variable? n

H Why is $17 + n$ used in the condition instead of $17 - n$? $17 + n$

I Did Ernie have 32 model cars at the end of the summer? 32

J Why do you use the idea of equality in the condition? $17 + n = 32.$

Read the problem in D4. First it is necessary to develop the condition for the problem.

K Do you know how many stamps Ann bought? For what is y a variable? y

L Why is $y - 14$ used in the condition instead of $y + 14$? $y - 14$

M Does Ann have 18 stamps left? 18

N Why do you use the idea of equality in the condition? $y - 14 = 18.$

Read the problem in D5. Then read the sentence in D5 that expresses the condition for the problem.

Sue had 15 quarters. After she spent some of them, she had 9 quarters left. How many quarters did Sue spend?

D1

George collects coins. After Joe gave him 5 coins, he had 39 coins. How many coins did George have before Joe gave him the 5 coins?

D2

In May, Ernie had 17 model cars. During the summer, he built some more cars. Then he had 32 model cars. How many model cars did Ernie build during the summer?

D3

Ann bought some postage stamps. She has used 14 of them. Now she has 18 stamps left. How many stamps did Ann buy?

D4

The temperature was 38 degrees above zero at 6 A.M. By noon it had risen 7 degrees. What was the temperature at noon?

$$38 + 7 = x.$$

D5

Nancy had 25 tickets to sell for the school play. She has sold 14 of these tickets. How many tickets does Nancy have left to sell?

$$25 - 14 = n.$$

D6

O For what is x a variable?

P Why is $38 + 7$ used in the condition instead of $38 - 7$? Why is the idea of equality used in the condition?

Read the problem in D6. Then read the sentence in D6 that expresses the condition for the problem.

Q For what is n a variable?

R Why is $25 - 14$ used in the condition instead of $25 + 14$? Why is the idea of equality used in the condition?

In some problems, you must compare the number of objects in one group with the number of objects in another group. Now you will learn how to develop conditions for problems of this kind.

Read the problem in D7 and the sentence that expresses the condition for the problem. You will learn why you can use $37 - 26 = x$ as the condition for this problem.

A How many dimes are there? How many nickels are there?

You cannot, of course, remove the group of 26 nickels from the group of 37 dimes, but you can remove a group of dimes equal in number to the group of nickels. Imagine that a group of 26 dimes is removed from the group of 37 dimes. The number of dimes left tells you how many more dimes than nickels Joe has.

When you find how many more or how many fewer objects there are in one group than in another, you are finding the *difference* of the numbers of objects in the two groups. When we say "the difference of 100 and 74," we mean that the second number, 74, is subtracted from the first number, 100. The difference of 100 and 74 is 26.

In this kind of comparison problem, there are three things to think about: the number of objects in the larger group, the number of objects in the smaller group, and the difference of the numbers.

Joe has 37 dimes and 26 nickels. He has how many more dimes than nickels?

$$37 - 26 = x.$$

D7

Joe has 11 more dimes than nickels. He has 26 nickels. How many dimes does he have?

$$x - 26 = 11.$$

D8

Now read the problem in D8. You will learn why you can use $x - 26 = 11$ as the condition for this comparison problem.

B In this problem, what two groups are compared?

C Do you know the number of objects in the larger group? Do you know the number of objects in the smaller group?

D Which does the x in the condition refer to, the number of dimes or the number of nickels? The 26 refers to the number of dimes in a group that has the same number of objects as the group of nickels.

E How many more objects are there in the larger group than in the smaller group?

F Is 11 the difference of the numbers?

G Which does the problem in D8 ask you to find, the number of objects in the larger group, the number of objects in the smaller group, or the difference of the numbers? How do you know?

H Why do you imagine that a group of 26 dimes has been removed from the total group of dimes? Will the number of dimes left be the same as the difference of the numbers in the two groups?

Joe has 11 fewer nickels than dimes. He has 37 dimes. How many nickels does he have?

$$37 - x = 11.$$

D9

Read the problem in D9. You will learn why you can use $37 - x = 11$ as the condition for this comparison problem.

I What two groups have been compared in this problem?

J Do you know the number of objects in the larger group? In the smaller group?

K The 37 in the condition refers to the number of objects in which group? The x refers to the number of dimes in a group that has the same number of objects as what other group?

L Is 11 the difference of the numbers?

M Which does the problem in D9 ask you to find, the number of objects in the larger group, the number of objects in the smaller group, or the difference of the numbers?

N Why do you imagine that a group of dimes is removed from the 37 dimes? Does the group removed have the same number of objects as the group of nickels? Will the number of dimes left be the same as the difference of the numbers in the two groups?

Now you know how to write sentences that express conditions for equality for problems.

On your own

For each problem, write a sentence that expresses the condition for the problem. Use whatever letter you wish to express the variable. Do not find the solution set. U = N.

1 When Margaret went to camp, she weighed 98 pounds. She lost 3 pounds while she was at camp. How many pounds did Margaret weigh when she came home from camp?

2 Sam scored 6 points during the first quarter of a basketball game. By the end of the second quarter, he had scored a total of 14 points. How many points did Sam score during the second quarter?

3 Judy promised to make 12 posters for a school party. She has made 8 of the posters. How many more posters does she need to make?

4 The height of Mt. McKinley in the United States is 20,320 feet. The height of Mt. King in Canada is 17,130 feet. Mt. McKinley is how many feet higher than Mt. King?

5 In a federal election in 1957, 92,858 votes were cast in Newfoundland, and 394,130 votes were cast in Nova Scotia. How many votes in all were cast in these two provinces?

6 Jerry had 72 cents. He spent some of this money and had 63 cents left. How many cents did Jerry spend?

7 There were 3,638 Canadian post offices in 1868. By 1958 there were 12,500 post offices. How many more Canadian post offices were there in 1958 than in 1868?

8 Mr. Martin bought 40 lambs at a sale. Then he had a total of 117 lambs. How many lambs did Mr. Martin have before he bought the 40 lambs?

9 During a baseball season, Lou Gehrig of the New York Yankees hit 34 more doubles than triples. He hit 18 triples. How many doubles did he hit?

10 After Helen spent 34¢ of the money in her purse, she had 18¢ left. How many cents did Helen have in her purse before she spent the 34¢?

11 Alice collects pictures of famous singers. She has 63 pictures of folk singers. She has 25 fewer pictures of opera singers than she has of folk singers. How many pictures of opera singers does Alice have?

1 | 18 **Exploring problems**

Problems involving conditions for inequality

Conditions help you to solve problems. You have made conditions for equality for some problems. You will now learn to make conditions for inequality for problems. U = N.

Read the problem in D1. First you will develop the condition for this problem.

You know how many airplanes Allan has and how many airplanes Pete has. The markers below represent the boys' airplanes.

13  Allan has 13 airplanes.

10 Pete has 10 airplanes.

Imagine that Pete's airplanes are put with Allan's airplanes. Because the 10 airplanes are put with the 13 airplanes, you use $13 + 10$ in the condition. $13 + 10$ refers to the total number of airplanes that Allan and Pete have.

$13 + 10$

You do not know how many airplanes Jim can have, but you do know that, together, Allan and Pete have more airplanes than Jim.

x

$13 + 10 > x.$

Use x as a variable for the number of airplanes Jim can have. Together, Allan and Pete have more airplanes than Jim has. Now you have the condition for the problem.

Allan has 13 model airplanes, and Pete has 10. Together, Allan and Pete have more model airplanes than Jim. How many model airplanes can Jim have?

D1

Margaret bought 27 post cards. She mailed some of them and then had fewer than 8 post cards left. How many post cards could Margaret have mailed?

D2

Now read the problem in D2. The first thing to do is to develop the condition for the problem. You know the number of post cards Margaret bought. The markers at the left represent the 27 post cards that Margaret bought.

27

Margaret mailed some post cards, but you do not know how many. Use n as a variable for the number of post cards that Margaret could have mailed.

n

Because she removed some of the 27 post cards, use $27 - n$ in the condition. $27 - n$ refers to the number of cards she had left.

$27 - n$

$27 - n < 8.$

Margaret had fewer than 8 post cards left. Now you have the condition for the problem.

In later lessons you will find solution sets of conditions like $13 + 10 > x$ and $27 - n < 8$. The solutions of the conditions will be used to obtain answers to the problems.

A Read the problem in D1 again. Why is $13 + 10$, and not $13 - 10$, in the condition for this problem?

B Now reread the problem in D2. Why is $27 - n$, and not $27 + n$, in this condition?

C What name is given to such conditions as ? $13 + 10 > x$ and $27 - n < 8$? How are these conditions different from the conditions you made for problems in lesson 17?

Read the problem in D3. You will develop the condition for this problem.

D Do you know how many boards Ken could have bought? For what is x a variable?

x

E Is 16 the number of boards that Ken used?

16

F Why is $x - 16$ used in the condition instead of $x + 16$? Why is $x - 16$ used to refer to the number of boards that Ken had left?

$x - 16$

G Why is the idea of "less than" used in the condition?

$x - 16 < 5.$

Read the problem in D4. The exercises that follow will help you to develop the condition for this problem.

H Do you know how many snapshots Judy could have had at first? For what is n a variable?

n

I Is 9 the number of new snapshots that Judy put into her album?

9

J Why is $n + 9$, and not $n - 9$, used in the condition? For what do you use $n + 9$?

$n + 9$

K Why is the idea of "greater than" used in the condition?

$n + 9 > 50.$

Read the problem in D5. A sentence that expresses the condition for the problem is also shown.

L For what is n a variable?

Allan has 13 model airplanes, and Pete has 10. Together, Allan and Pete have more model airplanes than Jim. How many model airplanes can Jim have?

D1

Margaret bought 27 post cards. She mailed some of them and then had fewer than 8 post cards left. How many post cards could Margaret have mailed?

D2

Ken bought some boards to build a bookcase and a shelf. He used 16 of the boards and had fewer than 5 boards left. How many boards could Ken have bought?

D3

After Judy put 9 new snapshots into her album, she had more than 50 snapshots in it. How many snapshots could Judy have had in her album before she put in the 9 new ones?

D4

Martha had 73 shells. She gave 18 of the shells to Rosemary. Then Martha had fewer shells than Ruth. How many shells could Ruth have had?

$$73 - 18 < n.$$

D5

M Why is $73 - 18$, and not $73 + 18$, used in the condition? What does $73 - 18$ refer to in the problem? Why is the idea of "less than" used in the condition?

Read the problem in D6. A sentence that expresses the condition is also shown.

N For what is y a variable?

O Why is $15 + y$, and not $15 - y$, used in the condition? For what do you use $15 + y$? Why is the idea of "greater than" used in the condition?

P Read the problem in D7. You are to write a sentence that expresses the condition for this problem. For what, in the problem, will you use a variable?

Q Why will you use $10 + 5$, and not $10 - 5$, in the condition?

R Why will you use the idea of "less than" in the condition?

S Write a sentence that expresses the condition for the problem.

Now you know how to write sentences that express conditions for inequality for problems.

On your own

For each problem write a sentence that expresses the condition. To express the variable, use whatever letter you wish. Do not find the solution set. U = N.

1 Dick had $7. After he earned $3, he had more dollars than John. How many dollars could John have had?

2 Ann bought 24 buttons. After she had sewed some of the buttons on a dress, she had more than 12 buttons left. How many buttons could Ann have sewed on the dress?

3 Virginia spent less than 75 cents for a notebook and pencils. She spent 49 cents for the notebook. How many cents could she have spent for the pencils?

4 Fred sold 29 papers, and Jim sold 33 papers. Together, Fred and Jim sold fewer papers than Don. How many papers could Don have sold?

5 Jane put 8 fish into her aquarium. Then she had more than 19 fish in the aquarium. How many fish could have been in the aquarium before Jane put in the 8 fish?

George had 15 arrowheads. After he found some more on his vacation, he had more than 40 arrowheads. How many arrowheads could George have found on his vacation?

$$15 + y > 40.$$

D6

Sarah had 10 phonograph records. She bought 5 more records, but she still has fewer records than Alice. How many phonograph records can Alice have?

D7

6 The total population of Saskatchewan and Manitoba is less than 1,810,000. The population of Manitoba is 885,000. What can the population of Saskatchewan be?

7 Jay had 17 feet of track for his miniature railroad. He bought more track and now has more than 31 feet of track. How many feet of track could Jay have bought?

8 A school auditorium can seat three hundred persons. Fewer than twelve seats were empty for the school play. How many persons could have attended the school play?

9 The area of Ontario is 412,582 square miles. The area of New Brunswick is 28,354 square miles. The difference in area of these provinces is greater than the area of British Columbia. What can be the area of British Columbia?

THINK What two groups are compared in problem 9?

10 During the year, Miss Green added $300 to her savings account. By the end of the year, she had more than $850 in her account. How many dollars could she have had in her account at the beginning of the year?

11 Ralph has 26 model cars. John has fewer model cars than Ralph. The difference in the number of cars they have is less than 9. How many model cars can John have?

12 Together, the students at Flint School and at Boone School collected less than $425 for playground equipment. The students at Boone collected $195. How many dollars could the students at Flint have collected?

13 Mr. Williams owns a ranch in Alberta. He sold 1280 acres of his land. Now he has more than 2480 acres of land left. How many acres of land could Mr. Williams have owned before he sold the 1280 acres?

KEEPING SKILFUL

Make one sketch for exercises 1 through 5.

1 Make a sketch of a plane.

2 Locate points A, B, and C in the plane. A, B, and C are noncollinear.

3 How many lines are determined by points A, B, and C? Make sketches of these lines.

4 Locate point D between A and C.

5 How many lines are determined by A, D, C, and B?

Make one sketch for exercises 6 through 12.

6 Make a sketch of circle K.

7 Make a sketch of diameter FG.

8 Make a sketch of chord FH. Locate J between F and H.

9 Locate L and M in the exterior of circle K.

10 Tabulate the subset of {F, G, H, J, K, L, M} that is included in circle K.

11 Tabulate the subset of {F, G, H, J, K, L, M} that is included in the interior of circle K.

12 Tabulate the subset of {F, G, H, J, K, L, M} that is included in the exterior of circle K.

13 Locate seven points, no three of which are collinear. How many lines are determined by these points? Make sketches of these lines.

1 | 19 Exploring problems

Solution sets of conditions for equality

In this lesson you will use conditions for equality to help solve problems. You will compute to find the solutions of the conditions. U = N.

Read problems A and B in D1. Does the sentence in red express the condition for problem A? Does it also express the condition for problem B?

$15 + n = 27.$

Why is $15 + n$, and not $15 - n$, in the condition? For what, in problem A, is n a variable? For what, in problem B, is n a variable?

The 27 markers at the left represent the 27 place cards Mary needs in problem A. What do the 27 markers represent for problem B?

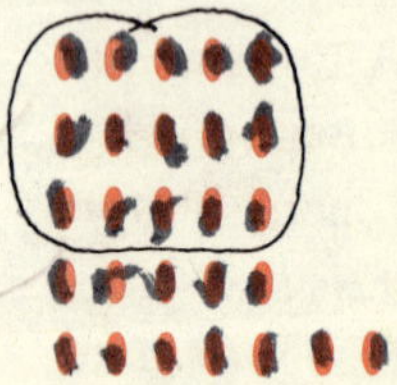

15 of the 27 markers represent the number of place cards that Mary has already made. What do the 15 markers represent for problem B?

Notice that 15 of the 27 markers are dimmed. Imagine that 15 of the place cards are removed from the 27 place cards. What does the dimming of the 15 markers suggest for problem B?

A Mary is making place cards for her birthday party. She has made 15 of them, but she needs 27 place cards in all. How many more place cards should she make?

B Jim had 15 pictures of old automobiles. He bought more pictures and now has 27 pictures of old automobiles. How many more pictures of old automobiles did Jim buy?

D1

C Bob did not have as many nails as he needed for building a shelf. After he found 8 more, he had 17 nails. How many nails did Bob have before he found the 8 nails?

D Joan made some paper flowers. She made 8 more and then had 17 flowers in all. How many flowers had Joan made before she made the 8 extra ones?

D2

A The removal of 15 markers from 27 markers suggests subtracting 15 from 27 to get the solution of $15 + n = 27$. Tabulate the solution set.

B When you replace n by 12 in $15 + n = 27$, do you obtain a true statement?

C Does 12 satisfy $15 + n = 27$?

Now you can answer the questions asked in problems A and B.

Mary should make 12 more place cards. Jim bought 12 more pictures.

D You can verify the answers by asking yourself these questions: If Mary has 15 place cards and makes 12 more, will she have the 27 she needs? If Jim had 15 pictures of old automobiles and bought 12 more, does he now have 27 pictures?

E Read the problem below. Can you also use the condition $15 + n = 27$ to solve this problem?

Jane had 15 pennies in her penny collection. She put in some new pennies. Then she had a total of 27 pennies. How many new pennies did she put in her collection?

F ? Make another problem that can be solved by using the condition $15 + n = 27$.

Read problems C and D in D2. Does the sentence in red express the condition for problem C? Does it express the condition for problem D?

$x + 8 = 17.$

Why is $x + 8$, and not $x - 8$, in the condition? For what, in problem C, is x a variable? For what, in problem D, is x a variable?

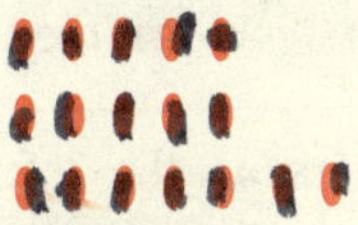

The 17 markers at the left represent the 17 nails Bob had. What do the 17 markers represent for problem D?

8 of the 17 markers represent the nails Bob found. What do the 8 markers represent for problem D?

8 of the 17 markers are dimmed. For problem C, imagine that 8 of the 17 nails are removed. What does the dimming of 8 markers suggest for problem D?

G The removal of 8 markers from 17 markers suggests subtracting 8 from 17 to get the solution of $x + 8 = 17$. Tabulate the solution set.

H When you replace x by 9 in $x + 8 = 17$, do you obtain a true statement?

I Does 9 satisfy $x + 8 = 17$?

Now you can answer the questions asked in problems C and D.

Bob had 9 nails before he found the 8 nails. Joan had made 9 paper flowers before she made the 8 extra flowers.

J You can verify these answers by asking yourself these questions: If Bob had 9 nails and found 8 more, did he then have 17 nails? If Joan had made 9 paper flowers and then made 8 more, had she then made 17 paper flowers in all?

K Make another problem that can be solved **?** by using the condition $x + 8 = 17$.

Read the problems in D3. Does the sentence in red express the condition for problem E?

$n - 9 = 15.$

Does it also express the condition for problem F?

Why is $n - 9$, and not $n + 9$, in the condition? For what, in problem E, is n a variable? For what, in problem F, is n a variable?

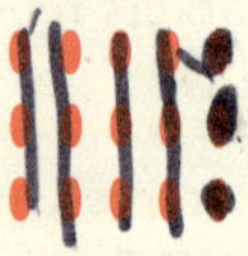

The 15 markers at the left represent the number of elms left. What do the 15 markers represent for problem F?

These 9 markers represent the number of elms cut down. What do the 9 markers represent for problem F?

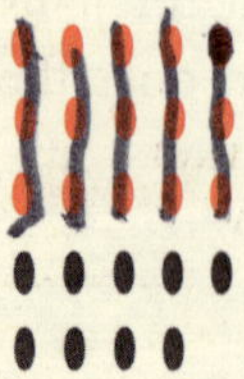

The 9 markers are put with the 15 markers. Think of the 9 elms as put back with the 15 elms. What does putting 9 markers with 15 markers suggest for problem F?

L Putting 9 markers with 15 markers suggests adding 9 and 15 to get the solution of $n - 9 = 15$. Tabulate the solution set.

M Does 24 satisfy $n - 9 = 15$?

E One day 9 of the elms in the park were cut down. Then only 15 elms were left. How many elms were in the park before the 9 were cut down?

F Phyllis bought some ribbon. She used 9 yards of the ribbon and then had 15 yards left. How many yards of ribbon had she bought?

D3

G Tom had 32 tickets to sell for the school play. After one day of sales, he had 13 tickets left. How many tickets had he sold that day?

H Mrs. Ross had saved 32 dollars to buy a lamp. She bought a lamp on sale and had 13 dollars left. How many dollars had she spent for the lamp?

D4

N Use the solution of $n - 9 = 15$ to answer the question asked in problem E.

You have found that there were 24 elms in the park before 9 of them were cut down. To verify your answer, read the problem again and decide whether or not your answer is correct. If 9 of the 24 trees were cut down, you know that 15 trees were left. So 24 is the correct answer.

It is sensible to verify an answer because you may have the wrong condition for the problem or your computation may be incorrect. You can verify many answers mentally.

O Use the solution of $n - 9 = 15$ to answer the question asked in problem F.

P Verify your answer to problem F.

Q Make another problem that can be solved **?** by using the condition $n - 9 = 15$.

Read problems G and H in D4. Does the sentence in red below express the condition for problem G? Does it also express the condition for problem H?

$32 - n = 13.$

Why is $32 - n$, and not $32 + n$, in the condition? For what, in problem G, is n a variable? For what, in problem H, is n a variable?

The 32 markers at the left represent the 32 tickets Tom had. What do the 32 markers represent for problem H?

13 of the 32 markers represent the 13 tickets Tom had left. What do the 13 markers represent for problem H?

13 of the 32 markers are dimmed. For problem G, imagine that 13 of the 32 tickets are removed. What does the dimming of 13 markers suggest for problem H?

R The removal of 13 markers from 32 markers suggests subtracting 13 from 32 to get the solution of $32 - n = 13$. Tabulate the solution set.

S Does 19 satisfy $32 - n = 13$?

T Answer the questions asked in problems G and H.

U Verify your answers to problems G and H.

V ? Make another problem that can be solved by using the condition $32 - n = 13$.

You can use what you have just learned about conditions and their solutions to help you think about familiar problems in a new way.

Don had 18 baseball cards. After he bought 24 more, he had how many baseball cards?

$$18 + 24 = w.$$

D5

Tim sold 49 of his 237 United States stamps to Ken. How many United States stamps did Tim have left?

$$237 - 49 = n.$$

D6

A Read the problem in D5. Why is $18 + 24$, and not $18 + w$, in the condition?

B For what, in the problem in D5, is w a variable?

C Suppose you were using markers to help you think about this problem. Why would you need a group of 18 markers and a group of 24 markers?

D Why would you put the 24 markers with the 18 markers? What computing should you do to find the solution of $18 + 24 = w$?

E Tabulate the solution set of $18 + 24 = w$.

F Does 42 satisfy $18 + 24 = w$?

G How many baseball cards did Don have after he bought 24?

H Verify your answer.

I ? Make another problem that can be solved by using the condition $18 + 24 = w$.

J Read the problem in D6. Why is $237 - 49$, and not $237 + 49$, in the condition?

K For what, in the problem in D6, is n a variable?

L Why must you think of 49 stamps as being removed from 237 stamps? What computing should you do to find the solution of $237 - 49 = n$?

M Tabulate the solution set of $237 - 49 = n$.

N Does 188 satisfy $237 - 49 = n$?

O Use the solution of $237 - 49 = n$ to answer the question asked in the problem. Verify your answer.

P Make another problem that can be solved ? by using the condition $237 - 49 = n$.

Now you know how to use computation to find the solutions of conditions for equality.

On your own

For each of the following problems, write a sentence that expresses the condition. Then tabulate the solution set of the condition and answer the question asked in the problem. Verify each answer. U = N.

1 At noon, the temperature was 28 degrees above zero. By seven o'clock in the evening, the temperature had dropped 15 degrees. What was the temperature at seven o'clock?

2 One week Mr. Brown travelled 798 miles. The following week he travelled 1092 miles. How many miles in all did Mr. Brown travel during these two weeks?

3 In 1959, 9942 vessels entered ports in Nova Scotia, and 6192 vessels entered ports in New Brunswick. How many fewer vessels entered in New Brunswick than in Nova Scotia?

4 Mrs. Reed picked 23 pints of strawberries. She sold some of these strawberries and then had 7 pints left. How many pints of strawberries had Mrs. Reed sold?

5 Elizabeth's weight now is 4 pounds less than her weight a month ago. She weighs 98 pounds now. Elizabeth weighed how many pounds a month ago?

THINK Why can $n - 98 = 4$ be thought of as the condition for problem 5?

6 John bought a bicycle with some of the money he had saved. He paid $34 for the bicycle and had $9 of his savings left. How many dollars had John saved?

7 Mr. Jones travelled by plane from Seattle to Chicago and from Chicago to Montreal. He flew a distance of 2489 air miles. The air distance from Seattle to Chicago is 1737 miles. The air distance from Chicago to Montreal is how many miles?

8 Carolyn was given $17 for her birthday. She earned some more money by baby-sitting. Then she had $23. How many dollars did she earn by baby-sitting?

9 After Mr. Hubert withdrew $75 from his savings account, he had $245 left in the account. How many dollars did Mr. Hubert have in his savings account before he withdrew the $75?

10 The Canadian Senate was established in 1867. The Supreme Court of Canada was established 8 years later. In what year must the Supreme Court of Canada have been established?

11 Mauvoisin Dam in Switzerland is 188 feet higher than Tignes Dam in France. The height of Tignes Dam is 592 feet. What is the height of Mauvoisin Dam?

12 The students at Rockville High School had 1513 tickets to sell for the spring music festival. They sold all but 195 of these tickets. How many tickets had the students sold?

13 After the Oakwood basketball team scored 43 points in a game with Clark, they had scored a total of 149 points against all their opponents. How many points had the Oakwood team scored before their game with Clark?

14 After Mr. Jameson bought 75 stamps, he had 423 stamps in his collection. How many stamps did he have before he bought the 75 new ones?

15 The Takakkaw Falls in British Columbia are 1038 feet higher than the Horseshoe Falls at Niagara. The height of the Takakkaw Falls is 1200 feet. How high are the Horseshoe Falls?

1 | 20 Exploring problems

Solution sets of conditions for inequality

In this lesson, you will use conditions for inequality to help you solve problems. You will learn how a condition for equality can be used to help obtain the solutions of a condition for inequality.

So far in your work with conditions, you have used the set of natural numbers as the universe for the variable. However, other sets of numbers can be used. For example, the universe can be the set whose members are 1, 2, 3, and so on. This set is also an infinite set and is often called the set of *counting numbers*. In this book, we will use the letter C as a name of this set.

Notice that the only difference between set C and the set of natural numbers is that zero is not included in set C.

From now on, when you see the sentence "U = C," remember that the replacements for the variable are members of the set of counting numbers.

A Read problems A and B in D1. What is the universe for the variable in each problem?

$13 + x < 30.$

B Does the sentence at the left express the condition for problem A? For problem B?

C You can use a condition for equality to help you find the solutions of $13 + x < 30$. For problem A, imagine that Ann now has exactly 30 records. For problem B, imagine that the boys together have exactly 30 cars.

$13 + x = 30.$

U = C.

A Ann had 13 phonograph records. She bought more, but she still had fewer than 30 records. How many records could Ann have bought?

B Together, Stan and Gordon have fewer than 30 model cars. Stan has 13 cars. How many model cars can Gordon have?

D1

D How do the markers below at the left suggest that you subtract to find the solution of $13 + x = 30$? The solution set of $13 + x = 30$ is $\{17\}$. Is 17 a solution of $13 + x < 30$?

E Is any number greater than 17 a solution of $13 + x < 30$? Explain your answer.

F Now you can decide if any numbers less than 17 are solutions of $13 + x < 30$. Is 16 a solution of $13 + x < 30$? Is 15 a solution?

G Is each member of the universe that is less than 17 a solution of $13 + x < 30$?

H Look at the tabulation of the set at the left below. Is this set the solution set of $13 + x < 30$? Why is 0 not included in the solution set?

$\{1, 2, 3, \ldots, 16\}$

I Now you can write a standard description of the solution set of $13 + x < 30$ in the way shown at the left. Is $\{x \mid x < 17\}$ the same set as $\{x \mid 13 + x < 30\}$?

$\{x \mid x < 17\}$

You can give the answers to problems A and B as follows:

Ann could have bought from 1 through 16 phonograph records. Gordon can have from 1 through 16 model cars.

J Now verify these answers. If Ann had 13 phonograph records and bought from 1 through 16 more, would she now have fewer than 30 records?

K If Stan has 13 model cars and Gordon has from 1 through 16 cars, would the boys have fewer than 30 model cars in all?

Now you will develop conditions for two more problems. You will use conditions for equality to help obtain the solutions of the conditions for inequality. This time you will use a different universe.

A Read problems C and D in D2. What is the universe for the variable in each problem?

$x + 12 > 40.$

B Does the sentence at the left express the condition for problem C? For problem D?

C You can use a condition for equality to help you find the solutions of $x + 12 > 40$. Imagine that Mr. Blake had exactly 40 mathematics books; imagine that the temperature at two o'clock was exactly 40 degrees.

$x + 12 = 40.$

D What computation does the picture below suggest for finding the solution of $x + 12 = 40$?

The solution set of $x + 12 = 40$ is $\{28\}$. Is 28 a solution of $x + 12 > 40$?

E Is any number less than 28 a solution of $x + 12 > 40$? Explain your answer.

F Now you can decide if any numbers greater than 28 are solutions of $x + 12 > 40$. Is 29 a solution of $x + 12 > 40$?

G Is each member of the universe greater than 28 a solution of $x + 12 > 40$?

H Is the set tabulated below the solution set of $x + 12 > 40$?

$\{29, 30, 31, \ldots\}$

I Is the solution set an infinite set?

U = N.

C Mr. Blake did not have enough mathematics textbooks to give one to each student in his third-period class. He got 12 more, and then had more than 40 textbooks. How many mathematics textbooks could he have had at first?

D At two o'clock in the afternoon the temperature in Elm Park was more than 40 degrees above zero. It had risen 12 degrees since noon. What could the temperature have been at noon?

D2

J How do you know that $\{x \mid x > 28\}$ is the same set as $\{x \mid x + 12 > 40\}$?

K Why is it convenient to use a standard description to describe the solution set of a condition for inequality like $x + 12 > 40$?

You know that solutions of the condition for the problem are used to obtain the answer to the problem. However, when the solution set is an infinite set, it is not sensible to use each solution in obtaining the answer to the problem. For example, 1000 is a member of $\{x \mid x > 28\}$, but it is unlikely that Mr. Blake would have had 1000 mathematics textbooks. Is it likely that the temperature could have been 1000 degrees at noon?

When the solution set of a condition for a problem is infinite, you usually need more information before you can find a sensible answer to the problem.

L Suppose that you are given the following information about problem C: "Mr. Blake had 36 students in his third-period class." Now you know that Mr. Blake had fewer than 36 textbooks at first. From the solution set of the condition, you know that Mr. Blake had more than 28 textbooks at first. Each solution of $x + 12 > 40$ that satisfies all the requirements of the problem can be used to get an answer to the problem. Use the information just given to tabulate the set of numbers that can be used to answer problem C.

Now you can give a sensible answer to problem C.

Mr. Blake had from 29 through 35 textbooks at first.

M Verify this answer. If Mr. Blake had from 29 through 35 textbooks and got 12 more, would he have more than 40 textbooks?

N Why do you need more information before you can give a sensible answer to problem D?

O Suppose you know that the temperature was lower than 38 degrees at noon. What is the greatest number that could be used to get an answer to problem D?

P From the solution set of $x + 12 > 40$, you know that the temperature was higher than 28 degrees at noon. What is the least number of degrees the temperature could have been at noon?

Q With the new information, what set of numbers can you use to obtain the answer to problem D? Tabulate this set.

R Now you can give a sensible answer to problem D.

The temperature at noon could have been any number of degrees from 29 through 37.

S ? Why are the numbers that we used to answer the question in problem C different from those we used to answer the question in problem D?

You observed for problems C and D that you had to have more information before you could find sensible answers to the problems. Later on in this book, you will learn how to write sentences to express conditions that contain all the information needed for such problems. The solutions of these conditions will be used to obtain the answers to the problems.

$U = N$.

Mary made 24 popcorn balls for a party. After the party, she had fewer than 7 popcorn balls left. What is the least number of popcorn balls that could have been eaten at the party?

$$24 - y < 7.$$

D3

$U = N$.

Jim had a reading assignment. After he had read 9 pages of his assignment, he still had more than 15 pages to read. What is the least number of pages that could have been in the assignment?

$$n - 9 > 15.$$

D4

A Read the problem in D3. What is the universe for the variable?

B You can use $24 - y = 7$ to help find the solutions of $24 - y < 7$. Do you add, or do you subtract, to find the solution of $24 - y = 7$? Tabulate the solution set of $24 - y = 7$.

C Is 17 a solution of $24 - y < 7$?

D If you replace y in $24 - y < 7$ by any number less than 17, do you get a true statement?

E Does each solution of $24 - y < 7$ have to be a number greater than 17?

F Were more than 17 popcorn balls eaten? What is the least number of popcorn balls that could have been eaten?

G Verify your answer.

H Read the problem in D4. What is the universe for the variable? Why is $n - 9$ used in the condition?

I Use $n - 9 = 15$ to help find the solutions of $n - 9 > 15$. Do you add, or do you subtract, to find the solution of $n - 9 = 15$? Tabulate the solution set.

J Is 24 a solution of $n - 9 > 15$? Explain your answer.

K Is any number less than 24 a solution of $n - 9 > 15$?

L Tabulate the solution set of $n - 9 > 15$. What is the least solution?

M Is the least solution the least number of pages that Jim could have had to read?

N Verify your answer.

In this lesson you have learned to use conditions for equality to help find solutions of conditions for inequality.

On your own

For each problem, write a sentence that expresses the condition. Tabulate the solution set of the condition and give the answer to the problem. The universe is given for each problem.

1 After Betty deposited 7 dollars in her savings account, she had less than 100 dollars in the account. What is the greatest number of dollars Betty could have had in her account before she deposited the 7 dollars? U = N.

2 Ken answered all 60 questions in a test. He had more than 4 incorrect answers. How many correct answers could Ken have had? U = N.

3 Mr. King plowed fewer than 35 acres of land in two days. He plowed 19 acres the first day. How many acres could he have plowed the second day? U = C.

4 Henry had 128 stamps. He bought 36 more, and now he has more stamps than Terry. What is the greatest number of stamps that Terry can have? U = N.

5 Sally made 8 place mats for her mother. She said, "Now I have made fewer than 20 place mats." How many place mats could Sally have made before she made the 8 for her mother? U = N.

6 Evelyn had 82¢. She spent 35¢ and still had more money than Phyllis. How many cents could Phyllis have had? U = N.

7 Mr. Owen drove from his house to the Toronto airport, and then he flew 962 miles to Winnipeg. He travelled a total distance of less than 1000 miles. How many miles can his house be from the Toronto airport? U = C.

8 Dick has 45 arrowheads, and John has 29. The difference in the number of their arrowheads is greater than the number of Jack's arrowheads. How many arrowheads can Jack have? U = N.

9 The highest temperature in Danville one summer was 105 degrees. One afternoon that summer, the temperature dropped 25 degrees, but it was still higher than 60 degrees. What could the temperature have been before it started to drop? U = N.

10 Miss Jasper typed 590 words in ten minutes. In the first five minutes, she typed fewer than 325 words. What is the least number of words she could have typed in the last five minutes? U = N.

11 The highest peak in Canada is Mount Logan in the Yukon, some 19,850 feet above sea level. Mount Logan is more than 8,213 feet higher than Mount Temple in Alberta. What is the greatest height in feet Mount Temple can be? U = N.

12 During the first game of the football season, Ed scored more than 6 points. By the end of the season, he had scored 36 points. How many points could Ed have scored after the first game of the season? U = N.

13 Last spring Mr. Hansen planted 112 acres of his land in oats and corn. He planted more than 67 acres in corn. How many acres could he have planted in oats? U = C.

APPLYING MATHEMATICS

In this lesson you will solve problems by using conditions for equality and conditions for inequality. You will compute to find the solutions of the conditions. The universe is given for each problem.

After you have read each problem, write a sentence that expresses the condition for the problem. Then find the solution, or solutions, of the condition and answer the question asked in the problem.

1 Hayes School has a new auditorium. There are 823 seats on the main floor and 518 seats in the balcony. What is the total number of main-floor and balcony seats in the new auditorium? U = N.

2 David and John share a paper route. Last Sunday they delivered fewer than 105 papers. David delivered 67 of the papers. How many papers could John have delivered? U = C.

3 The Harrison Electronics Company bought 500 large envelopes. Some of these envelopes were used to mail the annual report. 245 envelopes were left. How many envelopes were used to mail the annual report? U = N.

4 Alice spent 8 hours doing homework during a two-week period. She spent more than 3 hours on homework the first week. How many hours could she have spent on homework the second week? U = N.

5 Mr. Johnson's weekly salary was increased by $19. Now his salary is $103 per week. What was Mr. Johnson's weekly salary before he received the increase? U = N.

6 The length of the Mackenzie River is 2635 miles. The length of the Peace River is 1195 miles. The Mackenzie is how many miles longer than the Peace? U = N

7 Ted had 201 foreign stamps. He gave 84 of them away and still had more foreign stamps than Phil. What is the greatest number of foreign stamps that Phil could have had? U = N.

8 Alex had $14. He was given some money for his birthday and now has $21. How many dollars was he given for his birthday? U = N.

9 After Mrs. Jones wrote a check for $145, she had $278 in her checking account. How many dollars did she have in her checking account before she wrote the check for $145? U = N.

10 A nursery owner had 531 pine trees to sell. He sold all but 76 of these trees. How many pine trees did he sell? U = N.

11 Last weekend Ann read the first 179 pages of a new book. Now she has fewer than 165 pages to read. What is the greatest number of pages that the book can contain? U = N.

12 Mr. Butler borrowed $1350 from a bank. At the end of the year, he repaid this amount plus $81 for the use of the money. How many dollars did he pay the bank at the end of the year? U = N.

13 Charles spent $51 for a camera and flash attachment. He spent $44 for the camera. How many dollars did he spend for the flash attachment? U = N.

14 The Richardson family drove from their home to Lake Louise in two days. Lake Louise is 421 miles from their home. The first day they drove more than 295 miles. How many miles could they have driven the second day? U = C.

15 It took Mr. Williams 3 hours to set out 140 tomato plants. He set out 46 plants the first hour and at least one plant during each of the remaining two hours. What is the greatest number of plants he could have set out the second hour? U = C.

THINK Is the number of tomato plants he set out in the first two hours less than 140?

1 | 21 Exploring problems

Conditions for abstract problems

In lessons 19 and 20, you used solutions of conditions to get answers to problems about persons and things. Now you will learn to use solutions of conditions as answers to problems that concern numbers only. $U = N$.

A Read problems A and B in D1.

B Does the sentence in D2 express the condition for problem A? Does it also express the condition for problem B?

C For what, in problem A, is x a variable? For what, in problem B, is x a variable?

D Why is $16 + x$, and not $16 - x$, in the condition?

E Why is the idea of equality used in the condition?

F What computation should you use to find the solution of $16 + x = 33$?

G Tabulate $\{x \mid 16 + x = 33\}$.

H If Frank had 16 model cars and Jerry gave him 17 more, does Frank now have 33 cars?

I If 17 is added to 16, is the sum 33?

J Read problems C and D in D3. Does the sentence in D4 express the condition for problem C? Does it also express the condition for problem D?

K Use $13 + x = 20$ to help find the solution set of $13 + x < 20$. What computation should you use to find the solution of $13 + x = 20$?

L Tabulate $\{x \mid 13 + x = 20\}$.

M Is each solution of $13 + x < 20$ greater than 7? Less than 7?

N Tabulate $\{x \mid 13 + x < 20\}$.

A Frank had 16 model cars. Jerry gave him some more. Now Frank has 33 model cars. How many model cars did Jerry give to Frank?

B If a number is added to 16, the sum is 33. What is the number?

D1

$$16 + x = 33.$$

D2

C Dick scored 13 points during the first half of a basketball game. He scored fewer than 20 points during the entire game. How many points could he have scored during the second half?

D What numbers can be added to 13 so that each sum is less than 20?

D3

$$13 + x < 20.$$

D4

A farmer had 85 steers. He shipped some of them to market and then had 47 steers left. How many steers did he ship to market?

D5

O Does each member of the set that you tabulated in exercise N satisfy the condition for problem C? For problem D?

P Read the problem in D5. Write the sentence that expresses the condition for this problem.

Q Write a problem whose condition is the same as the condition for the problem in D5. Your problem should concern numbers only.

Now you know how to write sentences that express conditions for problems that are about numbers only. You also know how to find the solutions of these conditions.

On your own

For each problem, first write a sentence that expresses the condition. Then tabulate the solution set of the condition. U = N.

1 The difference of 42 and 18 is what number?

2 What numbers can be added to 29 so that each sum is less than 35?

3 If 6 is added to a number, the sum is 25. What is the number?

4 The product of 16 and 12 is less than what numbers?

5 You can subtract 37 from what number to get a difference of 14?

6 The quotient of 1134 and 42 is greater than what numbers?

7 What number can you subtract from 120 so that the difference is 57?

8 To what numbers can you add 8 so that each sum is greater than 17?

9 When you add 139 to 376, what is the sum?

10 To what number can 16 be added so that the sum is 12?

THINK Can a solution set be the empty set?

11 What numbers can be subtracted from 26 so that each difference is greater than 12?

12 The difference of 147 and 15 is less than what numbers?

13 What number do you get when you multiply 108 by 350?

14 To what numbers can you add 13 so that each sum is greater than 15?

15 What number do you get when you divide 95,676 by 476?

16 What is the greatest number from which 6 can be subtracted so that the difference is less than 9?

17 What is the least number that can be subtracted from 28 so that the difference is less than 15?

KEEPING SKILFUL

Find the sum.

1 6851, 2334, 1815

2 8230, 694, 19

3 24768, 34619, 52116

4 86347, 49818, 60004

5 72683, 14931, 12386

6 29318, 3647, 7802

7 5655, 656, 19290

8 63147, 82598, 14006

Find the difference.

9 74160, 39890	14 42321, 35312
10 41934, 67	15 35700, 24894
11 62346, 12547	16 19258, 18369
12 61842, 3457	17 27125, 18864
13 36809, 6909	18 97325, 58320

Multiply	Divide
19 67 by 39.	26 4502 by 92.
20 125 by 80.	27 5764 by 68.
21 409 by 53.	28 10606 by 52.
22 348 by 46.	29 9225 by 123.
23 275 by 128.	30 10005 by 279.
24 106 by 349.	31 26780 by 103.
25 297 by 502.	32 77558 by 214.

Tabulate the solution set of each condition expressed below. For exercises 33 through 44, U = {1, 2, 3, 4, 5}. For exercises 45 through 56, U = N.

33 $y + 12 > 12$.	45 $97(102) = z$.
34 $8 - d > d$.	46 $13 - y > 6$.
35 $3z + z = 4$.	47 $3x + 1 < 3x$.
36 $9 - x < 6$.	48 $65 - x = 60$.
37 $97 - z = 95$.	49 $34(76) > m$.
38 $144 \div 48 < c$.	50 $z + 2z = 6$.
39 $41 - c < 32$.	51 $n + 7 > 59$.
40 $17 + n > 47$.	52 $24 + n < 24$.
41 $14 - d = 9$.	53 $n + 100 > 300$.
42 $x + 37 < 41$.	54 $5y = 4y + y$.
43 $96 \div 16 > m$.	55 $x - 5 > 0$.
44 $7 - b > 2$.	56 $43 - m > 42$.

CHECKING UP

The small numeral within parentheses tells you what page to turn to if you need help with an exercise.

Test 11

For each of exercises 1 through 4, choose the word from the following list that most clearly expresses the idea described by the exercise.

collinear	geometry
congruent	line
diameter	plane

1 The study of sets of points (29)

2 A chord of a circle (47)

3 Separates a plane into two half-planes (41)

4 Is contained in the same line (34)

For each of exercises 5 through 8, choose the word from the following list that most clearly expresses the idea described by the exercise.

equation	numeral
finite	tabulation
graph	universe

5 A way to name a set (11)

6 A true statement that includes the idea of equality (17)

7 A set consisting of all the objects that can be used as replacements for the variable (16)

8 A name of a number (5)

Test 12

Which of the following sentences express true statements? Which of the following sentences express false statements?

9 The number of members in an infinite set is a natural number. (23)

10 A circle has infinitely many radii. (46)

11 A variable may be used only once in a condition. (21)

12 The solution set of a condition must have fewer members than the universe. (25)

13 If $U = N$, then $\{x \mid 2 + x < 5\}$ contains exactly two members. (27)

14 If a line is included in a plane, then each point in the line is in the plane. (32)

15 Three noncollinear points determine two planes. (35)

16 A point separates space into two half-spaces. (41)

17 If three points are collinear, then one of the points is between the other two. (37)

18 Assume that $\overline{AB} \cong \overline{CD}$ and $\overline{CD} < \overline{EF}$. Then $\overline{EF} < \overline{AB}$. (43)

Test 13

What words or symbols best complete exercises 19 through 27?

19 The set that has no members is called the ___. (25)

20 An object that belongs to a set is a ___ of the set. (10)

21 A name of the line that contains points A and B is ___. (33)

22 $\{1, 3\}$ is a ___ of $\{0, 1, 2, 3, 4\}$. (11)

23 If $U = N$, then $\{0, 1, 2\}$ is the ___ of $x + 4 < 7$. (18)

24 The sentence $13 - 2 < 11$ expresses a ___ statement. (13)

25 $\{3, 6, 9, \ldots, 30\}$ has exactly ___ members. (23)

26 The sentence $0(5) < 1$ expresses a ___ statement. (13)

27 $\{1, 2, 3, \ldots\}$ is the set of ___ numbers. (73)

Test 14

For each of the conditions expressed in exercises 28 through 31, first tabulate the solution set. Then make a graph of the universe and encircle each dot that represents a point associated with a member of the solution set. $U = \{0, 1, 2, 3, 4, 5\}$.

28 $x + 3 < 5$. (53)

29 $4 \neq 7 - x$. (53)

30 $2 + x = x + 2$. (53)

31 $x + 9 > 8$. (53)

Test 15

From the list given below each exercise, choose the expression that correctly completes the exercise.

32 The sentence ∼∼∼ expresses a false statement. (13)

a $2+3>4$. **c** $1+4<5$.

b $7-3=4$. **d** $5+2\neq 6$.

33 The set whose members are ∼∼∼ is an infinite set. (23)

a all the known planets in our solar system

b the natural numbers from 2 through 10,000

c all the people in the world

d the counting numbers greater than 5000

34 The symbol ∼∼∼ expresses the idea of "greater than." (20)

a $<$ **b** $>$ **c** $\cong$ **d** $\neq$

35 The symbol ∼∼∼ expresses the idea of "not equal to." (20)

a $>$ **b** $\cong$ **c** $\neq$ **d** { }

36 Sentence ∼∼∼ expresses an inequality. (21)

a $x+4\neq 5$. **c** $7-3<6$.

b $2+3=8$. **d** $1-0>1$.

37 If the universe is {2, 3, 4}, then ∼∼∼ is a solution of $5<2+x$. (24)

a 2 **b** 3 **c** 4 **d** 5

38 Segments of the same size are ∼∼∼. (39)

a collinear **c** coplanar

b congruent **d** infinite

Test 16

Use the display above for exercises 39 through 44.

39 What three radii of circle K are represented? (46)

40 What two chords of circle K are represented? (47)

41 Name the diameter of circle K that is represented. (47)

42 What points in circle K are named? (46)

43 What points in the exterior of circle K are named? (48)

44 What points in the interior of circle K are named? (48)

Test 17

For each of the following problems, first write a sentence that expresses the condition. Next tabulate the solution set of the condition. Then give the answer to the problem.

45 Ann bought 15 post cards and then had fewer than 31 post cards. How many post cards could she have had before she bought the 15? U = N. (73)

46 In the 1867 Canadian House of Commons, there were 181 members. In 1961 there were 265 members. The Canadian House of Commons had increased by how many members during this period of time? U = N. (68)

47 Sue had 57 magazines. She threw away the oldest ones, and then had more than 39 left. How many magazines could she have thrown away? U = C. (73)

48 Kay's weight now is 4 pounds more than it was a month ago. She weighs 101 pounds now. How many pounds did she weigh a month ago? U = N. (68)

49 What numbers can be subtracted from 71 so that each difference is greater than 13? U = N. (78)

50 To what number can 482 be added to get a sum of 620? U = N. (78)

Test 18

Multiply

51 359 by 9. (55)

52 105 by 46. (55)

53 77 by 77. (55)

54 812 by 238. (55)

55 768 by 552. (55)

Test 19

Divide

56 5280 by 6. (58)

57 6636 by 84. (58)

58 15542 by 38. (58)

59 14484 by 213. (59)

60 76000 by 125. (59)

Unit 2

Intersection and union of sets

2 | 22 **Exploring ideas**

Intersection of sets

In this lesson you will learn how to obtain a new set from two given sets. In later lessons you will use this knowledge to help you solve problems.

A Look at the sets in D1. Set A is the set of South American countries that border on Bolivia. Set B is the set of South American countries that border on the Pacific Ocean.

B Is Peru a country that borders on Bolivia? Is Peru a country that borders on the Pacific Ocean? Name another country that borders on Bolivia and also on the Pacific Ocean.

C Read the tabulation in D2. Is each member of the set a member of set A? Of set B?

D Does the set tabulated in D2 contain any objects that are not members of both set A and set B?

E {Peru, Chile} is the set of countries that border on Bolivia and also on the Pacific Ocean. Why is Brazil not a member of this set? Why is Paraguay not a member of this set?

F How were A and B used to obtain {Peru, ? Chile}?

{Peru, Chile} is the set that contains those objects, and only those objects, that belong to both set A and set B. {Peru, Chile} is the *intersection* of set A and set B.

The intersection of two sets is the set that contains all the objects that belong to both sets. It does not contain any other objects.

G Look at D3. Is 6 a member of the intersection of C and D? Is 3 a member of the

Forming the intersection of two sets; using Venn diagrams to represent intersections of sets intersection? Is 4 a member of the intersection? Explain your answers.

H How do you know that {1, 3, 6} is not the intersection of C and D?

I Is {2, 4} the intersection of C and D? How do you know?

The symbol below is used to express the idea of intersection. The words in D4 show how to write and read a name of the intersection of {1, 2, 3, 4} and {2, 4, 6}.

$$\cap$$

J Read the sentence in D5. How do you know that $\{1, 2, 3, 4\} \cap \{2, 4, 6\}$ and {2, 4} are the same set? Does the sentence in D5 express a true statement?

K D6 shows you how to read a sentence about the intersection of sets C and D. Does the sentence in D6 express the same statement as the sentence in D5? Explain your answer.

L Is the intersection of D and C the same ? set as the intersection of C and D? Is $C \cap D = D \cap C$ a true statement? Explain your answers.

M Look at D7. Tabulate set E. Tabulate set F. Which of these sets is an infinite set?

N Is 5 a member of the intersection of E and ? F? Is 10 a member of the intersection of E and F? Explain your answers.

O Tabulate $E \cap F$. Is $E \cap F$ a finite set?

A = {Brazil, Paraguay, Chile, Argentina, Peru}.
B = {Colombia, Peru, Ecuador, Chile}.

D1

{Peru, Chile}

D2

C = {1, 2, 3, 4}.
D = {2, 4, 6}.

D3

"The intersection of

$\{1, 2, 3, 4\} \cap \{2, 4, 6\}$

the set whose members are one, two, three, four and

the set whose members are two, four, six"

D4

$\{1, 2, 3, 4\} \cap \{2, 4, 6\} = \{2, 4\}$.

D5

"The intersection of C and D

equals

$C \cap D = \{2, 4\}$.

the set whose members are two, four."

D6

U = N.
$E = \{x \mid x > 5\}$.
$F = \{x \mid x < 10\}$.

D7

in ter sec tion (in′tər sek′shən). The intersection of two sets is the set that contains those objects, and only those objects, that belong to both sets. The intersection of {1, 2, 3} and {2, 3, 4, 5} is {2, 3}.

P Look at D8. Tabulate set K. Tabulate set L.
Q Tabulate $K \cap L$. Is $K \cap L$ an infinite set?
R Tabulate set M. What members of $K \cap L$ are also members of M?

{7, 8} is the intersection of set K, set L, and set M. Notice that the intersection of these three sets is the set that contains only those objects that are members of both $K \cap L$ and set M. In other words, the intersection of K, L, and M ($K \cap L \cap M$) contains only those objects that belong to all three sets.

S Is $K \cap L \cap M = \{7, 8\}$ a true statement?
T Sets I and J are tabulated in D9. Is any member of I also a member of J? Is any member of J also a member of I?

No member of I is a member of J, and no member of J is a member of I. No object in either set is a member of both sets. Sets I and J have *no common members.* Two sets that have no common members, are *disjoint sets.*

U Why are set I and set J disjoint sets?
V Look again at D9. Is the intersection of I and J the empty set? Explain your answer.

$U = N$.
$K = \{x \mid x > 6\}$.
$L = \{x \mid x > 2\}$.
$M = \{x \mid x < 9\}$.

D8

$I = \{5, 10, 15, 20\}$.
$J = \{7, 14, 21, 28\}$.

D9

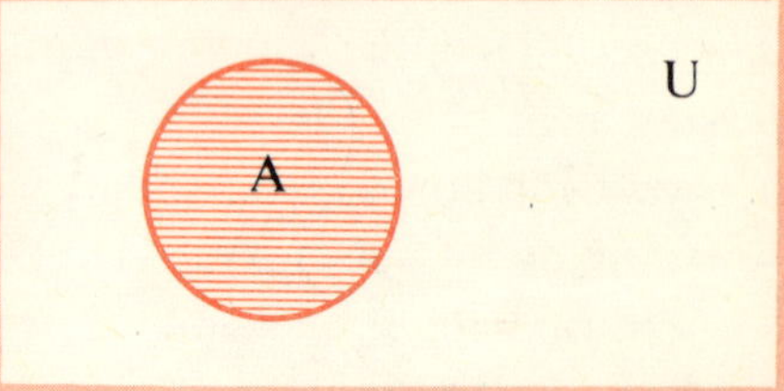

D10

You can use diagrams to learn more about the intersection of sets. Such diagrams are called *Venn* diagrams.

A Two sets are represented by the Venn diagram in D10. The picture of the rectangle and of its interior represents a universe. The picture of the circle and of its interior represents set A. How does the diagram show that A is a subset of the universe?
B Suppose that U is the set of all Canadian citizens and that A is the set of all Canadian citizens who are registered voters. Is A a subset of U?
C Suppose that U is the set of all automobiles. Describe three sets, each of which is a subset of U.

Now you will study a Venn diagram that represents disjoint sets.

D What three sets are represented by the Venn diagram in D11? Notice that the pictures of A and B are shaded in different ways. These different shadings will help you remember that A is different from B.
E U and A are the same sets described in exercise B. Suppose that set B is the set of all Canadian citizens who are younger than ten years of age. Is B a subset of U?
F Do the set of all registered voters and the set of all Canadian citizens younger than ten have common members? Are A and B disjoint sets? Explain your answer.

dis joint sets (dis joint′). Two sets are disjoint sets only when they have no common members. {0, 1, 2} and {3, 4, 5} are disjoint sets. {0, 1, 2} and {2, 3, 4} are not disjoint sets.

G For the sets described in exercises B and E, is $A \cap B$ the empty set? Explain your answer.

H Suppose that U is the set of natural numbers. Suppose also that A is the set of even numbers less than 10. Describe three subsets of U whose intersections with A are the empty set.

I If two sets are disjoint, what do you know about their intersection?

$A \cap B$ when A and B are disjoint sets

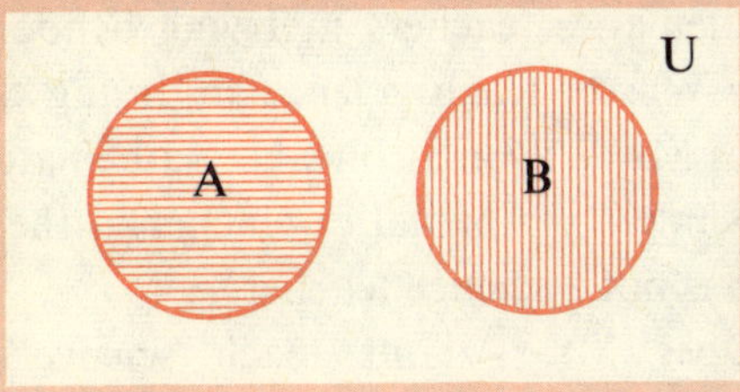

D11

$A \cap B$ when A and B meet

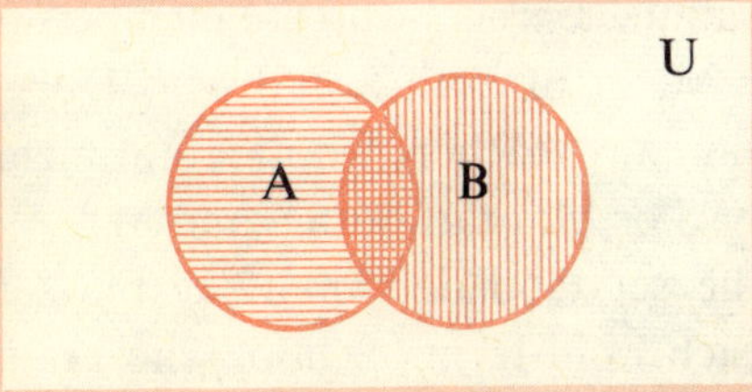

D12

$A \cap B$ when B is a subset of A

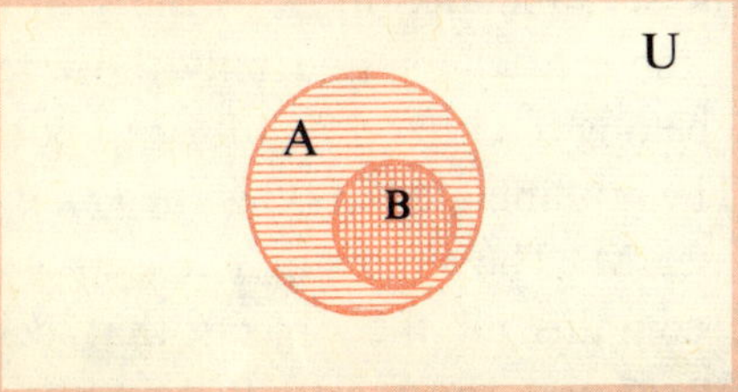

D13

J The Venn diagram in D12 represents sets that have some common members. Sets that have some common members are sets that *meet*. Again suppose that U is the set of all Canadian citizens and that A is the set of all Canadian citizens who are registered voters. Now suppose that B is the set of all Canadian citizens living in Ontario. How do you know that B is a subset of U?

K For the sets described in exercise J, is $A \cap B$ the set of all registered voters living in Ontario? How do you know?

L Look again at D12. How is $A \cap B$ represented by the Venn diagram?

M Suppose that C is the set of all citizens living in Quebec. Describe $A \cap C$.

N Suppose that U is the set of natural numbers and A is the set of odd numbers. Describe three subsets of U whose intersections with A are not the empty set.

O If two sets meet, what do you know about their intersection?

P Now look at D13. Again suppose that U is the set of all Canadian citizens and that A is the set of all Canadian citizens who are registered voters. Suppose that B is the set of all registered voters living in Manitoba. How do you know that B is a subset of A?

Q How does the diagram in D13 show that B is a subset of A?

R For the sets described in exercise P, is $A \cap B$ the set of all registered voters living in Manitoba? How is $A \cap B$ represented by the diagram in D13?

S For the sets described in exercise P, is $A \cap B$ the same set as B? Explain your answer.

T Suppose that U is the set of students in your school and that A is the set of all members of the school band. Describe three sets that are subsets of A.

U What is the intersection of A and each set that you described in exercise T?

V If one set is a subset of a second set, what **?** do you know about the intersection of the two sets?

W What is the intersection of a set with itself? **?** Explain your answer.

X Is the intersection of two sets a subset of **?** each of the sets? Explain your answer.

Y What is the intersection of a set and the **?** empty set? Explain your answer.

Now you know how to find the intersection of two sets. You also know that the intersection depends on how the two sets are related.

On your own

For each of exercises 1, 2, and 3, tabulate $A \cap B$.

1 $A = \{4, 8, 12, 16, 20, 24\}$.
$B = \{6, 12, 18, 24, 30\}$.

2 $A = \{0, 1, 2, \ldots\}$.
$B = \{0, 2, 4, \ldots\}$.

3 $A = \{1, 3, 5, \ldots\}$.
$B = \{0, 2, 4, \ldots\}$.

For each of exercises 4 through 7, tabulate set C and set D. Then tabulate $C \cap D$. $U = N$.

4 $C = \{x \mid x < 8\}$.
$D = \{x \mid x > 4\}$.

5 $C = \{x \mid x = 27\}$.
$D = \{x \mid x < 35\}$.

6 $C = \{x \mid x + 3 < 10\}$.
$D = \{x \mid x + 2 > 6\}$.

7 $C = \{x \mid 8 > x\}$.
$D = \{x \mid x + 2 > 13\}$.

Sets E, F, and G are described below. Use the descriptions to make a Venn diagram for each set named in exercises 8, 9, and 10. The universe is the set of students enrolled in Emerson High School.

E is the set of twelfth-grade students.

F is the set of tenth-grade students.

G is the set of students who are in the twelfth-grade chorus.

8 $F \cap E$ **9** $F \cap G$ **10** $E \cap G$

2 | 23 **Exploring ideas**

Union of sets

You have learned how to obtain the intersection of two sets. In this lesson you will learn how to obtain another set from two given sets.

A Look at D1. Set S is the set of all science teachers in Irving School. Set M is the set of all mathematics teachers in Irving School. Does Mr. Wilson teach science in Irving School? Does Mr. Wilson also teach mathematics?

B Name a mathematics teacher in the school who is not a science teacher.

C Does Mr. Adams teach science in the school? Does Mr. Adams also teach mathematics? Name another science teacher who is also a mathematics teacher.

D Read the tabulation in D2. Does the set contain all the teachers who are members of either S or M, or of both S and M? Does the set contain any teachers who are not members of either S or M, or of both S and M?

E The set tabulated in D2 is the set of all **?** teachers in Irving School who are teachers of either science or mathematics, or of both science and mathematics. How were sets S and M used to obtain {Mr. Adams, Miss Evans, Mr. Wilson, Mr. Cox}?

The set tabulated in D2 is the set that contains those teachers, and only those teachers, who belong to either S or M, or to both S and M. The set tabulated in D2 is the *union* of set S and set M. The union of two sets is the set that contains all the objects that belong to either set or to both sets. It does not contain any other objects.

un ion (ūn′yən). The union of two sets is the set that contains those objects, and only those objects, that belong to either set or to both sets. The union of {1, 3, 5} and {0, 1, 2, 3} is {0, 1, 2, 3, 5}.

F Suppose that E is the set of all English teachers in Irving School. E = {Mrs. Robbins, Miss Schroeder, Mr. Johnson, Mr. Barnes, Miss Hansen}.

G Is any member of E also a member of S? Tabulate the union of E and S.

H Is any member of E also a member of M? Tabulate the union of E and M.

I Look at D3. Is 5 a member of the union of C and D? Is 6 a member of the union? Is 10 a member of the union? Is any other number a member of the union? If so, what is the number?

J How do you know that {5, 6, 7, 8, 9, 10} is not the union of C and D?

K Tabulate the union of C and D. Remember that, when you tabulate a set, you list the name of each member only once.

The symbol below is used to express the idea of union. Be careful not to confuse this symbol with the letter U that is often used as a name for a universe. The words in D4 show how to write and read a name of the union of {5, 10} and {6, 8, 10}.

L Now read the sentence in D5. Does the sentence express a true statement? How do you know?

M D6 shows how to read another sentence about the union of C and D. Does this sentence express the same statement as the sentence in D5?

N Is the union of D and C the same set as the **?** union of C and D? Is $C \cup D = D \cup C$ a true statement? Explain your answers.

S = {Mr. Adams, Miss Evans, Mr. Wilson}.
M = {Mr. Adams, Miss Evans, Mr. Cox}.

D1

{Mr. Adams, Miss Evans, Mr. Wilson, Mr. Cox}

D2

C = {5, 10}.
D = {6, 8, 10}.

D3

"The union of

{5, 10} ∪ {6, 8, 10}

the set whose members are five, ten and

the set whose members are six, eight, ten"

D4

{5, 10} ∪ {6, 8, 10} = {5, 6, 8, 10}.

D5

"The union of C and D

equals

C ∪ D = {5, 6, 8, 10}.

the set whose members are five, six, eight, ten."

D6

$U = N$.
$E = \{x | x < 6\}$.
$F = \{x | x + 5 = 16\}$.
$G = \{x | x - 2 = 7\}$.

D7

$U = N$.
$K = \{x | x + 4 < 15\}$.
$L = \{x | x + 2 > 5\}$.

D8

O Look at D7. Tabulate set E. Tabulate set F. Tabulate set G.

P Do E and F meet? Explain why E and F are disjoint sets.

Q Is 6 a member of the union of E and F? Is ? 0 a member of the union? Is 11 a member of the union? Explain your answers.

R Tabulate $E \cup F$. Is $E \cup F$ an infinite set?

S Is each member of E a member of $E \cup F$? Is each member of F a member of $E \cup F$?

T Is each member of $E \cup F$ a member of either E or F?

U The union of $E \cup F$ and G is {0, 1, 2, 3, 4, 5, 9, 11}. Is the union of E, F, and G ($E \cup F \cup G$) the set that contains only those objects that belong to either $E \cup F$ or G, or to both $E \cup F$ and G?

Notice that the union of three sets contains all the objects that belong to the three sets. Some of the objects may belong to just one of the sets. Some objects may belong to two of the sets. Some objects may belong to all three sets.

V Look at D8. Tabulate K. Tabulate L.

W Is K a finite set? Is L a finite set? Tabulate $K \cup L$. Is $K \cup L$ a finite set?

X Is each member of K a member of $K \cup L$? Is each member of L a member of $K \cup L$?

Y Is each member of $K \cup L$ a member of either K or L? Which members of $K \cup L$ are members of both K and L?

Z Tabulate the intersection of K and L. Is ? $K \cap L$ a subset of $K \cup L$? How do you know?

In lesson 22 you used Venn diagrams to represent the intersection of sets. Venn diagrams can also be used to represent the union of sets.

A The Venn diagram in D9 represents disjoint sets. How is the universe represented? How are the disjoint sets represented?

B Suppose that U is the set of all cities in Canada. Suppose also that A is the set of all cities located in the Prairie Provinces, and B is the set of all cities in Ontario. Is A a subset of U? Is B a subset of U?

C Are A and B disjoint sets? Explain your answer.

D Is $A \cup B$ the set of all cities that are either in the Prairie Provinces or in Ontario? How do you know?

E How is $A \cup B$ represented by the diagram in D9?

F Suppose that U is the set of natural numbers and A is the set of odd numbers less than 20. Give descriptions of two other subsets of U so that A and each set that you describe will be disjoint sets.

G What is the union of A and each set that you just described?

H The diagram in D10 represents sets that meet. Suppose that U and A are the sets described in exercise B. Suppose that set B is the set of all cities that are provincial capitals. Is B a subset of U?

I Describe $A \cup B$. How is $A \cup B$ represented by the diagram in D10?

J Suppose that U is the set of natural numbers and A is the set of even numbers less

$A \cup B$ when A and B are disjoint sets

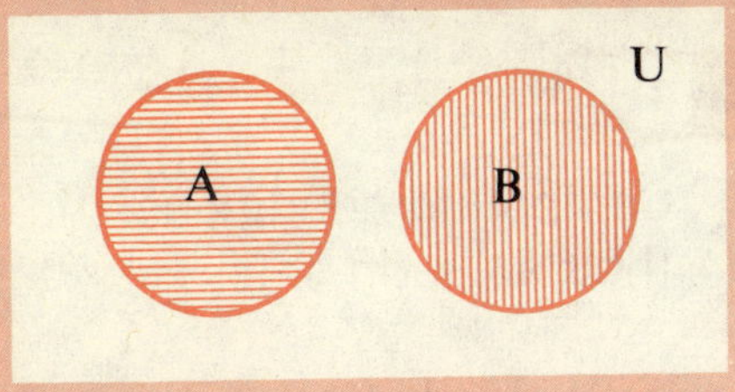

D9

$A \cup B$ when A and B meet

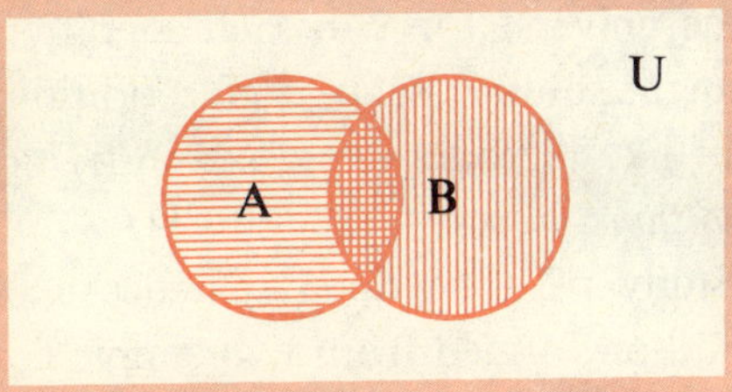

D10

$A \cup B$ when B is a subset of A

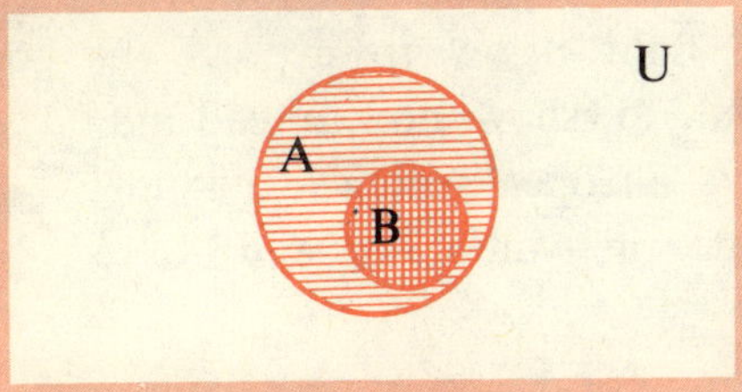

D11

than 10. Give descriptions of two other subsets of U so that A and each set that you describe will meet.

K For each set that you described in exercise J, what is the union of that set and A?

L Now look at D11. How is the statement that B is a subset of A represented by the diagram in D11?

M Again suppose that U is the set of all cities in Canada and that A is the set of all cities that are in the Prairie Provinces. Suppose that set B is the set of all cities in Alberta. Is B a subset of A? Explain your answer.

N For the sets described in exercise M, describe $A \cup B$. How is $A \cup B$ represented by the diagram in D11?

O Is $A \cup B$ the same set as A? Explain your ? answer.

P Suppose that U is the set of natural numbers and that A is the set of odd numbers. Give descriptions of two other sets so that each set is a subset of A.

Q What is the union of A and each set that you described in exercise P?

R If one set is a subset of a second set, what ? do you know about their union?

S Suppose A and B are two sets. Is A a sub- ? set of $A \cup B$? Is B a subset of $A \cup B$? Is $A \cap B$ a subset of $A \cup B$? Explain your answers.

T What is the union of any given set and the ? empty set? Explain your answer.

U What is the union of a set with itself? Ex- ? plain your answer.

V If the union of two sets is the empty set, ? what do you know about the two sets?

W If the union of two sets is the same set as ? the intersection of the two sets, and the two sets are not empty, what do you know about the two sets?

Now you know how to find the union of two sets. You also know that the union depends on how the two sets are related.

On your own

For each of exercises 1 through 5, tabulate $A \cup B$.

1 A = {bluebird, crow, hawk, owl}.
B = {eagle, hawk, owl, vulture}.

2 $A = \{3, 6, 9, 12\}$.
$B = \{5, 10, 15\}$.

3 $A = \{0, 1, 2, \ldots\}$.
$B = \{1, 3, 5, \ldots\}$.

4 $A = \{1, 2, 5, 9\}$.
$B = \{2, 9, 5, 1\}$.

5 $A = \{0, 2, 4, \ldots\}$.
$B = \{1, 3, 5, \ldots\}$.

6 Sets E, F, and G are tabulated below. Tabulate $E \cup F \cup G$.

$E = \{1, 5, 7, 9\}$.
$F = \{1, 7, 13\}$.
$G = \{7, 9, 11, 13\}$.

First tabulate sets C and D. Next tabulate $C \cap D$. Then tabulate $C \cup D$. $U = N$.

7 $C = \{x \mid x + 2 < 9\}$.
$D = \{x \mid x + 3 > 4\}$.

8 $C = \{x \mid x + 14 < 31\}$.
$D = \{x \mid x - 2 = 13\}$.

9 $C = \{x \mid x > 8\}$.
$D = \{x \mid x + 4 < 13\}$.

10 $C = \{x \mid x - 3 > 10\}$.
$D = \{x \mid x + 6 > 19\}$.

11 $C = \{x \mid x + 16 < 30\}$.
$D = \{x \mid x - 6 > 6\}$.

12 First tabulate sets R, S, and T. Next tabulate $R \cap S \cap T$. Then tabulate $R \cup S \cup T$. $U = N$.

$R = \{x \mid x + 5 < 6\}$.
$S = \{x \mid x - 2 > 2\}$.
$T = \{x \mid x + 7 < 13\}$.

Sets W, X, Y, and Z are described below. Use the descriptions to make a Venn diagram for each set named in exercises 13 through 18. The universe is the set of all animals.

W is the set of all pets.
X is the set of all dogs.
Y is the set of all rabbits.
Z is the set of all four-legged animals.

13 $Z \cup X$ **15** $W \cup Y$ **17** $Z \cup Y$
14 $W \cup Z$ **16** $Z \cup W$ **18** $Y \cup X$

Compound conditions and their solution sets

You have already learned how to find solution sets of conditions. In this lesson you will learn how two conditions can be combined to form a new condition.

A What conditions are expressed in D1? What is the universe for x in each condition? Tabulate the solution set of each condition. Conditions like the ones expressed in D1 are *simple conditions.*

B Study D2. The open sentence expresses a condition formed from two simple conditions and the connective "and."

The connective "and" means that each solution of the condition must satisfy not only $x + 3 > 7$ but also $6 + x < 14$.

Mathematicians use the symbol shown at the right below to express the connective "and." D3 shows how to read and write an open sentence that includes the symbol for "and."

$\wedge$

$U = \{0, 1, 2, \ldots, 10\}$.
A $x + 3 > 7$.
B $6 + x < 14$.

D1

$U = \{0, 1, 2, \ldots, 10\}$.
$x + 3 > 7$ and $6 + x < 14$.

D2

com pound condition (kom′pound). A condition that is made up of two or more simple conditions and one or more connectives. $y < 6 \wedge 3 < y$ is a compound condition. It contains two simple conditions, $y < 6$ and $3 < y$, and includes the connective "and."

A condition like $x + 3 > 7 \wedge 6 + x < 14$, which is made up of two simple conditions and a connective, is a *compound condition.*

C A standard description of the solution set of $x + 3 > 7 \wedge 6 + x < 14$ is given in D4. Read the description.

Now you will learn how to find the solution set of $x + 3 > 7 \wedge 6 + x < 14$. The solution set of each simple condition is tabulated in D5. The solution set of the compound condition is also tabulated in D5.

D Which members of $\{x | x + 3 > 7\}$ are also members of $\{x | 6 + x < 14\}$?

E Does $\{5, 6, 7\}$ contain all the members of the universe that satisfy both $x + 3 > 7$ and $6 + x < 14$? Is $\{5, 6, 7\}$ the same set as $\{x | x + 3 > 7 \wedge 6 + x < 14\}$?

F Is $\{x | x + 3 > 7 \wedge 6 + x < 14\}$ the same set as $\{x | 6 + x < 14 \wedge x + 3 > 7\}$? Explain your answer.

G Study D6. It shows how to write and read a name of the intersection of $\{x | x + 3 > 7\}$ and $\{x | 6 + x < 14\}$.

REMINDER

The intersection of two sets is the set that contains only those objects that belong to both sets.

See lesson 22, page 83.

H Read the sentence in D7. Does the sentence **?** express a true statement? Explain your answer.

"x plus three is greater than seven

and

$x + 3 > 7 \wedge 6 + x < 14.$

six plus x is less than fourteen."

D3

$\{x | x + 3 > 7 \wedge 6 + x < 14\}$

D4

$U = \{0, 1, 2, \ldots, 10\}.$

$\{x | x + 3 > 7\} = \{5, 6, 7, 8, 9, 10\}.$

$\{x | 6 + x < 14\} = \{0, 1, 2, 3, 4, 5, 6, 7\}.$

$\{x | x + 3 > 7 \wedge 6 + x < 14\} = \{5, 6, 7\}.$

D5

"The intersection of

$\{x | x + 3 > 7\} \cap \{x | 6 + x < 14\}$

the solution set of $x + 3 > 7$ and

the solution set of $6 + x < 14$"

D6

$\{x | x + 3 > 7\} \cap \{x | 6 + x < 14\} = \{5, 6, 7\}.$

D7

I Is the intersection of the solution set of ? $x + 3 > 7$ and the solution set of $6 + x < 14$ the same set as the solution set of $x + 3 > 7 \wedge 6 + x < 14$? How do you know?

J Read the open sentence in D8. What two simple conditions must be satisfied by each member of $\{x | x < 9 \wedge x + 2 < 8\}$?

K What members of N satisfy $x + 2 < 8$?

L What members of N that satisfy $x + 2 < 8$ also satisfy $x < 9$? Are these the only natural numbers that satisfy $x < 9 \wedge x + 2 < 8$?

M What members of N are in the intersection of $\{x | x < 9\}$ and $\{x | x + 2 < 8\}$? Are these the same natural numbers that satisfy $x < 9 \wedge x + 2 < 8$?

N Look at the Venn diagram in D9. How many sets are represented? How is the universe represented? The pictures of the two circles and of their interiors represent sets A and B. Set A is the solution set of a simple condition. Set B is the solution set of another simple condition.

O Which portion of the diagram represents the solution set of a compound condition that includes the connective "and"? Which portion of the diagram represents $A \cap B$?

P The solution set of a compound condition ? that includes "and" is the intersection of the solution sets of the two simple conditions that form the compound condition. Explain why this statement is true.

Now you will learn to make graphs of the solution sets of conditions like $x + 3 > 7 \wedge 6 + x < 14$ and $x < 9 \wedge x + 2 < 8$.

REMINDER

The graph of a set of numbers is a set of dots.

See lesson 13, page 52.

$U = N.$

$x < 9 \wedge x + 2 < 8.$

D8

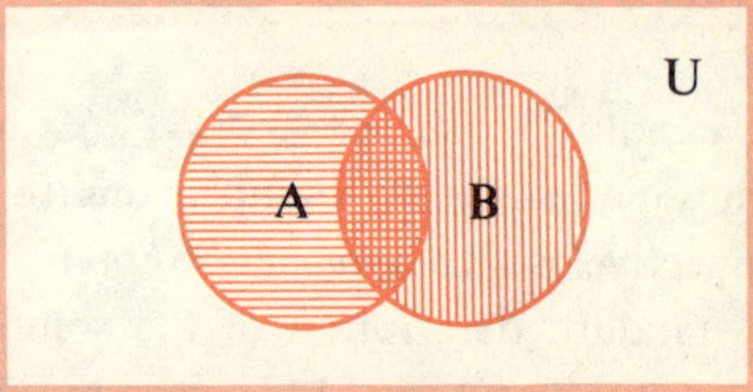

D9

$U = \{0, 1, 2, \ldots, 10\}.$

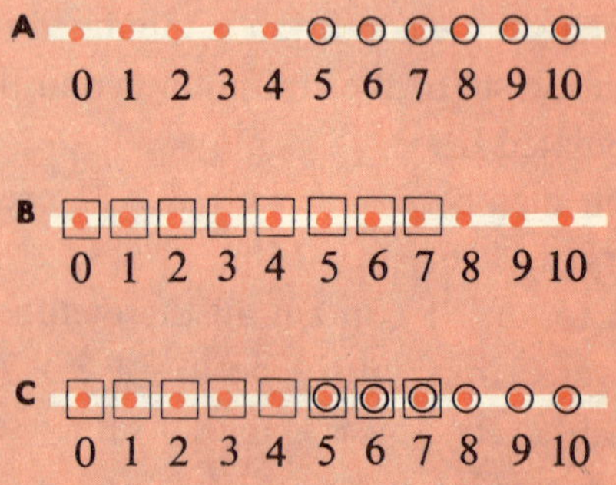

D10

$U = N.$

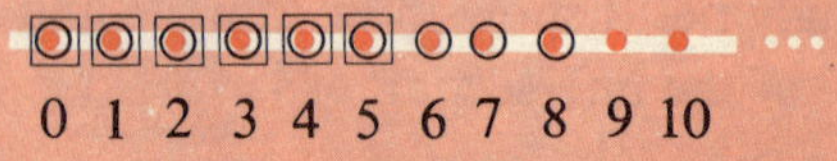

D11

A Look at graph A in D10. Do the encircled dots form the graph of $\{x | x + 3 > 7\}$?

B Look at graph B. Do the dots enclosed by squares form the graph of $\{x | 6 + x < 14\}$?

C Graphs A and B are combined in graph C. How can you tell which dots form the graph of $\{x | x + 3 > 7 \wedge 6 + x < 14\}$?

D Look at D11. Which dots form the graph of $\{x | x < 9 \wedge x + 2 < 8\}$?

E $A = \{x | x < 9\}$. $B = \{x | x + 2 < 8\}$. Make a Venn diagram to represent $A \cap B$.

F Which portion of the diagram represents $\{x | x < 9 \wedge x + 2 < 8\}$?

G How do the graphs in D11 and the Venn diagram you made for exercise E show that $\{x | x < 9 \wedge x + 2 < 8\}$ is a subset of $\{x | x < 9\}$? How do the graphs and the diagram show that $\{x | x < 9 \wedge x + 2 < 8\} = \{x | x + 2 < 8\}$?

In earlier lessons you learned that sometimes the solution set of a simple condition can be the empty set or an infinite set. The exercises that follow show that the solution set of a compound condition can also be the empty set or an infinite set.

H Read the open sentence in D12. What members of the universe satisfy $x < 2$?

I What numbers that satisfy $x < 2$ also satisfy $x + 1 > 4$?

J How many members of the universe satisfy $x < 2 \wedge x + 1 > 4$?

K Tabulate $\{x | x < 2 \wedge x + 1 > 4\}$.

L Now look at D13. Tabulate $\{x | x + 1 > x\}$. Is $\{x | x + 1 > x\}$ an infinite set?

M What solutions of $x + 1 > x$ also satisfy $x + 2 > 10$?

N Tabulate $\{x | x + 2 > 10 \wedge x + 1 > x\}$. Is $\{x | x + 2 > 10 \wedge x + 1 > x\}$ an infinite set?

O Suppose you want to find $\{x | x + 4 > 13 \wedge x + 2 = 16\}$. Which is easier to find, the solution set of $x + 4 > 13$, or the solution set of $x + 2 = 16$?

P Tabulate $\{x | x + 4 > 13 \wedge x + 2 = 16\}$.

$U = N$.
$x < 2 \wedge x + 1 > 4$.

D12

$U = N$.
$x + 2 > 10 \wedge x + 1 > x$.

D13

Now you know how to find the solution set of a compound condition that includes the connective "and." You also know that this solution set is the intersection of the solution sets of the simple conditions that make up the compound condition.

On your own

For exercises 1 through 6, tabulate the solution set of each compound condition. $U = N$.

1 $x < 14 \wedge x > 8$.

2 $x < 19 \wedge x + 1 = 11$.

3 $x = 5 \wedge 4 + x = 15$.

4 $x < 13 \wedge 15 - x > 6$.

5 $x + 3 > 12 \wedge 14 < x$.

6 $x > 100 \wedge x + 18 > x$.

For each compound condition expressed in exercises 7, 8, and 9, first make a graph of the set of natural numbers. Extend your picture of the line to contain as many dots as you need for the particular exercise. Encircle the dots in the graph of the solution set of the first simple condition. Draw squares around the dots in the graph of the solution set of the second simple condition. Finally, tabulate the solution set of the compound condition. $U = N$.

7 $14 = 8 + x \wedge x < 10$.

8 $x + 9 < 17 \wedge x > 2$.

9 $4 + x < 11 \wedge 4 + x > 11$.

For each of exercises 10, 11, and 12, let A be the solution set of one simple condition and let B be the solution set of the other simple condition. For each exercise make a Venn diagram to represent a compound condition formed from the two simple conditions and the connective "and." $U = N$.

10 The solution set of the compound condition is the same set as B.

11 The solution set of the compound condition is the empty set.

12 The solution set of the compound condition contains at least one member of A. It does not contain all members of either A or B.

For each of exercises 13 through 16, tell which of the Venn diagrams you just made could be used to represent the solution set of the compound condition expressed in the exercise. U = N.

13 $x - 1 > 5 \wedge x + 3 < 13$.

14 $x > 17 \wedge x + 5 < 22$.

15 $x > 20 \wedge x + 15 > 17$.

16 $x + 15 > 15 \wedge x + 2 < 7$.

KEEPING SKILFUL

Multiply

1 372 by 49.

2 609 by 25.

3 132 by 578.

4 903 by 264.

5 352 by 710.

6 405 by 180.

Divide

7 3164 by 24.

8 5000 by 78.

9 6448 by 31.

10 23498 by 62.

11 8742 by 186.

12 4750 by 214.

13 157700 by 456.

14 54032 by 176.

For each of exercises 15 through 20, first tabulate sets F and G. Next tabulate F ∩ G. Then tabulate F ∪ G. U = N.

15 $F = \{s \mid 3 + s > 4\}$.
$G = \{s \mid 8 - s > 4\}$.

16 $F = \{d \mid d + 24 = 51\}$.
$G = \{d \mid d - 7 > 18\}$.

17 $F = \{c \mid 14 + c > 20\}$.
$G = \{c \mid c < 9\}$.

18 $F = \{n \mid n + 172 < 180\}$.
$G = \{n \mid 294 - n = 276\}$.

19 $F = \{v \mid v - 14 = 25\}$.
$G = \{v \mid 28 + v = 67\}$.

20 $F = \{c \mid c - 42 > 38\}$.
$G = \{c \mid c + 59 > 64\}$.

2 | 25 Exploring problems

Problems involving compound conditions

So far, you have solved problems by using only one simple condition. For some problems you used additional information to decide which solutions of the condition could be used to get sensible answers. However, problems like these really involve more than one simple condition. In this lesson you will solve problems by using compound conditions and finding solution sets of these conditions. U = N.

Read the problem in D1. First you will develop a compound condition for this problem.

A How do you know that Mrs. Ames had fewer than 10 hamburger buns to begin with? Use x as a variable for the number of buns she could have had before she bought more.

$x < 10$. Does the sentence at the left express one simple condition for the problem?

B Mrs. Ames bought a package of 6 buns and then had more than 12. Why do you again use x as a variable for the number of buns she could have had before she bought 6 more?

$x + 6 > 12$. **C** Does the sentence at the left express another simple condition for the problem?

$x < 10 \wedge x + 6 > 12$. **D** Does the sentence at the left express the compound condition for the problem?

$\{7, 8, 9, \ldots\}$ **E** How do you know that the set tabulated at the left is the solution set of $x + 6 > 12$?

Mrs. Ames needed 10 hamburger buns for lunch. She did not have enough buns on hand. So she bought a package of 6. Then she had more than 12 buns. How many buns could she have had before she bought 6 more?

D1

The record for consecutive push-ups in George's gym class is 14. George's own record is fewer than 14. One day George missed his own record by 1, but he still did more than 9 push-ups. What can George's record be?

D2

What numbers greater than 5 can be added to 6 so that each sum is less than 16?

D3

F Can you use each member of $\{x | x + 6 > 12\}$? to get an answer to the problem? Explain your answer.

G How do you know that each number used to get an answer to the problem must be less than 10?

H Tabulate $\{x | x < 10 \wedge x + 6 > 12\}$. Remember that each member of $\{x | x < 10 \wedge x + 6 > 12\}$ must satisfy each of the simple conditions.

I Is $\{x | x < 10 \wedge x + 6 > 12\}$ the intersection ? of $\{x | x < 10\}$ and $\{x | x + 6 > 12\}$, or is it the union of the two solution sets?

J Can you use each member of $\{x | x < 10 \wedge x + 6 > 12\}$ to get an answer to the problem?

You can use each solution of the compound condition to get an answer to the problem.

Mrs. Ames could have had 7, 8, or 9 buns before she bought 6 more.

K Verify 7 buns as an answer. Are 7 buns fewer than 10 buns? If Mrs. Ames had 7 buns and bought 6 more, would she have had more than 12 buns?

L Verify each of the other answers.

M Read the problem in D2. George's record for consecutive push-ups is fewer than 14. Is $x < 14$ a condition for the problem? For what is x a variable?

N The day George missed his record by 1, he still did more than 9 push-ups. Is $x - 1 > 9$ a condition for the problem? For what is x a variable?

O What is the compound condition for the problem in D2?

P Tabulate $\{x | x - 1 > 9\}$ and $\{x | x < 14\}$.

Q Which do you find, the intersection or the union of $\{x | x < 14\}$ and $\{x | x - 1 > 9\}$?

R Tabulate $\{x | x < 14 \wedge x - 1 > 9\}$.

S Give the answers to the problem.

T Verify your answers.

Now you will solve problems that concern numbers only. U = N.

A Read the problem in D3. Is $x > 5$ one simple condition for the problem? Is $6 + x < 16$ the other simple condition? For what is x a variable? What is the compound condition for the problem?

B Tabulate $\{x | 6 + x < 16\}$. Is each member of this solution set an answer to the problem in D3?

C Which members of the set you tabulated satisfy $x > 5$?

D Tabulate $\{x | x > 5 \wedge 6 + x < 16\}$.

Now you can use each solution of the compound condition as an answer to the problem.

The numbers are the natural numbers from 6 through 9.

When 3 is added to a number, the sum is 40. When 15 is subtracted from the number, the difference is 25. What is the number?

D4

E Read the problem in D4. Use s as a variable for the number you are to find. What is the compound condition for the problem?

F Tabulate $\{s | s + 3 = 40\}$.

G Is the member of $\{s | s + 3 = 40\}$ also a member of $\{s | s - 15 = 25\}$?

H Tabulate $\{s | s + 3 = 40 \wedge s - 15 = 25\}$.

Since there are no solutions of the compound condition, there are no answers to the problem.

Now you know how to solve problems by using compound conditions that include the connective "and."

On your own

For each problem, write a sentence that expresses the compound condition. Use any letter you wish to express the variable. Tabulate the solution set of the compound condition. Then give the answer to the problem. U = N.

1 Bob has 13 model cars, and Jerry has 9 model cars. Pete has fewer model cars than Bob and Jerry have together, but he has more model cars than Bob. How many model cars can Pete have?

2 Three years from now, Bill will still be less than 21 years old. Five years ago, he was more than 9 years old. How old can Bill be now?

3 In April, Henry sold 62 magazine subscriptions. In May, he sold fewer than 25 subscriptions. Altogether he sold more than 81 subscriptions during these two months. How many subscriptions could he have sold in May?

4 Last week, Mr. Ray drove fewer than 1790 miles. If he had driven 175 miles more, he would have driven more than 1900 miles. How many miles could Mr. Ray have driven last week?

5 Mr. Hill bought 144 tomato plants. He set out more than 96 of these plants in one hour, and still had more than 12 plants left to set out. How many tomato plants could he have left to set out?

6 Mrs. Johnson bought 60 postage stamps. She used more than 27 of these stamps, but still had more than 24 stamps left. How many stamps could she have used?

7 Mr. Jones bought 315 pairs of overshoes to sell in his shoe store. He sold more than 269 pairs and then had more than 27 pairs left to sell. How many pairs of overshoes could he have had left?

8 When a number is added to 2950, the sum is 4010. When the number is subtracted from 3000, the difference is 1940. What is the number?

9 What numbers greater than the product of 406 and 850 can be added to 279,379 so that each sum is less than 600,000?

10 What numbers greater than the difference of 5010 and 3465 can be added to 4276 so that each sum is less than 5826?

11 What numbers greater than the quotient of 68,068 and 187 can be added to 576 so that each sum is less than 1000?

12 When 1496 is added to a number, the sum is 2130. When the number is added to 373, the sum is 1000. What is the number?

13 When 9568 is subtracted from a number, the difference is 3627. When the number is added to 1708, the sum is 14,903. What is the number?

APPLYING MATHEMATICS

Some of the problems in this lesson involve simple conditions. Others involve compound conditions. For each problem, write a sentence that expresses the condition for the problem. Tabulate the solution set of the condition and give the answer to the problem. U = N.

1 The area of Lake Huron is 23,010 square miles. The area of Lake Michigan is 22,400 square miles. The area of Lake Michigan is how many square miles less than the area of Lake Huron?

2 Dan scored 5 points during the first quarter of a basketball game. During the whole game, he scored fewer than 24 points. How many points could Dan have scored during the last three quarters of the game?

3 627 votes were cast in a school election. The seventh grade cast 276 of these votes. The eighth and ninth grades cast the rest of the votes. How many votes were cast by the eighth and ninth grades together?

4 David had 98 coins in his collection. After he sold 19 coins, he still had more coins than Arthur. How many coins could Arthur have had?

5 Harold, who is 13 years old, is younger than Jim. The difference in their ages is less than 6 years. How old can Jim be?

6 One year there were 166,629 telephones in use in Nova Scotia and 122,205 telephones in New Brunswick. The total number of telephones in Nova Scotia and New Brunswick was less than the number of telephones in Alberta. What is the least number of telephones there could have been in Alberta that year?

7 In 7 years, Janet will be more than 18 years old. Six years ago, she was less than 9 years old. How old can Janet be now?

8 Dave has 9 Mexican coins. He also has some European coins. He has 17 more European coins than Mexican coins. How many European coins does he have?

9 The weight of the Discoverer V satellite was 1700 pounds. This satellite weighed 1455 pounds more than the Discoverer I satellite. How many pounds did the Discoverer I satellite weigh?

10 Miss Jones had 35 students in her first-period class. She did not have enough history books so that each student could have one. After she obtained 9 more history books, she had more than 37. How many of these books could she have had before she obtained the 9 books?

11 One year in Canada, there were fewer than 8,402,000 persons of voting age. 5,701,000 of these persons voted in the federal election that year. What could be the greatest number of persons of voting age who did not vote in this election?

12 The "Enterprise," an atomic-powered aircraft carrier, is longer than the "Queen Elizabeth," an ocean liner. The difference in the lengths of these ships is less than 71 feet. The length of the "Queen Elizabeth" is 1031 feet. What is the greatest length the aircraft carrier can be?

13 What numbers less than the quotient of 48 and 4 can be subtracted from 13 so that each difference is greater than 3?

14 What numbers less than the difference of 243 and 195 can be added to 64 so that each sum is greater than 112?

15 What numbers less than the sum of 137 and 48 can be subtracted from 211 so that each difference is greater than 19?

16 What numbers greater than the product of 42 and 19 can be added to 124 so that each sum is greater than 912?

CHECKING UP

You should restudy lessons 22 through 25 if you are unable to do the work in these tests.

Test 20

Using the sets tabulated below, tabulate each of the sets named in exercises 1 through 9.

$A = \{1, 2, 3, 4, 5\}$. $D = \{\ \}$.
$B = \{0, 2, 4, 6\}$. $E = \{3\}$.
$C = \{1, 3, 5\}$. $F = \{1, 3, 5\}$.

1 $A \cap B$ **4** $B \cup C$ **7** $F \cap C$
2 $A \cup B$ **5** $E \cap D$ **8** $C \cup F$
3 $C \cap B$ **6** $E \cup D$ **9** $A \cap C$

Test 21

Using the standard descriptions given below, for each of exercises 10 through 15, make a Venn diagram to represent the sets named. $U = N$.

$G = \{x \mid x + 2 = 14\}$. $J = \{x \mid x > 7\}$.
$H = \{x \mid x + 2 < 14\}$. $K = \{x \mid x < 3\}$.

10 G and H **12** J and H **14** H and K
11 K and G **13** J and K **15** G and J

Test 22

For exercises 16 through 23, $U = N$.

16 Tabulate $\{x \mid x + 3 < 9\}$.

17 Tabulate $\{x \mid x - 2 > 1\}$.

18 Using the tabulations that you made for exercises 16 and 17, tabulate
$\{x \mid x + 3 < 9 \wedge x - 2 > 1\}$.

19 Make a graph of N.

20 On the graph that you just made for exercise 19, encircle the dots that are in the graph of $\{x \mid x + 2 < 12\}$.

21 On the graphs that you made for exercises 19 and 20, draw squares around the dots that are in the graph of $\{x \mid 6 + x < 9\}$.

22 Using the graphs that you made for exercises 19, 20, and 21, tabulate $\{x \mid x + 2 < 12 \wedge 6 + x < 9\}$.

23 How do you know that $\{x \mid 6 + x < 9\}$ is a subset of $\{x \mid x + 2 < 12\}$?

2 26 Exploring ideas

Intersection of lines and planes

You know that the intersection of two sets is the set that consists of only those objects that belong to both sets. In this lesson you will learn about the intersection of sets of points.

Each photograph on page 99 represents an idea about sets of points. The objects shown suggest lines and planes. As you study the les-

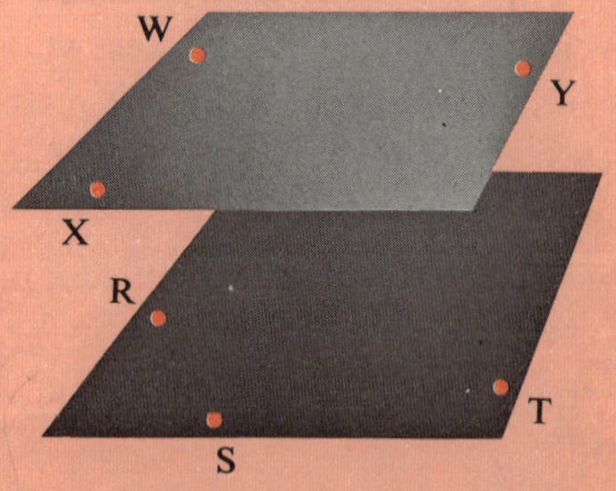

D1

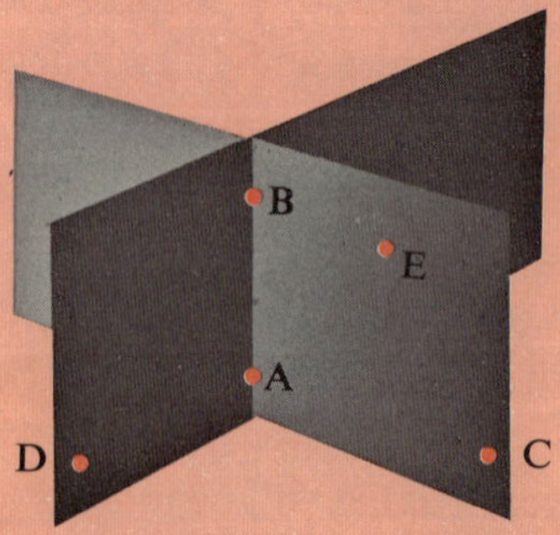

D2

son, you can use objects like these to help you understand the ideas presented in this lesson.

A Name the planes represented in D1. Is each plane an infinite set of points?

B Remember that a plane is unlimited in extent. We will assume that the planes represented in D1 have no points in common. In other words, they do not meet. Are planes WXY and RST disjoint sets? Explain your answer.

> REMINDER
>
> Two sets that have no common members are disjoint sets.
>
> *See lesson 22, page 84.*

Two planes, like plane WXY and plane RST, that have no points in common, are *parallel planes.*

C Are any two parallel planes disjoint sets? Explain your answer.

D In which photograph on this page do the objects suggest parallel planes?

E You know that the intersection of two sets is also a set. Describe the intersection of the two planes represented in D1.

F If any two planes are parallel, what do you know about the intersection of the two planes?

You have been studying an important property of two parallel planes. This property is expressed below.

The intersection of two parallel planes is the empty set.

Next you will learn about planes that are not parallel.

G Name the planes represented in D2. Is A in each of the planes? Is B in each of the planes?

> **par al lel planes** (par′ə lel). Two planes that have no points in common.

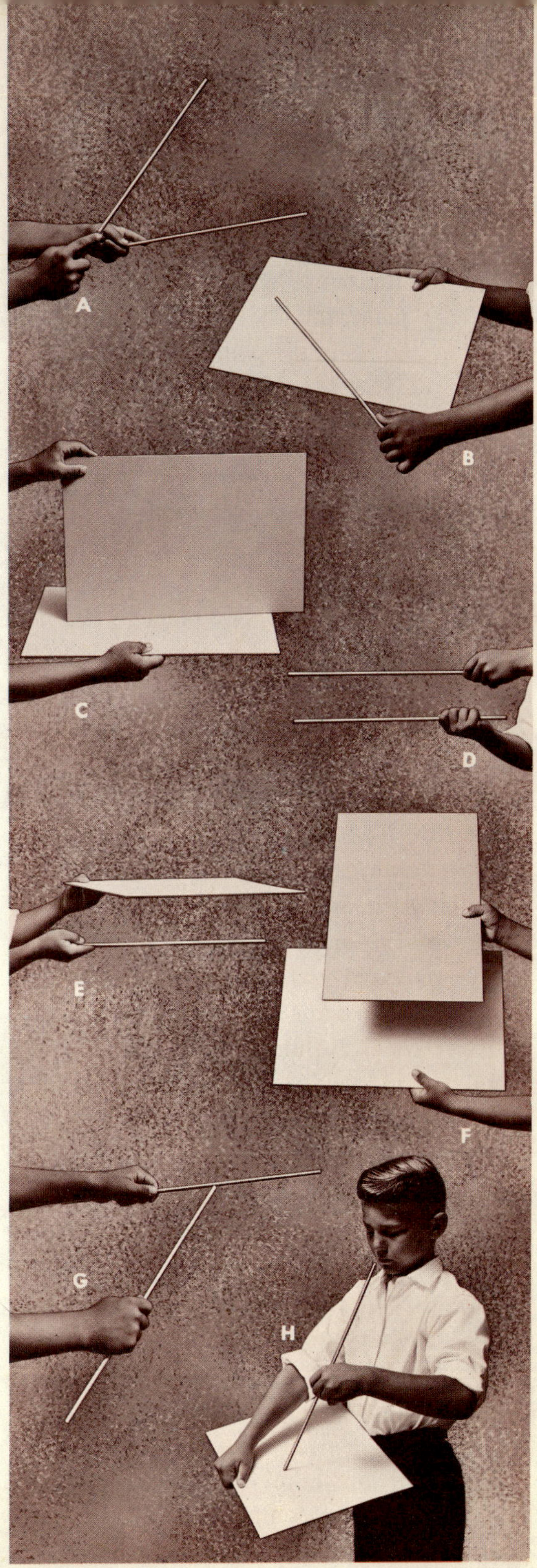

H Look again at D2. Explain why $\overleftrightarrow{AB}$ is included in each of the planes represented.

> REMINDER
>
> If a line contains two points of a plane, the line is included in the plane.
>
> *See lesson 9, page 34.*

You remember that two sets that have common members are said to meet. Geometric figures that have common members are said to meet, or to *intersect.*

I Look again at D2. Do plane ABD and plane ABC have common members? Do the two planes intersect?

J In which photograph on page 99 do the objects suggest planes that intersect?

K What is the intersection of plane ABD and plane ABC?

L How many planes are determined by **?** points A, B, and E, represented in D2? Explain why E cannot be a common member of plane ABD and plane ABC. Remember that plane ABD and plane ABC are different planes.

Exercises G through K help you to understand an important property of two planes that intersect. This property is expressed below.

The intersection of two planes that meet is a line.

M Three points are in the intersection of two **?** planes. How do you know that the two planes are not parallel? How do you know that the three points are collinear?

N Describe the intersection of a plane FGH **?** and a plane EGH different from plane FGH.

You have learned that the intersection of two parallel planes is the empty set. You also know that if two planes meet, their intersection is a line. Next you will learn about the intersection of a line and a plane.

D3 represents the three ways in which a line and a plane may be related.

A ℓ_1 and plane LMN do not have any common members. ℓ_1 is parallel to plane LMN. What is the intersection of ℓ_1 and plane LMN?

B ℓ_2 intersects plane LMN. What is the intersection of ℓ_2 and plane LMN?

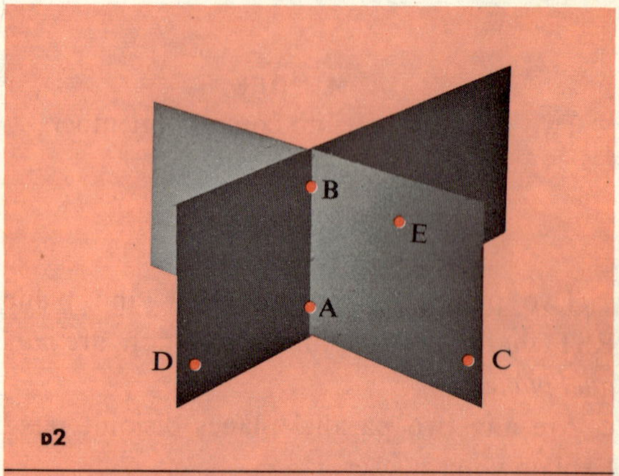

D2

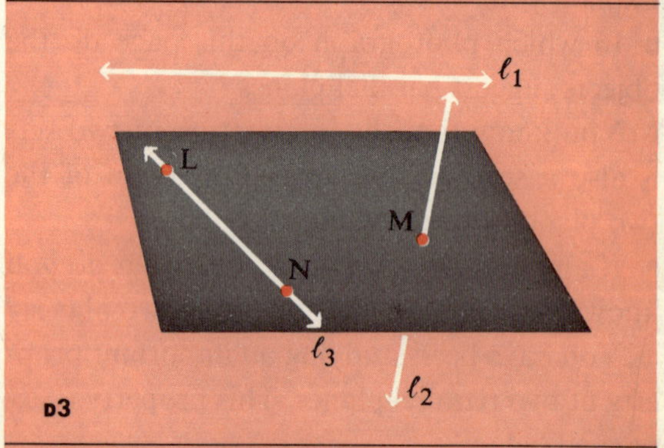

D3

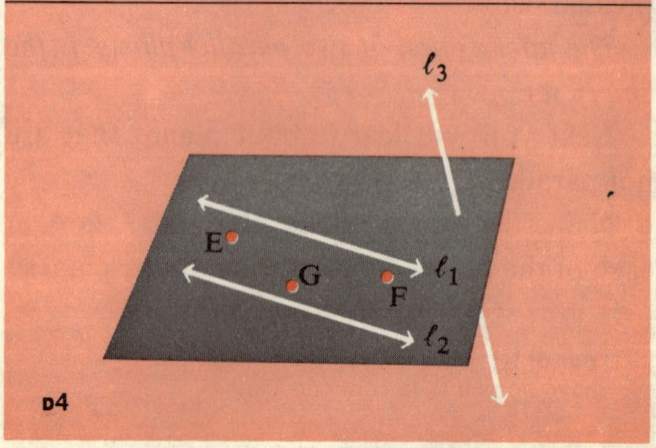

D4

We say that ℓ_2 intersects plane LMN *in* point M. We mean that point M is the only member common to ℓ_2 and plane LMN.

C Plane LMN contains points L and N. How ? do you know that ℓ_3 is a subset of plane LMN? What is the intersection of ℓ_3 and plane LMN?

You know that a line is either parallel to or intersects a given plane. The property expressed below concerns a line and a plane that are parallel.

The intersection of a line and a plane that are parallel is the empty set.

D In which photograph on page 99 do the objects suggest a line and a plane that are parallel?

The property expressed below concerns a line and a plane that intersect.

If a line and a plane intersect, their intersection either contains exactly one point or is the line.

E In which photograph on page 99 do the objects suggest a line that intersects a plane in one point?

F In which photograph on page 99 do the objects suggest a line and a plane whose intersection is the line?

So far you have learned about the intersection of two planes and the intersection of a line and a plane. Now you will learn about the intersection of two lines.

A Name the lines represented in D4. Which is each line, a finite set of points or an infinite set of points? Does each line extend endlessly in opposite directions?

B Lines ℓ_1 and ℓ_2 represented in D4 are included in the same plane. Name this plane. Is each line a subset of the plane?

C Lines ℓ_1 and ℓ_2 have no points in common. They do not intersect. Are ℓ_1 and ℓ_2 disjoint sets? Describe the intersection of ℓ_1 and ℓ_2.

Two lines like ℓ_1 and ℓ_2, that are subsets of the same plane and that do not intersect, are *parallel lines.*

D In which photograph on page 99 do the objects suggest parallel lines?

E Remember that two parallel lines are included in the same plane. Look again at D4. ℓ_1 and ℓ_3 have no points in common. Are ℓ_1 and ℓ_3 in the same plane? Are ℓ_1 and ℓ_3 parallel? Explain your answers.

Two lines that are not included in the same plane are *skew lines.* ℓ_1 and ℓ_3 are skew lines.

F In which photograph on page 99 do the objects suggest skew lines?

G $\overleftrightarrow{AB}$ and $\overleftrightarrow{CD}$ have no points in common. Do ? you know whether or not $\overleftrightarrow{AB}$ and $\overleftrightarrow{CD}$ are parallel? Explain your answer.

H Describe the intersection of two parallel lines. The intersection of two skew lines.

A property of parallel lines and a property of skew lines are expressed below.

The intersection of two parallel lines is the empty set. The intersection of two skew lines is the empty set.

REMINDER

The union of two sets is the set that contains only those objects that belong to either set or to both sets.

See lesson 23, page 87.

par al lel lines (par′ə lel). Two lines, included in the same plane, that do not have any points in common.

skew lines (skū). Two lines not included in the same plane.

I Suppose that $\ell_4 \cup \ell_5$ is not a subset of any **?** one plane. What do you know about ℓ_4 and ℓ_5?

J Suppose that $\ell_6 \cup \ell_7$ is a subset of a plane. **?** Suppose also that $\ell_6 \cap \ell_7 = \{\ \}$. What do you know about ℓ_6 and ℓ_7?

K Now look at D5. $\overleftrightarrow{WS}$ and $\overleftrightarrow{SJ}$ are included in plane WSJ. Are $\overleftrightarrow{WS}$ and $\overleftrightarrow{SJ}$ skew lines? Are $\overleftrightarrow{WS}$ and $\overleftrightarrow{SJ}$ parallel lines?

L What point do $\overleftrightarrow{WS}$ and $\overleftrightarrow{SJ}$ have in common? Are $\overleftrightarrow{WS}$ and $\overleftrightarrow{SJ}$ disjoint sets? Do $\overleftrightarrow{WS}$ and $\overleftrightarrow{SJ}$ intersect?

M Describe the intersection of $\overleftrightarrow{WS}$ and $\overleftrightarrow{SJ}$. Does $\overleftrightarrow{WS} \cap \overleftrightarrow{SJ} = \{S\}$?

$\overleftrightarrow{WS}$ and $\overleftrightarrow{SJ}$ intersect in point S. $\overleftrightarrow{WS}$ and $\overleftrightarrow{SJ}$ are included in the same plane, but they are not parallel. An important property of two lines like $\overleftrightarrow{WS}$ and $\overleftrightarrow{SJ}$ is expressed below.

If two lines intersect, their intersection contains exactly one point.

N In which photograph on page 99 do the objects suggest lines that intersect?

O Suppose that $\ell_8 \cap \ell_9$ is not the empty set. Describe $\ell_8 \cap \ell_9$.

P Two lines, ℓ_{10} and ℓ_{11}, intersect. How many **?** planes are determined by ℓ_{10} and ℓ_{11}?

In this lesson you have learned about the intersection of two sets of points and about geometric figures that are parallel.

On your own

Use D6 as you answer the questions in exercises 1 through 9.

1 What is the intersection of plane ABC and plane ACD?

2 What is the intersection of plane ABD and plane ACD?

3 $\overleftrightarrow{AB}$ is the intersection of what two planes?

4 Tabulate the intersection of $\overleftrightarrow{CA}$ and $\overleftrightarrow{AD}$.

5 How many planes represented in D6 contain A?

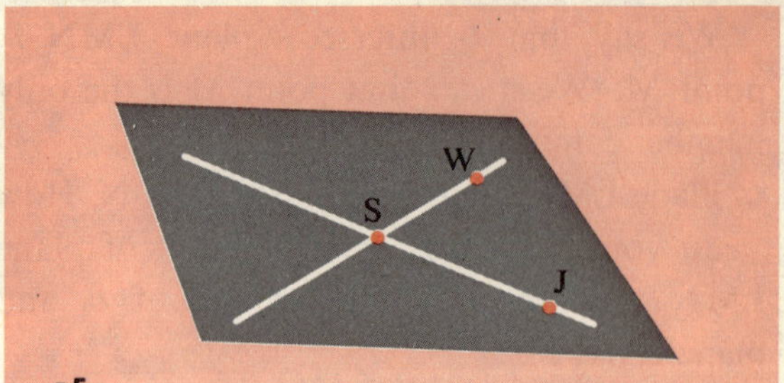

D5

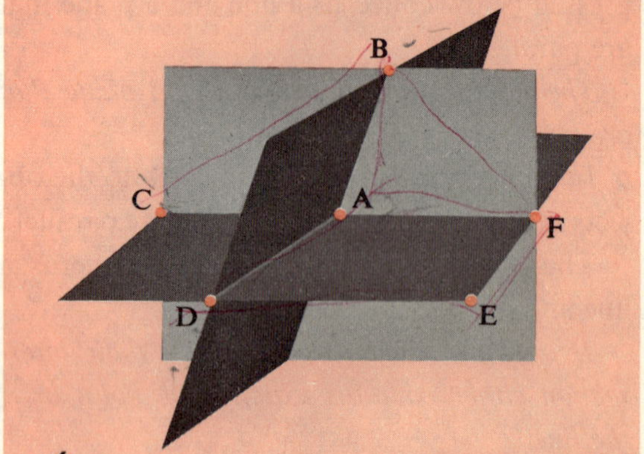

D6

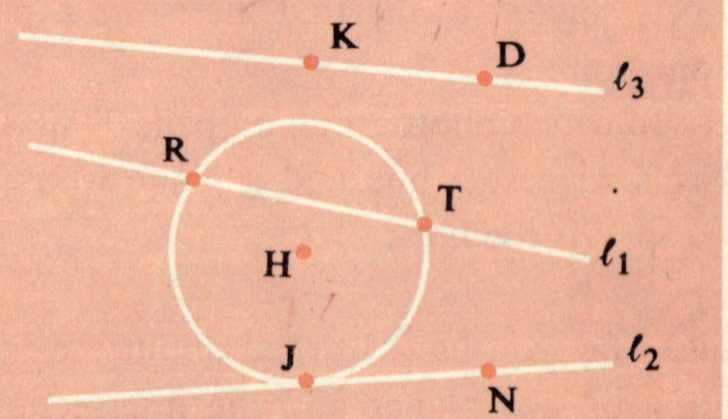

D7

6 Which pairs of lines represented in D6 do you think are skew lines?

7 Which pairs of lines represented in D6 do you think are parallel lines?

8 Tabulate the intersection of $\overleftrightarrow{AC}$ and plane ADB.

9 What is the intersection of $\overleftrightarrow{AB}$ and plane ADB?

For exercises 10 through 16, use D7. The geometric figures represented in D7 are all subsets of the same plane. Review lesson 12 if you need to recall certain ideas about a circle.

10 Tabulate the intersection of circle H and ℓ_1.

11 Tabulate the intersection of circle H and ℓ_2.

12 Tabulate the intersection of circle H and ℓ_3.

13 Describe the intersection of the interior of circle H and ℓ_1.

14 Tabulate the intersection of the interior of circle H and ℓ_2.

15 Tabulate the intersection of the interior of circle H and ℓ_3.

16 What is the intersection of ℓ_3 and the exterior of circle H?

17 Make a sketch of circle R. Next make a sketch of a line that intersects circle R in one point. Then make a sketch of a line that intersects circle R in two points.

18 Make a sketch of circle S. Then make a sketch of two parallel lines each of which intersects the circle in two points.

Use D8 to help answer the questions in exercises 19 through 21. Review lessons 10 and 11 if you need to recall certain ideas about segments and separation.

19 ℓ_1 separates the plane into two half-planes. Are points L and M in the same half-plane? Tabulate the intersection of $\overline{LM}$ and ℓ_1.

20 Are points V and W in the same half-plane? Tabulate the intersection of $\overline{VW}$ and ℓ_1.

21 How many points are in the intersection of $\overline{ZG}$ and ℓ_1? Are points Z and G in the same half-plane?

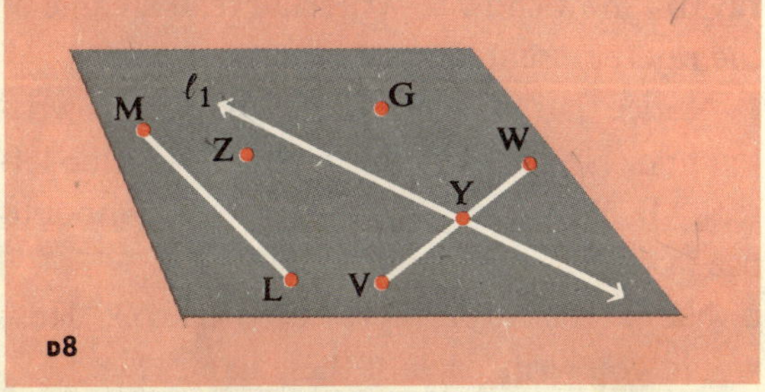

D8

22 Make a sketch of circle R. Make a sketch of radius RS. Tabulate the intersection of $\overline{RS}$ and circle R.

23 In the same drawing, make a sketch of chord MN of circle R. Tabulate the intersection of chord MN and circle R.

24 $\overline{LT}$ and $\overline{ST}$ are radii of circle T. Tabulate the intersection of these two radii.

KEEPING SKILFUL

Tabulate the solution set of each condition expressed in exercises 1 through 16. $U = \{1, 3, 5, 7, 9, 11\}$.

1 $69 + x < 74$.

2 $s + s > 8$.

3 $121 - w < 121$.

4 $2m + 3 = 17$.

5 $108 \div 12 > x$.

6 $2x = 22$.

7 $142 + y = 151$.

8 $v + 4 = 7$.

9 $12 + v > 13$.

10 $4y + 1 = 29$.

11 $27 - p > 17$.

12 $3x < 25$.

13 $216 \div 12 > w$.

14 $w + 159 < 170$.

15 $3y = 2y + y$.

16 $2z + 1 = z$.

Tabulate the solution set of each condition expressed in exercises 17 through 26. $U = N$.

17 $3806 - n = 1979$.

18 $17 + v < 33$.

19 $36(972) > d$.

20 $18 - b = 18$.

21 $13 - w > 4$.

22 $4497 + 8596 = m$.

23 $143 + c > 200$.

24 $2z + 5 = 23$.

25 $562 + n > 561$.

26 $3f = f$.

Tabulate the solution set of each condition expressed in exercises 27 through 36. $U = N$.

27 $m > 7 + 4 \wedge m + 9 < 24$.

28 $x > 27 \wedge x + 154 < 192$.

29 $765 \div 45 > s \wedge 80 - s > 59$.

30 $75 + x > 113 \wedge x < 300 - 176$.

31 $w < 15 \wedge w + 435 > 446$.

32 $b > 27(42) \wedge 237 + b < 1380$.

33 $s + 187 = 506 \wedge s - 298 = 21$.

34 $c < 347 + 962 \wedge c + 524 > 1833$.

35 $12m = 228 \wedge 124 + m = 143$.

36 $9068 - 8976 < z \wedge 182 + z > 274$.

2 | 27 Exploring ideas

Rays and angles

You have studied some geometric figures in previous lessons. In this lesson you will study some other geometric figures called rays and angles.

A Look at D1. Point A separates the line represented in D1 into two half-lines. Are points T and U in the same half-line? Are R and S in the same half-line? Explain your answers. Remember that you are thinking about the two half-lines bounded by A.

> REMINDER
>
> A point separates a line into two half-lines. The point is the boundary of each half-line. The boundary is not in either half-line.
>
> Each half-line is bounded by the point.
>
> *See lesson 11, page 42.*

B Is each of the half-lines bounded by A an infinite set of points? Does each half-line extend endlessly in one direction?

Look again at D1. Think about the set of points that contains A and all the points in the line to the right of A. This set of points is a *ray*. Point A is the *endpoint* of the ray.

C Describe another ray represented in D1 that ? has A as its endpoint.

A set of points that contains the boundary of a half-line and all the points in the half-line is a ray. The boundary of the half-line is the endpoint of the ray. A ray is a geometric figure.

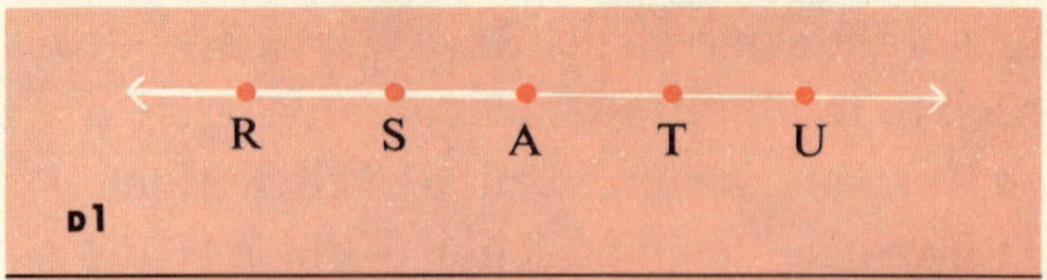

D1

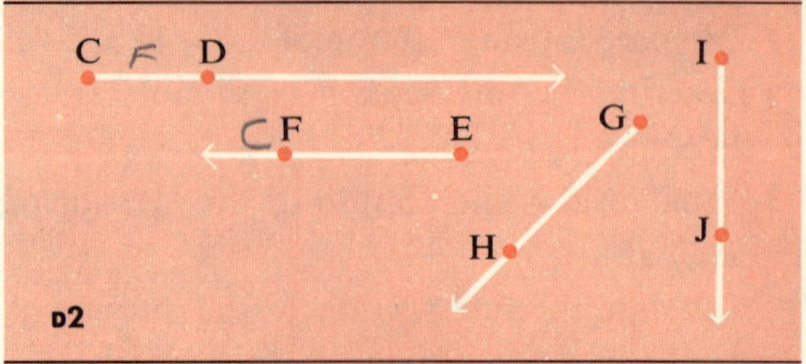

D2

D3

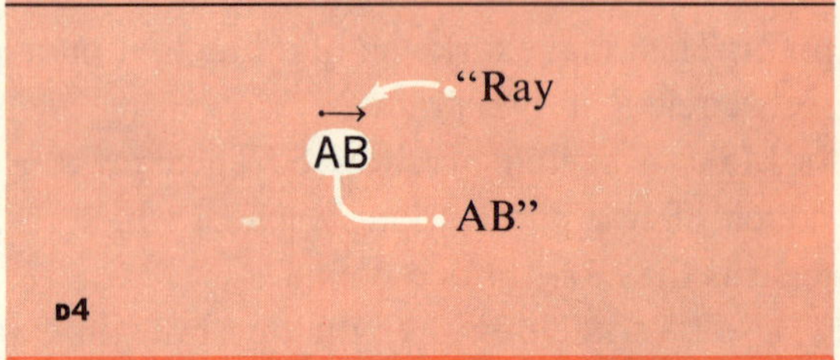

D4

ray (rā). A set of points containing the boundary of a half-line and all the points in the half-line. The boundary of the half-line is the **endpoint** of the ray.

D Several rays are represented in D2. Name the endpoint of each ray.

E Name the endpoint of the ray represented in D3. Name another point in the ray.

In naming a ray, we use the name of its endpoint and the name of one other point in the ray. D4 shows how to write and read a name of the ray represented in D3.

F Notice that the name of the endpoint is written first. Notice also the symbol above the letters AB. Why is this symbol a good symbol to use in writing a name of a ray?

G Name the rays represented in D2. How would you write each of these names?

H Is it sensible to ask if $\overrightarrow{CD}$ is longer than $\overrightarrow{EF}$? Explain your answer.

Use D5 to help you answer exercises I through N.

I $\overrightarrow{PQ}$ is the set of points consisting of P and all points in ℓ_1 to the right of P. Describe $\overrightarrow{QP}$.

J What is the endpoint of $\overrightarrow{PQ}$? Of $\overrightarrow{QP}$?

K Is ray PQ the same as ray QP? Explain your answer.

L What is the intersection of $\overrightarrow{PQ}$ and $\overrightarrow{QP}$?

M Is $\overrightarrow{PQ}$ the same as $\overrightarrow{PR}$? Explain your answer.

N What is the union of {P} and the half-line to the left of P?

D5

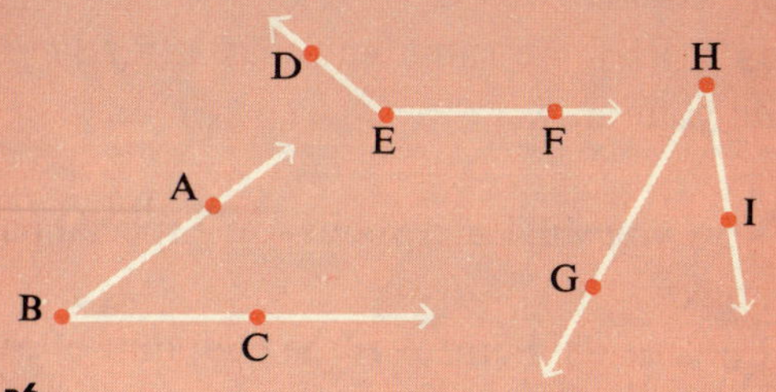

D6

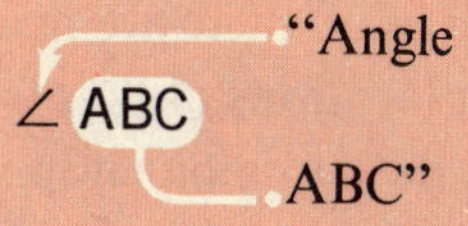

D7

> **an gle** (ang′gəl). The union of two rays that have a common endpoint, but that do not form a line. The common endpoint is the **vertex** (vėr′teks) of the angle. Each of the rays is a **side** of the angle.

Next you will use what you know about rays as you study another set of points that is a geometric figure.

A Look at D6. Point B is the common endpoint of $\overrightarrow{BA}$ and $\overrightarrow{BC}$. Point E is the common endpoint of which two rays represented in D6? Point H is the common endpoint of which two rays represented?

B The set that contains all the points in $\overrightarrow{BA}$ together with all the points in $\overrightarrow{BC}$ is an *angle*. Describe each of the other angles represented in D6.

An angle is the union of two rays that have a common endpoint, but that do not form a line. The common endpoint is the *vertex* of the angle. Each of the rays is a *side* of the angle. Since an angle is a set of points, it is a geometric figure.

C Name the sides and vertex of each angle represented in D6.

D Is each side of an angle a subset of the angle? Explain your answer.

E Are all the points in an angle contained in the same plane? Is an angle a subset of a plane?

F Is it sensible to ask which of the two sides of an angle is the longer? Is it sensible to ask which of two angles has longer sides? Explain your answers.

One way of naming an angle is to use the name of its vertex and the names of two other points, one in each side of the angle. D7 shows how to write and read a name of the angle represented at the left in D6.

The vertex of ∠ABC is point B. Notice that the name of the vertex is written between the names of the other two points. Mathematicians always put the name of the vertex in this middle position to indicate clearly which point is the vertex of the angle.

G Notice also the symbol to the left of the letters ABC. Why is this symbol a good symbol to use in writing a name of an angle?

H Look again at D6. Is ∠ABC the same angle as ∠CBA?

I Give two names for each of the other angles represented in D6.

J Is ∠RST the same angle as ∠RTS? Explain your answer.

Now you will learn about some special pairs of angles.

A Look at D8. Point A is the endpoint of each of the three rays represented in the display. Name these three rays.

Notice that in D8 there are no dots to represent the exact locations of points A, B, C, and D. Point A is the common endpoint of each of the three rays. Point B is some other point in $\overrightarrow{AB}$; point C is some other point in $\overrightarrow{AC}$; and point D is some other point in $\overrightarrow{AD}$. From now on, you will be given the exact locations of points only when you need such information to do your work.

B ∠DAB and ∠DAC are represented in D8. What is their common vertex? What is their common side? Sides AB and AC are not common to ∠DAB and ∠DAC.

C Points A, B, and C are collinear. Is the union of sides AB and AC a line?

If two angles have a common vertex and a common side, and if the union of the sides that are not common is a line, then the two angles are a *linear pair of angles*. ∠DAB and ∠DAC, represented in D8, are a linear pair of angles.

D Look at D9. Points A, B, and C, points E, F, and G, and points I, J, and K are collinear. ∠ABD and ∠DBC are a linear pair of angles.

> **lin e ar pair of angles** (lin′ē ər). Two angles that have a common vertex and a common side, and whose sides that are not common form a line.

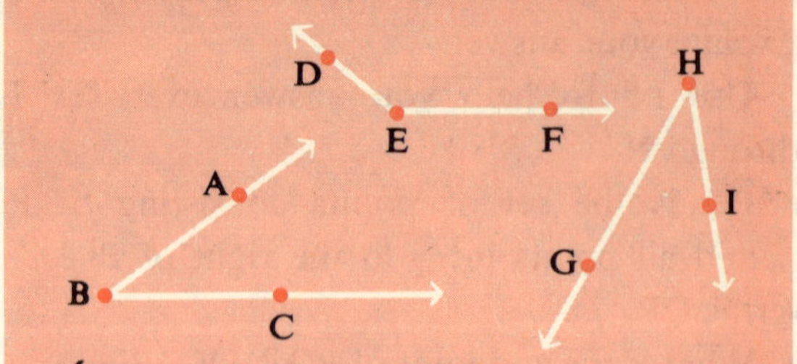

D6

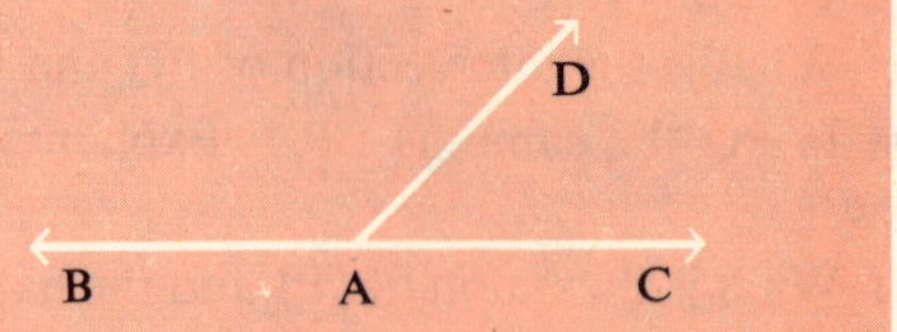

D8

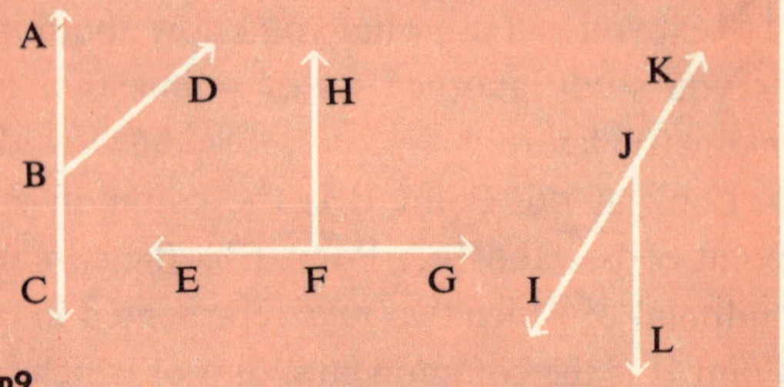

D9

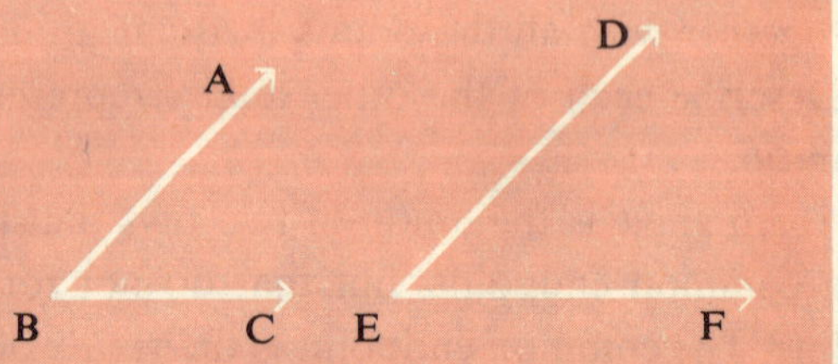

D10

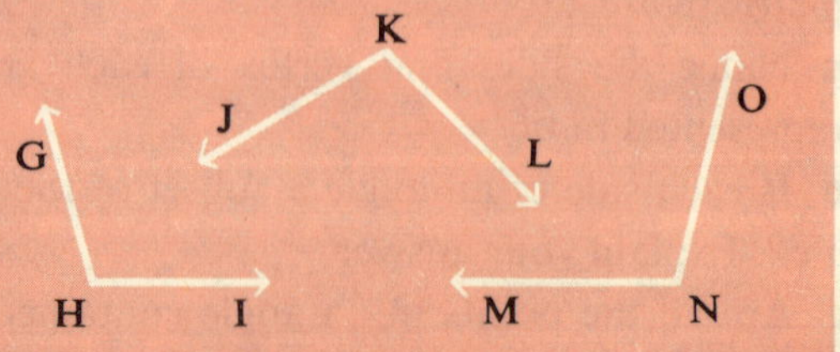

D11

Name two other linear pairs of angles represented in D9.

Each angle of a linear pair of angles is the *supplement* (sup′lə mənt) of the other angle of the pair. Thus, ∠ABD is the supplement of ∠DBC, and ∠DBC is the supplement of ∠ABD.

E Look again at D9. What angle is the supplement of ∠EFH? Of ∠IJL? Of ∠HFG? Of ∠KJL?

Now you will learn that congruence has the same meaning for angles that it has for segments. Congruent angles are "the same size."

F Look at D10. ∠ABC ≅ ∠DEF. Do you think that ∠DEF ≅ ∠ABC?

G Look at D11. ∠GHI ≅ ∠JKL. ∠JKL ≅ ? ∠MNO. Do you think that ∠GHI ≅ ∠MNO?

H Points A, B, and C, represented in D12, are collinear. Are ∠ABD and ∠DBC a linear pair of angles? What angle is the supplement of ∠ABD? Of ∠DBC?

Now suppose that ∠ABD ≅ ∠DBC. Then each of these two angles is a *right angle*. An angle that is congruent to its supplement is a right angle.

I Look at D13. Points R, S, and U are collinear. ∠TSU is a right angle. What angle is the supplement of ∠TSU? Is ∠TSU ≅ ∠TSR? Is ∠TSR a right angle? Explain your answers.

J ∠MNO, represented in D14, is a right angle. ? Explain how you would make a sketch of a

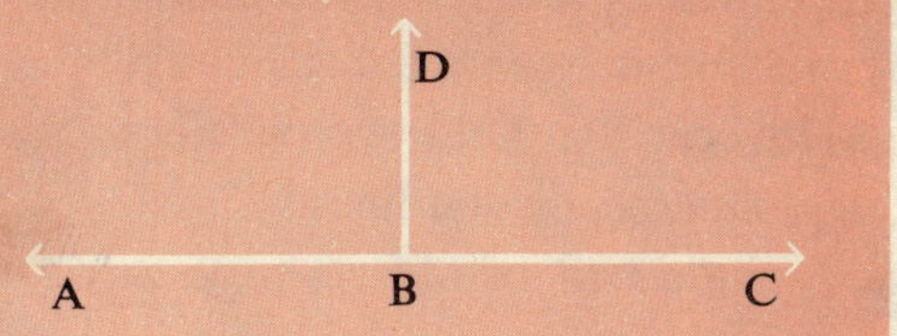

D12

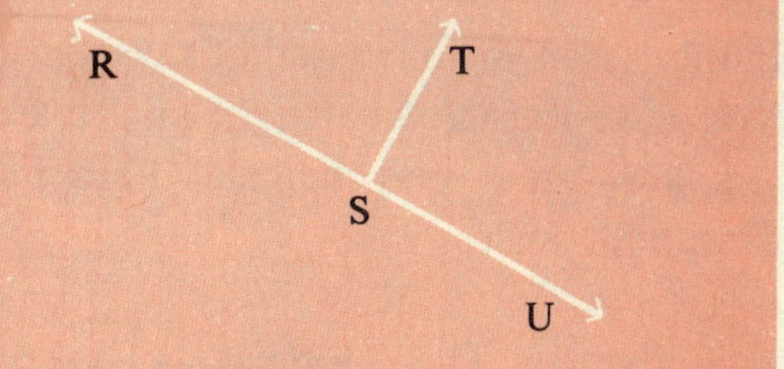

D13

D14

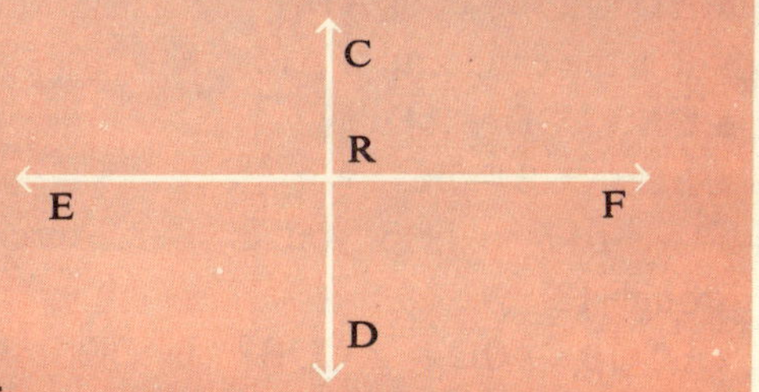

D15

supplement of ∠MNO. Is ∠MNO congruent to this supplement?

You have been learning about right angles. You can use what you know about right angles to learn more about lines that intersect.

K Look at D15. Lines CD and EF intersect in point R. Point R is the endpoint of the four rays represented in the display. Name the four rays. Name the four angles that are formed by these rays.

Suppose that the angles formed when $\overleftrightarrow{CD}$ and $\overleftrightarrow{EF}$ intersect are right angles. Then $\overleftrightarrow{CD}$ and $\overleftrightarrow{EF}$ are *perpendicular lines*. Two lines are

right an gle (rīt ang′gəl). An angle that is congruent to its supplement.

per pen dic u lar lines (pėr′pən dik′ū lər). Two lines that intersect so that right angles are formed.

perpendicular if they intersect and if the angles formed by these lines are right angles.

L How can you hold two pencils so that they suggest perpendicular lines?

M Name a pair of objects in your classroom that suggest perpendicular lines.

In this lesson you have studied rays and angles. You have learned what right angles are, and you know that perpendicular lines meet to form right angles.

On your own

Study D16. Then, for each of exercises 1 through 7, tell whether the sentence expresses a true statement or a false statement. A, B, C, and D are collinear points.

1 $\overrightarrow{AC} = \overrightarrow{AB}$.

2 $\overrightarrow{BC} = \overrightarrow{CB}$.

3 $\overrightarrow{AD}$ is a subset of $\overleftrightarrow{AD}$.

4 $\overrightarrow{AD}$ is a subset of $\overline{AD}$.

5 B is the endpoint of $\overrightarrow{AB}$.

6 $\overrightarrow{CA} \cup \overrightarrow{CD} = \overleftrightarrow{AD}$.

7 $\overrightarrow{BC} \cap \overrightarrow{CB} = \overline{BC}$.

Use D17 to help you answer exercises 8 through 12.

8 Is $\overrightarrow{OB} \cup \overrightarrow{OC} = \angle COB$? Is $\overrightarrow{OC} \cup \overrightarrow{OA} = \angle AOC$?

9 Name the sides and vertex of $\angle AOC$.

10 Name the sides and vertex of $\angle COB$.

11 Is $\overrightarrow{OC}$ a subset of $\angle COB$? Of $\angle AOC$?

12 $\angle AOC$ and $\angle COB$ have a common side and a common vertex. What else must you know to decide if $\angle AOC$ and $\angle COB$ are a linear pair of angles?

Use the following information for exercises 13, 14, and 15. $\overleftrightarrow{KL}$ and $\overleftrightarrow{MN}$ are any two lines that intersect in point Q. Point Q is between K and L and also between M and N.

13 Name the common vertex of $\angle MQL$ and $\angle NQL$. Name the common side of these two angles.

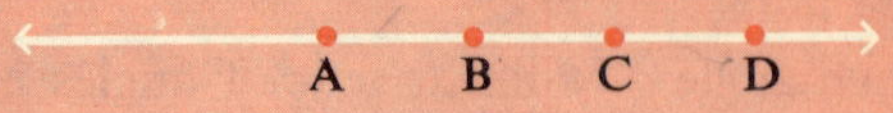

D16

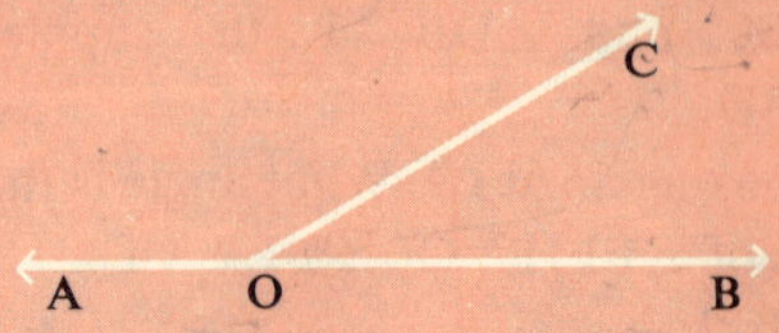

D17

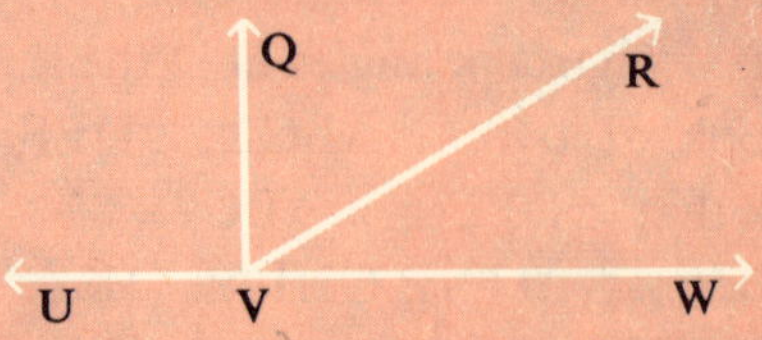

D18

14 Is $\overrightarrow{QM} \cup \overrightarrow{QN} = \overleftrightarrow{MN}$ a true statement about the sides of $\angle MQL$ and $\angle NQL$ that are not common? Are $\angle MQL$ and $\angle NQL$ a linear pair of angles?

15 Name another linear pair of angles formed by $\overleftrightarrow{KL}$ and $\overleftrightarrow{MN}$. Name the common side of these two angles.

Use D18 to help you with exercises 16 through 19. Points U, V, and W are collinear.

16 Are $\angle RVW$ and $\angle RVU$ a linear pair of angles? Name another linear pair of angles.

17 What is the supplement of $\angle RVW$?

18 What is the supplement of $\angle QVW$?

19 $\angle QVW \cong \angle QVU$. Name two right angles represented in D18.

Use the following information for exercises 20 and 21. $\overleftrightarrow{IJ}$ and $\overleftrightarrow{GH}$ are any two perpendicular lines that intersect in point R. Point R is between I and J and also between G and H.

20 Is $\angle JRG$ a right angle? Is $\angle GRI$ a right angle? Is $\angle JRG \cong \angle GRI$?

21 Name two other right angles formed by $\overleftrightarrow{IJ}$ and $\overleftrightarrow{GH}$.

2 28 **Exploring ideas**

The triangle

In this lesson you will learn about another plane geometric figure called a triangle.

A Look at D1. A, B, and C are three noncollinear points. How many segments are determined by A, B, and C?

> REMINDER
>
> Points that are not contained in the same line are noncollinear points.
>
> *See lesson 9, page 34.*

B ? Points A, B, and C determine segments AB, BC, and AC. Is the set containing all the points in $\overline{AB}$, all the points in $\overline{BC}$, and all the points in $\overline{AC}$ the union of these three segments? How do you know?

C Look again at D1. Is each of the points A, B, and C a member of the union of $\overline{AB}$, $\overline{BC}$, and $\overline{AC}$?

The union of $\overline{AB}$, $\overline{BC}$, and $\overline{AC}$ is a *triangle.* A triangle is a set of points whose members are all the points contained in the three segments determined by any three noncollinear points. Each of the segments is a *side* of the triangle. Each endpoint of the segments is a *vertex* of the triangle.

> **tri an gle** (trī′ang′gəl). The union of the three segments determined by any three noncollinear points. The three segments are the **sides** of the triangle. The endpoints of the segments are the **vertices** (vėr′tə sēz) of the triangle.

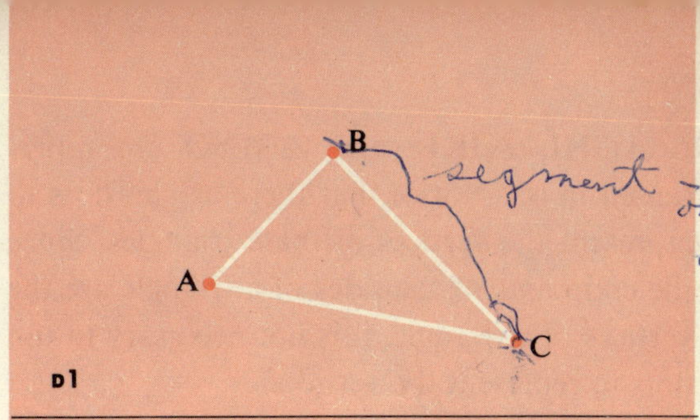

D1

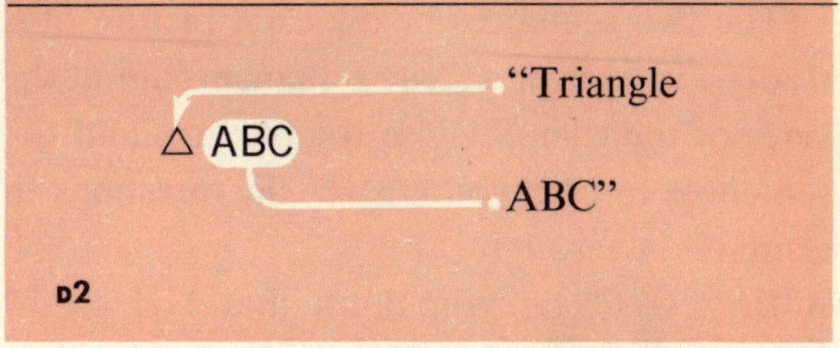

D2

D Name the three sides of the triangle represented in D1. Name the three vertices.

E ? Is a triangle a subset of more than one plane? Explain your answer.

In naming a triangle, we use the names of its three vertices. Study D2, which shows how to write and read a name of the triangle represented in D1.

F Look again at D1. Is △CBA the same triangle as △ABC? Is △BAC the same triangle as △ABC? Explain your answers.

You know that we sometimes talk about the center of a circle, but you know that the center is not in the circle. In the same way, we talk about the angles of a triangle. We know that a triangle does not include angles. The phrase "angles of a triangle" is only a way of identifying certain angles. In talking about △ABC, for example, we say that ∠BAC is an angle of △ABC. This statement means that each side of ∠BAC includes a side of the triangle. Thus, $\overleftrightarrow{AB}$ includes $\overline{AB}$, and $\overleftrightarrow{AC}$ includes $\overline{AC}$.

G ? Is ∠ABC a subset of △ABC? Explain your answer.

Now you will learn to identify triangles according to the number of congruent sides that each triangle has.

△GHI, △JKL, and △MNO are represented in D3. Notice that there are no dots to represent the vertices of these triangles. Since the endpoints of the sides of a triangle are the vertices of a triangle, it is not necessary to use dots to represent the vertices.

The two sentences below each picture of a triangle in D3 express true statements about the sides of the triangle. Use the pictures and the sentences to help you answer the questions in exercises A through I.

A In △GHI, do you think that $\overline{GH} > \overline{GI}$? How many sides of △GHI are congruent?

B Does △JKL have two congruent sides? What other triangle represented in D3 also has two congruent sides?

C Which triangle has three congruent sides?

A triangle with no two sides congruent is a *scalene triangle.*

D Which triangle represented in D3 is a scalene triangle?

A triangle with two congruent sides is an *isosceles triangle.*

E Which triangles represented in D3 are isosceles triangles?

A triangle with three congruent sides is an *equilateral triangle.*

F Which triangle represented in D3 is an equilateral triangle?

G Is any equilateral triangle also an isosceles ? triangle? How do you know?

H Is the set of all equilateral triangles a subset ? of the set of all isosceles triangles? How do you know?

I Is the set of all isosceles triangles a subset of ? the set of all equilateral triangles? Explain your answer.

J Make a sketch of an equilateral triangle. Make a sketch of an isosceles triangle that is not equilateral. Make a sketch of a scalene triangle.

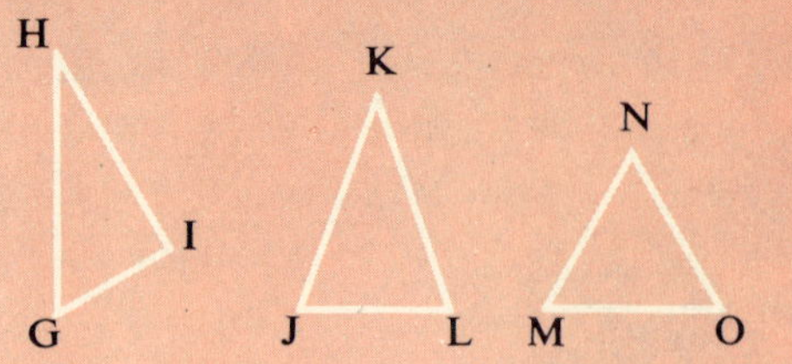

$\overline{GH} > \overline{HI}$. $\overline{JK} \cong \overline{KL}$. $\overline{MN} \cong \overline{NO}$.

$\overline{HI} > \overline{GI}$. $\overline{KL} > \overline{JL}$. $\overline{NO} \cong \overline{MO}$.

D3

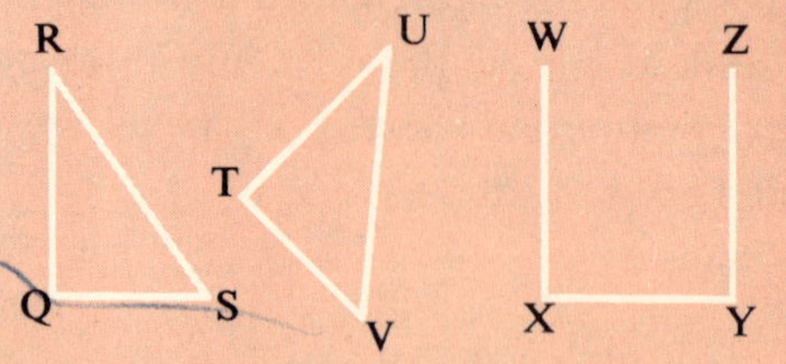

D4

sca lene triangle (skā lēn′). A triangle with no two of its sides congruent.

i sos ce les triangle (ī sos′ə lēz). A triangle with two of its sides congruent.

e qui lat er al triangle (ē′kwə lat′ər əl). A triangle with its three sides congruent.

right triangle. A triangle with one right angle.

In lesson 27 you learned about right angles. Now you will study right triangles.

K Look at D4. ∠RQS of △QRS is a right angle. Since one angle of △QRS is a right angle, △QRS is a *right triangle.*

L Look again at D4. ∠VTU of △TUV is a right angle. Is △TUV a right triangle?

M Look at the picture of the geometric figure WXYZ in D4. This figure has two right angles, ∠WXY and ∠XYZ. Is the figure a triangle?

N Do you think that a right triangle can have ? more than one right angle?

O Do you think that a right triangle can also **?** be an isosceles triangle? Do you think that a right triangle can also be an equilateral triangle?

P Suppose that U is the set of all triangles. **?** Suppose also that A is the set of all isosceles triangles, and that B is the set of all equilateral triangles. Make a Venn diagram to represent these sets. Describe $A \cap B$.

Q Suppose that C is the set of all right trian- **?** gles. Then $A \cap C$ is the set of all triangles that are both isosceles and right triangles. On the Venn diagram you made for exercise P, represent set C. Describe $B \cap C$.

R Suppose that D is the set of all scalene tri- **?** angles. Describe $C \cap D$.

You have already studied congruent segments and congruent angles. Now you will learn about congruent triangles.

A The sentences in D5 express true statements about the angles and sides of $\triangle IJK$ and $\triangle LMN$ represented in D5. Study D5.

B Is each angle of $\triangle IJK$ congruent to an angle of $\triangle LMN$? Is each angle of $\triangle LMN$ congruent to an angle of $\triangle IJK$?

C Is each side of $\triangle IJK$ congruent to a side of $\triangle LMN$? Is each side of $\triangle LMN$ congruent to a side of $\triangle IJK$?

Each angle of $\triangle IJK$ is congruent to an angle of $\triangle LMN$, and each angle of $\triangle LMN$ is congruent to an angle of $\triangle IJK$. Each side of $\triangle IJK$ is congruent to a side of $\triangle LMN$, and each side of $\triangle LMN$ is congruent to a side of $\triangle IJK$. Therefore, $\triangle IJK$ and $\triangle LMN$ are *congruent triangles*.

> **con gru ent triangles** (kong′grü ənt). Two triangles that have the same size and shape. Suppose that $\triangle ABC$ and $\triangle DEF$ are any two triangles. If $\angle ABC \cong \angle DEF$, $\angle BAC \cong \angle EDF$, $\angle BCA \cong \angle EFD$; and if $\overline{AB} \cong \overline{DE}$, $\overline{BC} \cong \overline{EF}$, $\overline{AC} \cong \overline{DF}$, then $\triangle ABC \cong \triangle DEF$.

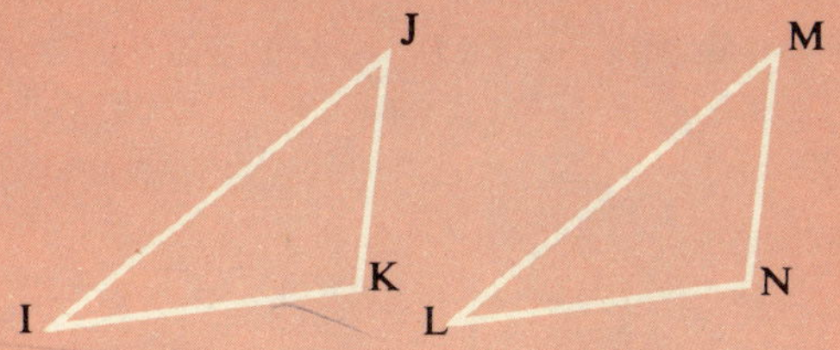

$\angle KIJ \cong \angle NLM$.	$\overline{IJ} \cong \overline{LM}$.
$\angle IJK \cong \angle LMN$.	$\overline{JK} \cong \overline{MN}$.
$\angle JKI \cong \angle MNL$.	$\overline{IK} \cong \overline{LN}$.

D5

Suppose that $\triangle ABC$ and $\triangle DEF$ are any two triangles. If $\angle ABC \cong \angle DEF$, $\angle BAC \cong \angle EDF$, $\angle BCA \cong \angle EFD$; and if $\overline{AB} \cong \overline{DE}$, $\overline{BC} \cong \overline{EF}$, $\overline{AC} \cong \overline{DF}$, then $\triangle ABC \cong \triangle DEF$.

D Look again at D5. $\triangle IJK \cong \triangle LMN$. Do you think that $\triangle LMN \cong \triangle IJK$?

E Suppose that $\triangle LMN$ is congruent to a third triangle, $\triangle OPQ$. Do you think that $\triangle IJK \cong \triangle OPQ$?

Now you know that if two triangles are congruent, they have three pairs of angles that are congruent and three pairs of sides that are congruent.

F Suppose that two triangles have three an- **?** gles of one triangle congruent to three angles of the other. Do you think that the three sides of one triangle are congruent to the three sides of the other triangle?

G Suppose that two triangles have three sides **?** of one triangle congruent to three sides of the other. Do you think that the three angles of one triangle are congruent to the three angles of the other triangle?

In this lesson you have studied different kinds of triangles. You also know what it means to say that two triangles are congruent.

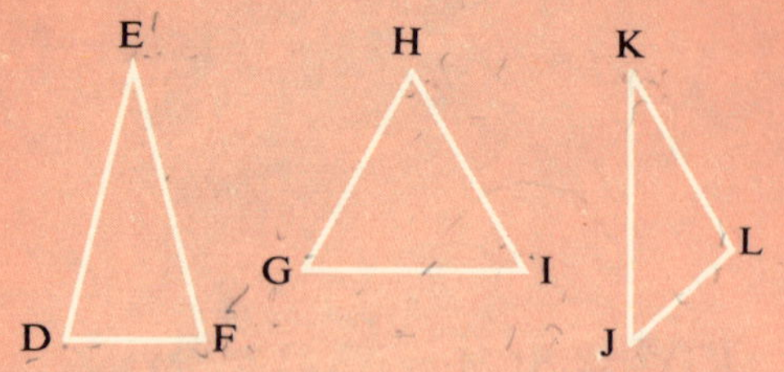

$\overline{DE} \cong \overline{EF}$. $\overline{GH} \cong \overline{HI}$. $JK > KL$.

$\overline{EF} > \overline{DF}$. $\overline{HI} \cong \overline{GI}$. $KL > JL$.

D6

On your own

1 Three noncollinear points determine exactly how many segments? What geometric figure is the union of these segments?

2 Make a sketch of a triangle determined by noncollinear points R, S, T. Name the sides of this triangle. Name the vertices.

3 $\triangle RST$ is the union of what segments?

4 Is $\overline{RS}$ a subset of $\triangle RST$?

5 Is $\{R\}$ a subset of $\triangle RST$?

6 Is $\angle SRT$ a subset of $\triangle RST$?

For exercises 7 through 12, use the sentences and the pictures in D6 to help you.

7 Is $\triangle DEF$ an isosceles triangle? Is $\triangle DEF$ an equilateral triangle? Explain your answers.

8 In $\triangle DEF$, do you think $\angle EFD \cong \angle FDE$?

9 Is $\triangle GHI$ an isosceles triangle? An equilateral triangle? Explain your answers.

10 In $\triangle GHI$, do you think $\angle HIG \cong \angle IGH$? Do you think $\angle IGH \cong \angle GHI$? Do you think $\angle HIG \cong \angle GHI$?

11 Is $\triangle JKL$ a scalene triangle? How do you know?

12 In $\triangle JKL$, do you think $\angle KLJ \cong \angle LJK$? Do you think $\angle LJK \cong \angle JKL$? Do you think $\angle KLJ \cong \angle JKL$?

13 Suppose that U is the set of all triangles; X is the set of all equilateral triangles; Y is the set of all right triangles. Make a Venn diagram to represent $X \cap Y$. Tabulate $X \cap Y$.

14 Could you make a sketch of a right equilateral triangle? Explain your answer.

15 In $\triangle LMN$, $\angle MLN$ is a right angle. $\overline{LM} \cong \overline{LN}$. Make a sketch of $\triangle LMN$.

16 Is $\triangle LMN$ a right triangle? What other kind of triangle is it?

17 In $\triangle OPQ$, $\angle POQ$ is a right angle, $\overline{QP} > \overline{PO}$, and $\overline{PO} > \overline{OQ}$. Make a sketch of $\triangle OPQ$.

18 Is $\triangle OPQ$ a scalene triangle? What other kind of triangle is it?

19 Make a sketch of a geometric figure with two right angles. Is the figure a triangle?

20 Make a sketch of a geometric figure with three right angles. Is the figure a triangle?

21 Can a triangle have more than one right angle?

22 Suppose that $\triangle RST$ and $\triangle UVW$ are any two triangles such that $\angle RST \cong \angle UVW$, $\angle STR \cong \angle VWU$, $\angle TRS \cong \angle WUV$; and that $\overline{RS} \cong \overline{UV}$, $\overline{ST} \cong \overline{VW}$, $\overline{RT} \cong \overline{UW}$. What do you know about $\triangle RST$ and $\triangle UVW$?

23 Now suppose that $\triangle XYZ$ is any triangle other than $\triangle UVW$ so that $\angle UVW \cong \angle XYZ$, $\angle VWU \cong \angle YZX$, $\angle WUV \cong \angle ZXY$; and that $\overline{UV} \cong \overline{XY}$, $\overline{VW} \cong \overline{YZ}$, $\overline{UW} \cong \overline{XZ}$. Is $\triangle UVW \cong \triangle XYZ$?

24 Use the information given in exercises 22 and 23 to answer the following question. Do you think that $\triangle RST \cong \triangle XYZ$?

25 Suppose that $\triangle BCD$ and $\triangle EFG$ are any two triangles such that $\angle BCD \cong \angle EFG$, $\overline{CB} \cong \overline{FE}$, and $\overline{CD} \cong \overline{FG}$. Do you think that $\overline{BD} \cong \overline{EG}$, that $\angle CDB \cong \angle FGE$, and that $\angle DBC \cong \angle GEF$?

26 Suppose that $\triangle EFG$ and $\triangle HIJ$ are any two triangles such that $\angle EFG \cong \angle HIJ$, $\angle FGE \cong \angle IJH$, and $\overline{FG} \cong \overline{IJ}$. Do you think that $\overline{EG} \cong \overline{HJ}$, that $\overline{FE} \cong \overline{IH}$, and that $\angle GEF \cong \angle JHI$?

2 | 29 **Exploring ideas**

Regions of the plane

You already know that a circle separates a plane into two regions. Now you will learn about other geometric figures that separate a plane. The geometric figures that you will study in this lesson are plane figures.

A Look at D1. How many points are contained in the intersection of $\overline{AB}$ and ℓ_1? How do you know that A and B are in the same half-plane?

B Look again at D1. How many points are contained in the intersection of $\overline{BC}$ and ℓ_1? How do you know that B and C are not in the same half-plane?

> REMINDER
>
> A line separates a plane into two sets of points. The two sets are called half-planes.
> A circle separates a plane into two regions.
>
> *See lesson 11, page 41. See lesson 12, page 49.*

C Circle R, represented in D1, separates the plane into two regions. Name these regions.

D Are A, B, and C in the exterior of circle R? What point named in D1 is in the interior of circle R?

E What is the boundary of a half-plane? What is the boundary of the interior of a circle? What is the boundary of the exterior of a circle?

F What is the intersection of a circle and its interior?

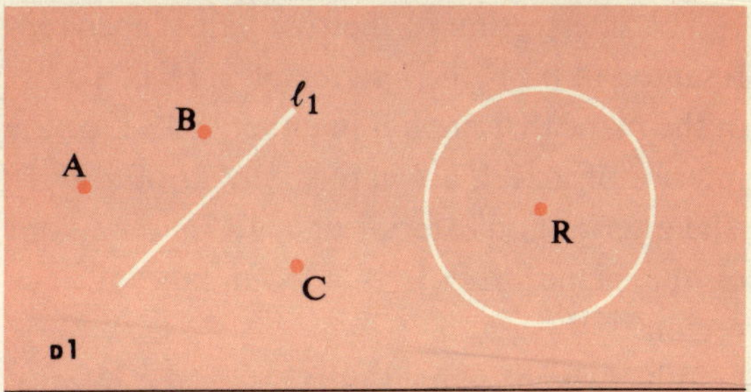

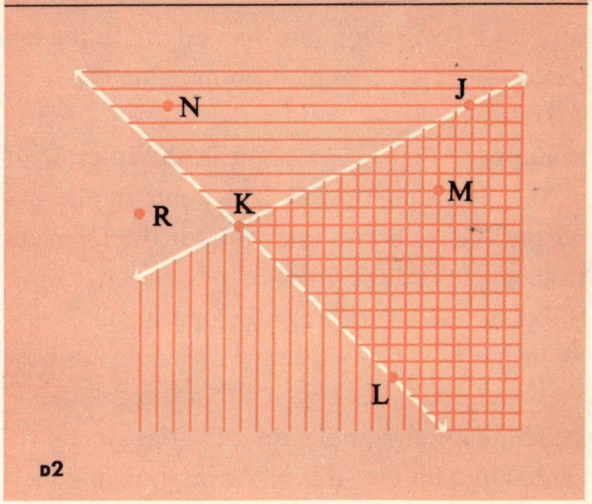

G What is the union of a circle, its interior, and its exterior?

H Now look at D2. $\overrightarrow{KJ}$ is one side of ∠JKL. What is the other side?

I Is $\overrightarrow{KJ}$ included in $\overleftrightarrow{KJ}$? Is $\overrightarrow{KL}$ included in $\overleftrightarrow{KL}$? Explain your answers.

You know that $\overleftrightarrow{KJ}$ separates plane JKL into two half-planes. One of these half-planes contains point L. This half-plane is represented by the part of D2 that is shaded by pictures of vertical lines.

J Does $\overleftrightarrow{KL}$ also separate plane JKL into two half-planes? One of these half-planes contains point J. How is this half-plane represented in D2?

K Now think of the half-plane represented by ? pictures of vertical lines and the half-plane represented by pictures of horizontal lines. How is the intersection of these two half-planes represented in D2?

The intersection of the two half-planes represented in D2 is the *interior* of $\angle$JKL. Points in the plane that are not in either $\angle$JKL or the interior of $\angle$JKL are in the *exterior* of $\angle$JKL. The interior and exterior of $\angle$JKL are regions of the plane. $\angle$JKL is a boundary of each region.

L Which point named in D2 is in the interior of $\angle$JKL? Which points named are in the exterior of $\angle$JKL? Which points named are in $\angle$JKL?

M ? Suppose that C is a point in the interior of an angle and that D is a point in the exterior. What do you know about the intersection of $\overline{CD}$ and the angle?

N Name the triangle represented in D3. A triangle has how many sides? A triangle has how many angles?

O Think of the angles of the triangle represented in D3. Point B is in the interior of which angle of $\triangle$ADF? Point H is in the interior of which angle of $\triangle$ADF? Point R is in the interior of which angle of $\triangle$ADF?

P Which point named in D3 is in the interiors of all three angles of $\triangle$ADF? Which point named is in the intersection of the interiors of the three angles of $\triangle$ADF?

The intersection of the interiors of the angles of a triangle is the *interior of the triangle*. Points that are not in either the triangle or the interior of the triangle are in the *exterior of the triangle*. The interior of a triangle and the exterior of a triangle are regions of the plane. The triangle is a boundary of each of these regions.

Q Look again at D3. Which point named is in the interior of $\triangle$ADF? Which points named are in $\triangle$ADF?

R ? Suppose that M is a point in the interior of a triangle, and that N is a point in the exterior. What do you know about the intersection of $\overline{MN}$ and the triangle?

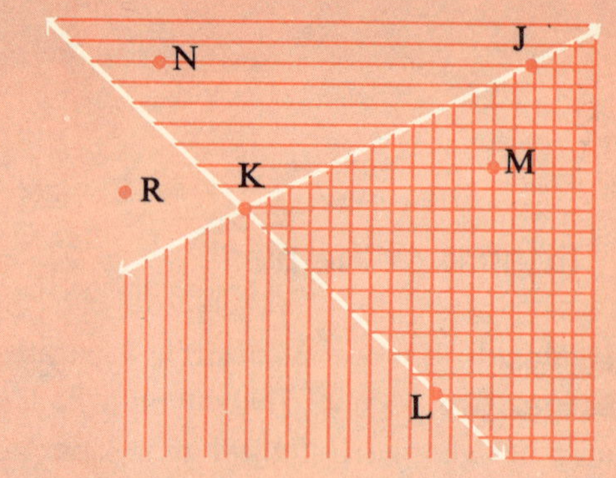

D2

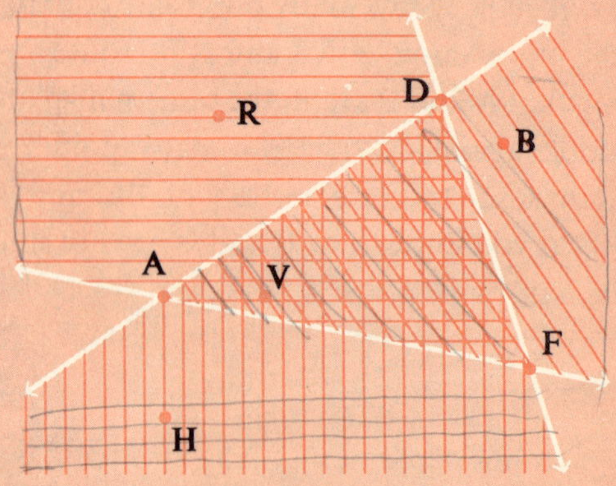

D3

in te ri or of an angle (in tēr′ē ər). The intersection of two half-planes. If $\angle$ABC is any angle, then the interior of $\angle$ABC is the intersection of the following two half-planes: the half-plane that is bounded by line AB and that contains point C and the half-plane that is bounded by line BC and that contains point A.

ex te ri or of an angle (eks tēr′ē ər). The set of points that are not in either the angle or the interior of the angle.

in te ri or of a triangle (in tēr′ē ər). The intersection of the interiors of the angles of the triangle.

ex te ri or of a triangle (eks tēr′ē ər). The set of points that are not in either the triangle or the interior of the triangle.

S What is the intersection of a triangle and its interior?

T What is the union of a triangle, its interior, and its exterior?

You have learned that circles, angles, and triangles separate planes into two regions. Now you will learn about some other geometric figures that separate a plane.

A Each picture in D4 represents a set of coplanar points. Is each set of points a plane figure? Explain your answer.

The plane geometric figure represented by picture A does not intersect itself. This geometric figure is a *simple closed curve*. Each of pictures B, C, D, E, and F also represents a simple closed curve.

Observe that in geometry the word "curve" has a meaning that differs from its meaning in everyday speech. Geometric figures like those represented by pictures A, C, and D are simple closed curves, even though they are the union of segments.

When you make a sketch of a simple closed curve, you will not need to lift your pencil from the paper, and you will not cross a pencil mark that you have already made. You will start and finish at the same place.

B Is a segment a simple closed curve? Is an angle a simple closed curve? Is a triangle a simple closed curve? Is a circle a simple closed curve? Explain your answers.

C Explain why pictures G, H, I, J, K, and L in D4 do not represent simple closed curves.

D Look at pictures A through F in D4. Into ? how many regions does each simple closed curve separate the plane?

Simple closed curves have the property expressed below.

A simple closed curve separates the plane into two regions.

D4

One of the regions is the *interior of the simple closed curve*, and the other region is the *exterior of the simple closed curve*.

E Suppose a plane figure does not separate the ? plane into two regions. What do you know about the figure?

F Suppose one point is in the interior of a ? simple closed curve and one point is in the exterior of the simple closed curve. What do you know about the intersection of the simple closed curve and the segment determined by the two points?

G What is the intersection of the interior of a simple closed curve and the exterior of the simple closed curve? Of a simple closed curve and the interior of the simple closed curve?

H What is the union of a simple closed curve, the interior of the simple closed curve, and the exterior of the simple closed curve?

I Is each of the plane figures represented in D5 a simple closed curve?

J Into how many regions does each geometric figure represented in D5 separate the plane?

In each simple closed curve represented in D5, each point of the simple closed curve is also a member of a segment included in the curve. A simple closed curve that is the union of segments is a *simple polygon*. The segments are sides of the polygon. The endpoints of the segments are vertices of the polygon.

In this book we will use the word "polygon" to mean "simple polygon." As you continue with your work in mathematics, you will learn about polygons that are not simple polygons. You will then learn how to describe a simple polygon without using the words "simple closed curve."

K Is a triangle a polygon? How do you know?

L Three polygons are represented in D6. What are the vertices and sides of polygon ABCDE? What are the vertices and sides of polygon FGHIJK? Notice that the names of the vertices are used to name a polygon.

M Look again at D6. Point S is in the interior of polygon LMNR. Which other point named is in the interior of polygon LMNR? What points named in D6 are in the exterior of polygon LMNR?

N Polygon LMNR is the union of what segments?

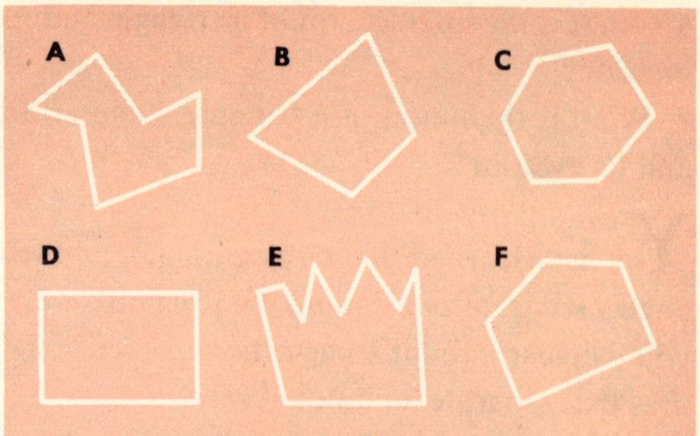

D5

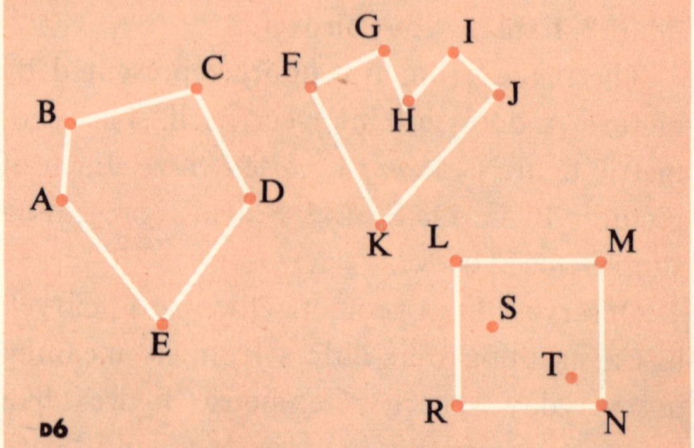

D6

sim ple pol y gon (sim′pəl pol′i gon). A simple closed curve that is the union of segments. The segments are the sides of the polygon. The endpoints of the segments are the vertices of the polygon.

Now you know that a simple closed curve separates a plane into two regions. You also know that a polygon is a special kind of simple closed curve.

On your own

Use D7 as you answer the questions in exercises 1 through 10.

1 What points named in D7 are in the interior of ∠CED?

2 What points named are in ∠DAB?

3 What point named is in the intersection of the interior of ∠DAB and the interior of ∠CED?

4 What point named is in the intersection of the exterior of ∠DAB and the exterior of ∠CED?

5 Tabulate ∠DAB ∩ ∠CED.

6 What points named are in the union of ∠DAB and ∠CED?

7 What point named is in the interior of △CDE?

8 What points named are in the exterior of △CDE?

9 What point named is in the intersection of the interior of ∠CED and the exterior of ∠DAB?

10 What points named are in the union of △CDE and the interior of △CDE?

Use D8 as you answer the questions in exercises 11 through 20.

11 Polygon ABCDEF has how many sides? Name the sides of this polygon.

12 Name the angles of polygon ABCDEF.

13 Tabulate circle R $\cap$ polygon ABCDEF.

14 What point named in D8 is in the intersection of the interior of circle R and the interior of polygon ABCDEF?

15 How many points named are in the intersection of the exterior of circle R and the exterior of polygon ABCDEF?

16 What points named are in the union of circle R and polygon ABCDEF?

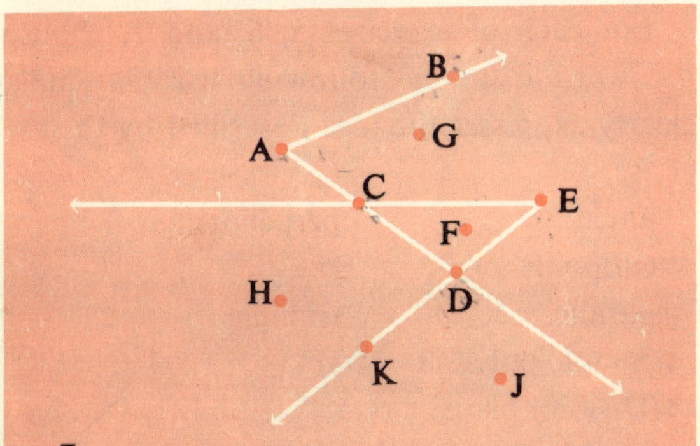

D7

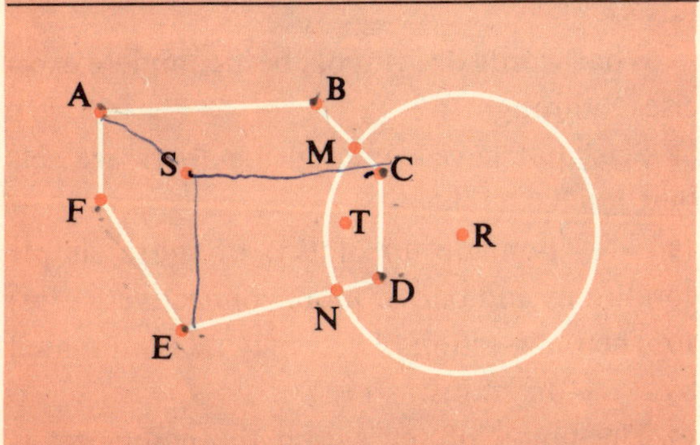

D8

17 What points named are in the union of the interior of polygon ABCDEF and the interior of circle R?

18 What points named are in the union of the exterior of circle R and the exterior of polygon ABCDEF?

19 How many points are in the intersection of $\overline{ST}$ and polygon ABCDEF? Are both S and T in the interior of polygon ABCDEF?

20 How many points are in the intersection of $\overline{SR}$ and polygon ABCDEF?

KEEPING SKILFUL

Make one sketch for exercises 1 through 7. The universe is the plane that includes circle W.

1 Make a sketch of circle W.

2 Make a sketch of radius WS.

3 Locate G in the interior of circle W and F in the exterior of circle W.

4 Write a standard description of circle W.

5 Write a standard description of the interior of circle W.

6 Write a standard description of the exterior of circle W.

7 Describe the intersection of circle W and $\overline{GF}$.

8 A, B, and C are collinear points. Suppose that B is between A and C. Write a sentence that expresses a true statement comparing $\overline{AB}$ and $\overline{AC}$.

9 Suppose that C is between A and B. Write a sentence that expresses a true statement comparing $\overline{AB}$ and $\overline{AC}$.

10 Suppose that C and B are the same point. Write a sentence that expresses a true statement comparing $\overline{AB}$ and $\overline{AC}$.

11 No three of the points A, B, C, D, E, F, and G are collinear. How many of the segments determined by these points contain point D?

SPECIAL CHALLENGE

Read the problem in D1. Then study D2 and D3. They show possible locations of farms A, B, and C and of wells J, K, and L.

A Make sketches similar to those in D2 and D3.

B Try to show how each farmer could arrange the pipes from his farm to each of the wells. Remember that no two pipes can cross.

C Make other sketches to show different locations of the farms and wells. In each sketch, try to show how the pipes can be arranged.

D Is it possible for the farmers to arrange the pipes under the conditions given in the problem? Use what you know about simple closed curves to explain your answer.

Each of three farmers wants to run a separate pipe from his farm to each of three wells. However, all the pipes must be at the same level, and no two of the pipes can cross. Is it possible for the farmers to arrange the pipes under these conditions?

D1

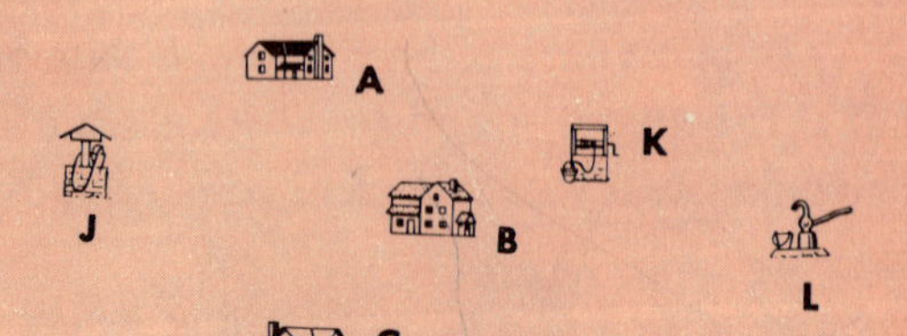

D2

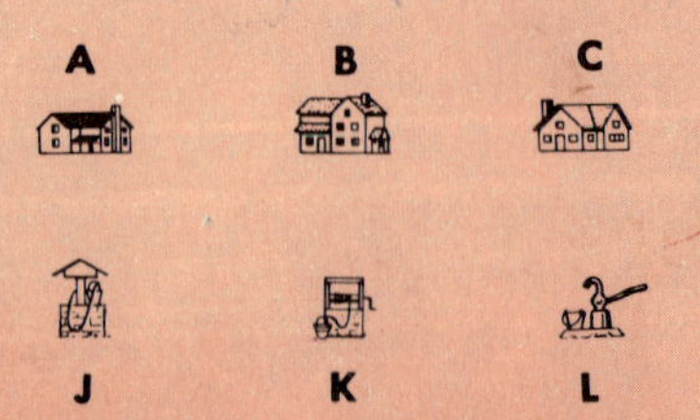

D3

CHECKING UP

The numeral within parentheses tells you what page to turn to if you need help with an exercise.

Test 23

For each of exercises 1 through 4, choose the word from the following list that most clearly expresses the idea described by the exercise.

equilateral	scalene
isosceles	skew
line	vertex

1 Common endpoint of two sides of a polygon (116)

2 Triangle with exactly two congruent sides (110)

3 Triangle with no two congruent sides (110)

4 Intersection of two planes that are not parallel (100)

For each of exercises 5, 6, and 7, choose the word from the following list that most clearly expresses the idea described by the exercise.

angle	perpendicular
endpoint	ray
parallel	triangle

5 Simple polygon (116)

6 Disjoint planes (98)

7 Half-line and its boundary (104)

Test 24

What words or symbols best complete exercises 8 through 16?

8 Sets that have common members are sets that ~~~~. (85)

9 ~~~~ is made up of two or more simple conditions and one or more connectives. (91)

10 The intersection of sets may be represented by ~~~~ diagrams. (84)

11 The union of set A and the empty set is ~~~~. (89)

12 Two lines that are not included in the same plane are —— lines. (101)

13 Segments AB, BC, CD, DE, and EA are the sides of polygon ——. (116)

14 The intersection of the empty set and a set that has 5 members is a set that has —— members. (86)

15 The intersection of two sets is a —— of each of the sets. (86)

16 A simple closed curve separates the plane into —— regions. (115)

Test 25

A list of symbols or expressions is given for each exercise. From each list choose the expression or symbol that correctly completes the exercise.

17 The symbol —— expresses the idea of intersection. (83)

a $\cup$ **b** $\cong$ **c** $\angle$ **d** $\cap$

18 The symbol —— expresses the connective "and." (90)

a $\triangle$ **b** $\wedge$ **c** $\longrightarrow$ **d** $<$

19 If the intersection of two lines that are included in the same plane is the empty set, then the two lines ——. (101)

a meet **c** are parallel

b are skew lines **d** intersect

20 —— is the same as $\angle$JKL. (105)

a $\overline{KJ} \cup \overline{KL}$ **c** $\overrightarrow{KJ} \cup \overrightarrow{KL}$

b $\angle$JLK **d** $\overline{KJ} \cap \overline{LK}$

21 Each angle of a linear pair of angles is —— the other angle of the pair. (107)

a the supplement of **c** the right angle of

b congruent to **d** perpendicular to

22 A triangle is the union of three —— determined by three noncollinear points. (109)

a rays **c** lines

b segments **d** half-lines

23 The greatest number of right angles a triangle may have is ——. (110)

a 3 **b** 2 **c** 1 **d** 0

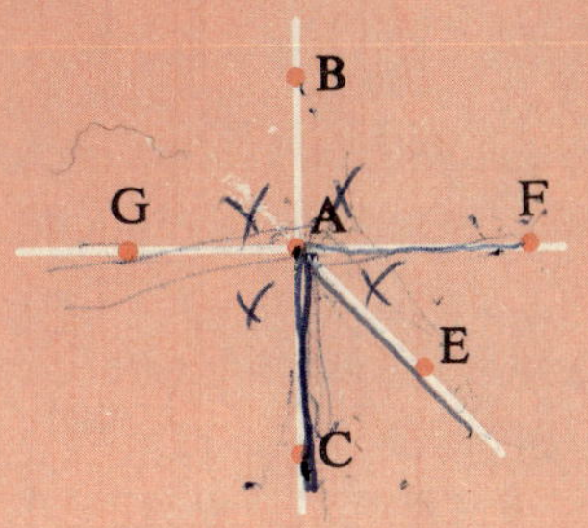

D1

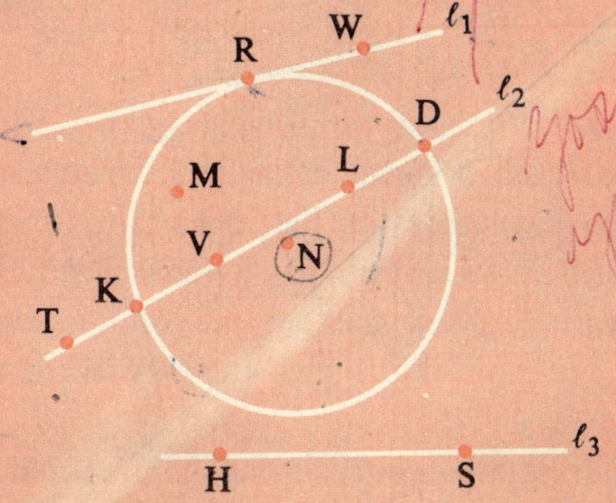

D2

Test 26

Use D1 to help you answer exercises 24 through 28. Lines BC and GF are perpendicular.

24 Name the sides of $\angle$EAC. (105)

25 Name the common side of $\angle$CAF and $\angle$GAC. (106)

26 What angle and $\angle$FAE are a linear pair of angles? (106)

27 Name a supplement of $\angle$EAC. (107)

28 Four right angles are represented in D1. Name these angles. (107)

Use D2 to help you with exercises 29 through 32. N is the center of the circle represented in the display.

29 Tabulate $\ell_1 \cap$ circle N. (103)

30 Tabulate $\ell_2 \cap$ circle N. (103)

31 Tabulate $\ell_3 \cap$ circle N. (103)

32 What points named are in the intersection of ℓ_2 and the interior of circle N? (103)

Test 27

Tabulate the solution set of each condition expressed in exercises 33 through 40. U = N.

33 $x > 7 \wedge x < 15$. (90)

34 $x > 4(3) \wedge x - 12 < 5$. (90)

35 $x + 3 < 14 \wedge 27 - x > 12$. (90)

36 $m > 6 \wedge m - 4 < 21$. (90)

37 $x + 6 > 13 \wedge x - 2 > 5$. (90)

38 $10 + x > 14 \wedge x + 3 < 5$. (90)

39 $9 - x > 8 \wedge x + 13 < 21$. (90)

40 $14 + x = 27 \wedge 27 - x = 13$. (90)

Test 28

For each problem below, first write a sentence that expresses the condition for the problem. You may use any letter as a name for the variable. Next tabulate the solution set of the condition. Then give the answer to the problem. U = N.

41 During a basketball game, Tom scored 18 points, and Bob scored 9 points. Jerry scored more points than Tom, but fewer than the total number of points scored by Tom and Bob. How many points could Jerry have scored during the game? (94)

42 Pat had fewer than 75 old pennies. He sold 15 of them to Harold, but still had more than 47 left. How many pennies could Pat have had before he sold the 15 to Harold? (94)

43 During the summer, Ray read fewer than 19 books. If he had read 9 more books, he would have read more than 26 books. How many books did Ray read during the summer? (94)

44 What numbers are less than 78 and greater than the sum of 19 and 31? (95)

45 What numbers less than 9 can be added to 15 so that each sum is greater than 20? (95)

46 What numbers less than 26 can be subtracted from 347 so that each difference is greater than 315? (95)

47 What numbers greater than 13 can be added to 98 so that each sum is less than 111? (95)

CHECKING UP

The numeral within parentheses tells you what page to turn to if you need help with an exercise.

Test 29

What words or symbols best complete exercises 1 through 9?

1 The sentence $95 - 47 > 45$ expresses ——— statement. (13)

2 The set of natural numbers that are greater than 155,000,000 is ——— set. (23)

3 ——— has infinitely many radii. (46)

4 The boundary of a half-plane is ———. (41)

5 {A, D} is ——— of {A, B, C, D, E}. (11)

6 ——— separates space into half-spaces. (41)

7 If three different points are ———, then one of the points is between the other two. (37)

8 $\overline{FG}$ is a segment whose ——— are F and G. (38)

9 A variable in a condition may be replaced only by a member of the ———. (16)

Test 30

Tabulate the solution set of each condition expressed in exercises 10 through 16.

U = {1, 2, 3, 4, 5, 6, 7, 8, 9, 10}.

10 $3x < 9$. (18)

11 $5 + c \neq 7$. (18)

12 $12 - y = 2$. (18)

13 $x - 1 > 5$. (18)

14 $k < 4 \wedge k > 1$. (90)

15 $x + 2 > 5 \wedge 2x > 8$. (90)

16 $x < 10 \wedge x + 2 = 2 + x$. (90)

Test 31

From the list that follows each exercise, choose the expression that correctly completes the exercise.

17 $17 \times 5 = 85$ is ———. (17)

a a condition for equality
b a condition for inequality
c an equation
d an inequality

18 $13 - 5 \neq x$ is ———. (21)

a a condition for equality
b a condition for inequality
c an equation
d an inequality

19 In the condition $m - 7 < 32$, the m is a ~~~~. (15)

a placeholder c numeral
b variable d number

20 {1, 3, 5, . . ., 1,000,001} is ~~~~. (23)

a a finite set c the set of all odd numbers
b a condition d an infinite set

21 A ~~~~ is the boundary of two half-lines. (42)

a point b plane c finite set d line

Test 32

For each problem, first write a sentence that expresses the condition for the problem. You may use any letter as a name for the variable. Next tabulate the solution set of the condition. Then give the answer to the problem. U = N.

22 After Phil found 7 golf balls, he had 23 golf balls. How many golf balls did he have before he found the 7? (68)

23 Kay has 57 autographs of famous persons. Betty has 24 more autographs than Kay. How many autographs does Betty have? (68)

24 Joyce had more than 21 picture postcards. After she mailed 17 of these cards, she had fewer than 9 left. How many postcards could she have had before she mailed the 17? (94)

25 What numbers can be added to 43 so that each sum is greater than 51? (78)

26 What numbers greater than 5 can be subtracted from 24 so that each difference is greater than 13? (94)

27 What numbers less than the difference of 300 and 172 can be added to 280 so that each sum is greater than 355? U = N.

Test 33

Multiply

28 38 by 5. (55)
29 76 by 18. (55)
30 124 by 86. (55)
31 699 by 413. (55)
32 207 by 390. (55)

Divide

33 423 by 9. (58)
34 480 by 32. (58)
35 6322 by 58. (58)
36 40120 by 472. (59)
37 251740 by 307. (59)

Unit 3

Conditions in two variables

3 30 Exploring ideas

Ordered pairs

For some time now you have been studying sets and conditions. In this lesson and in several of the lessons that follow, you will apply what you have learned to sets and conditions that differ in some ways from those you have already studied.

A Look at D1. Think of the capitals whose names are listed in D1 as a set of cities. Name this set of cities set A. Tabulate A.

B Think of the countries whose names are listed as a set of countries. Name this set of countries set B. Tabulate B.

C Is it possible to decide whether the idea expressed by the sentence in D2 is true or false? Explain your answer.

D How many different variables are there in the condition expressed in D2? How many different variables were there in the conditions that you studied in previous lessons?

E You will use the members of set A as replacements for *m* in the condition expressed in D2. Why can you use Paris as a replacement for *m*? Why should you not use Spain as a replacement for *m*?

F When you replace *m* by Paris, you obtain the condition expressed in D3. Why is it not possible to decide whether the idea expressed by the sentence in D3 is true or false?

G You will use the members of set B as replacements for *n* in the condition expressed in D2. Why can you use Spain as a replacement for *n*? Why should you not use Paris as a replacement for *n*?

CAPITAL CITIES	COUNTRIES
Paris	Norway
Ottawa	France
Madrid	Spain
	Canada

D1

m is the capital of *n*.

D2

Paris is the capital of *n*.

D3

m is the capital of Spain.

D4

Paris is the capital of Spain.

D5

H When you replace *n* by Spain, you obtain the condition expressed in D4. Is it possible to decide whether the idea expressed by the sentence in D4 is true or false? Explain your answer.

I When a condition contains two variables, must you make a replacement for each variable in order to obtain a statement?

J Now replace *m* by Paris and *n* by Spain. Do you obtain the statement expressed in D5? Is the statement true?

You used Paris as a replacement for *m* and Spain as a replacement for *n* in the condition "*m* is a capital of *n*." Notice that you used a pair of objects to obtain the statement expressed in D5.

K The first object of the pair, Paris, is the *first component* of the pair. The first component is a member of what set?

L The second object of the pair, Spain, is the *second component* of the pair. The second component is a member of what set?

In the exercises above, you used a city for the first component and a country for the second component of a pair of objects. A pair of objects whose components occur in a special order is an *ordered pair*.

M Look at D6. Notice that the names of the components of the ordered pair Paris, Spain are written within parentheses. D6 also shows how to read and write the name of this ordered pair.

N Think about the condition "*m* is the capital of *n*." When you replace *m* by a member of {Paris, Ottawa, Madrid} and *n* by a member of {Norway, France, Spain, Canada}, do you obtain a statement? Do the sentences in D7 express all the statements you can obtain?

O For each statement expressed in D7, write the name of the ordered pair that was used to make replacements. Which do you write first, the name of the replacement for *m* or the name of the replacement for *n*?

P Which of the statements expressed in D7 are true?

Q What ordered pairs were used to obtain true statements?

R Read the symbols (Paris, Norway) and ? {Paris, Norway}. How do the ideas expressed by these symbols differ?

Now you will study some conditions that concern numbers. You will also learn about ordered pairs whose components are numbers.

A Read the open sentence in D8. What are the variables in the condition expressed by the sentence?

"The ordered pair

(Paris, Spain)

whose first component is Paris and

whose second component is Spain"

D6

A Paris is the capital of Norway.
B Paris is the capital of France.
C Paris is the capital of Spain.
D Paris is the capital of Canada.
E Ottawa is the capital of Norway.
F Ottawa is the capital of France.
G Ottawa is the capital of Spain.
H Ottawa is the capital of Canada.
I Madrid is the capital of Norway.
J Madrid is the capital of France.
K Madrid is the capital of Spain.
L Madrid is the capital of Canada.

D7

$x < y$.
A = {1, 2, 3, 4}.
B = {2, 4, 6}.

D8

or dered pair (ôr′dərd pãr). A pair of objects in which the objects occur in a special order. The object that occurs first is the **first component** (kəm pō′nənt) of the ordered pair. The object that occurs second is the **second component** of the ordered pair.

B Also read the tabulations of sets A and B in D8. You will use the members of set A as replacements for x in $x < y$. You will use the members of set B as replacements for y in $x < y$.

C To obtain a statement from a condition in two variables, you must make replacements for how many variables?

D Do the sentences in D9 express all the statements that you can obtain from $x < y$ when you use the members of set A and set B, tabulated in D8, as replacements for x and y?

E Think of the statement expressed by the first sentence in D9. (1, 2) was used in making replacements to obtain this statement. D10 shows a short and convenient way to read and write the name of this ordered pair.

F Select four of the statements expressed in D9. For each statement, name the ordered pair that was used in making replacements for x and y.

G Which statements expressed in D9 are true? What ordered pairs were used to obtain true statements?

H The sentences $x + x = 4$ and $x + y = 4$ express two conditions. How many different variables are there in each condition? How do the two conditions differ?

In this lesson you have learned that ordered pairs are used to make replacements for two variables.

On your own

Write a name for each of the ordered pairs described in exercises 1 through 5.

1 The ordered pair whose first component is Robert Louis Stevenson and whose second component is *Treasure Island*

2 The ordered pair whose first component is Mary and whose second component is guitar

3 The ordered pair whose first component is 15° and whose second component is 8 P.M.

4 The ordered pair whose first component is Larry and whose second component is 141

5 The ordered pair whose first component is 1 and whose second component is 13

$x < y$.
A = {1, 2, 3, 4}.
B = {2, 4, 6}.

D8

$1 < 2$.	$2 < 2$.	$3 < 2$.	$4 < 2$.
$1 < 4$.	$2 < 4$.	$3 < 4$.	$4 < 4$.
$1 < 6$.	$2 < 6$.	$3 < 6$.	$4 < 6$.

D9

(1, 2) "The ordered pair one, two"

D10

Four conditions are expressed in exercises 6 through 9. Use the members of set C, tabulated below, as replacements for x. Use the members of set D, tabulated below, as replacements for y. For each exercise write sentences to express all the statements that you can obtain from the condition. Then write "T" after each sentence that expresses a true statement.

C = {2, 4, 6}. D = {5, 10, 15}.

6 $6 + x = y$. **8** $x + 4 = y$.

7 $x + 5 < y$. **9** $y > x + 1$.

10 In each ordered pair expressed below, the second component is 3 times the first component. One of the components is missing. Copy each symbol and supply the name of the missing component.

(1,) (4,) (, 9) (2,) (, 24)

11 In each ordered pair expressed below, the first component is 3 more than the second component. One of the components is missing. Copy each symbol and supply the name of the missing component.

(8,) (, 18) (12,) (, 29) (, 1)

APPLYING MATHEMATICS

The problems in this lesson are similar to the problems that you have studied so far in this book. For each problem, first write a sentence that expresses the condition for the problem. You may use any letter to name the variable. Next tabulate the solution set of the condition. Then give the answer to the problem. The universe is given for each problem.

1 Miss Larson had \$1405 in her savings account. She withdrew some of this money and then had \$890 left in her account. How much money did she withdraw from this account? U = N.

2 Martin scored 17 points during a basketball game. Together, Martin and Leo scored fewer than 32 points during the game. How many points could Leo have scored? U = C.

3 A restaurant owner had 315 dinner plates. He bought fewer than 150 new dinner plates and then had more than 434. How many new dinner plates could he have bought? U = N.

4 After Charles delivered 117 handbills, he had fewer than 43 handbills left to deliver. What is the greatest number of handbills that Charles could have had to deliver? U = N.

5 Susan collects unusual buttons. After her aunt had given her 18 buttons, Susan had 205 buttons in all. How many buttons had she collected before her aunt gave her the 18? U = N.

6 During a two-week business trip, Mr. Foster drove more than 913 miles. He drove 547 miles the first week. What is the least number of miles he could have driven the second week? U = N.

7 A survey stated that there were 6495 more private pilots than commercial pilots in Canada. There were 2548 commercial pilots at that time. How many private pilots were there in Canada at the time of the survey? U = N.

8 A merchant had more than 210 suits to sell. After he sold 89 of these suits, he had fewer than 131 suits left to sell. How many suits could he have had before he sold the 89? U = N.

9 Walter had 92¢ when he went to the school store. He spent some of this money and still had more than 34¢ left. How much money could he have spent? U = C.

10 Nine years ago, Mr. Roberts was less than 39 years old. Fifteen years from now, he will be more than 56 years old. How old can he be now? U = C.

11 In 1923, there were 680,772 fewer automobiles registered in Canada than in 1943. The number of automobiles registered in 1943 was 1,193,847. How many automobiles were registered in 1923? U = N.

12 The 2 P.M. temperature at an airport was 71 degrees above zero. The temperature had risen less than 16 degrees since 10 A.M., when it was less than 60 degrees. What could the temperature have been at 10 A.M? U = N.

13 What numbers can be subtracted from 62 so that each difference is greater than 53? U = N.

14 When 39 is subtracted from a number, the difference is 27. When the number is added to 39, the sum is 105. What is the number? U = N.

15 What number is the product of 148 and 203? U = N.

16 What numbers are less than the sum of 49 and 86? U = N.

17 What numbers can be added to 7224 so that each sum is greater than 7401? U = N.

18 What numbers less than the product of 13 and 18 can be added to 76 so that each sum is greater than 295? U = N.

19 What numbers greater than 75 can be subtracted from 3212 so that each difference is greater than 3137? U = N.

a is a holiday in b.

D1

A = {Thanksgiving, Labor Day, Christmas}.
B = {March, June, September, December}.

D2

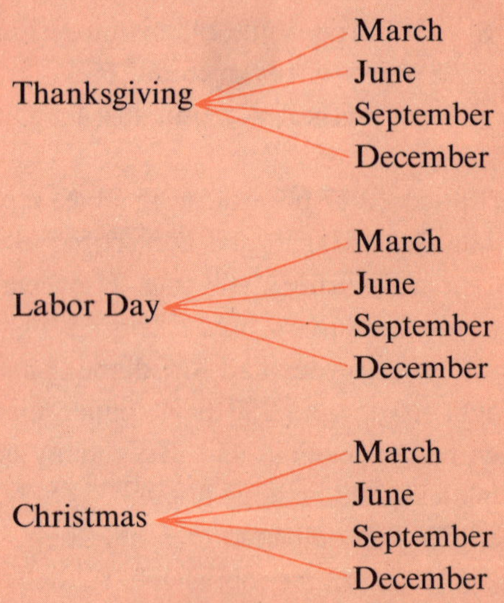

D3

3 31 **Exploring ideas**

Sets of ordered pairs

You have already learned what ordered pairs are and how to use them to make replacements in conditions in two variables. In this lesson you will learn about universes and solution sets whose members are ordered pairs.

A How many variables are there in the condition expressed in D1?

You know that you use ordered pairs to make replacements for two different variables in the same condition. Each component of an ordered pair is a member of a set of objects. Let us agree to use the members of set A, tabulated in D2, as replacements for a. Let us agree to use the members of set B as replacements for b.

B Think about the condition that is expressed in D1. Is (Labor Day, March) one ordered pair that you can use to make replacements for a and b?

C What are two other ordered pairs that you can use to make replacements for a and b?

To find all the ordered pairs that can be used to make replacements for a and b, match a member of A with each member of B in turn. Then match another member of A with each member of B, and so on. D3 shows one way to do this.

When each member of A is matched with each member of B, the result is a set of ordered pairs. This set is tabulated in D4.

Since the set tabulated in D4 was formed by matching each member of A with each member of B, you may use the symbol below at the right as a name of this set. D5 shows how to write and read this name of this set of ordered pairs.

A × B

D What does the name A × B tell you about the first component of each ordered pair in the set? What does it tell you about the second component of each ordered pair in the set?

A × B is the *Cartesian set* produced from sets A and B.

E Look again at D2. How many members are in A? How many members are in B? How many members are in the Cartesian set A × B?

{(Thanksgiving, March), (Thanksgiving, June), (Thanksgiving, September), (Thanksgiving, December), (Labor Day, March), (Labor Day, June), (Labor Day, September), (Labor Day, December), (Christmas, March), (Christmas, June), (Christmas, September), (Christmas, December)}

D4

F If you know the number of members in a set M and the number of members in a set N, how can you find the number of members in the Cartesian set M × N?

G Is (June, Thanksgiving) a member of A × B? Is (June, Thanksgiving) a member of B × A? Is B × A the same set as A × B? Explain your answers.

H Now you will use the members of A × B to make replacements for *a* and *b* in "*a* is a holiday in *b*." When you replace *a* by the first component of each ordered pair, and *b* by the second component of the same ordered pair, do you obtain the statements that are expressed in D6?

I Which statements expressed in D6 are true?

J Which members of the Cartesian set A × B are used to obtain true statements from "*a* is a holiday in *b*"?

You may tabulate the solution set of "*a* is a holiday in *b*" as shown in D7.

K Is each member of the solution set an ordered pair? Is the solution set a set of ordered pairs?

Car te sian set (kär tē′zhən). The set of all ordered pairs that can be formed by matching each member of one set in turn with each member of a second set. The Cartesian set S × R is the set of all ordered pairs that can be formed by matching each member of S in turn with each member of R. The members of S are the first components of the ordered pairs, and the members of R are the second components. If S = {1, 2} and R = {4, 5}, then S × R = {(1, 4), (1, 5), (2, 4), (2, 5)}.

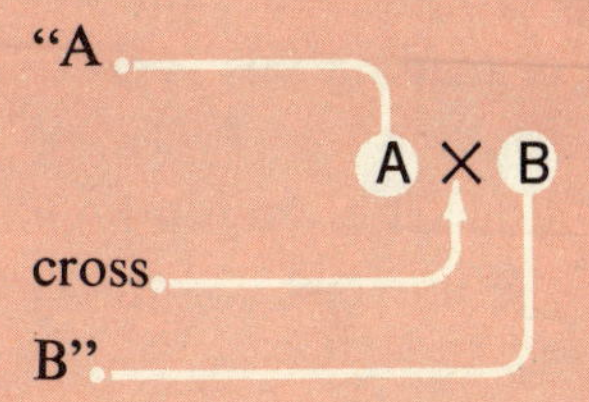

D5

A Thanksgiving is a holiday in March.
B Thanksgiving is a holiday in June.
C Thanksgiving is a holiday in September.
D Thanksgiving is a holiday in December.
E Labor Day is a holiday in March.
F Labor Day is a holiday in June.
G Labor Day is a holiday in September.
H Labor Day is a holiday in December.
I Christmas is a holiday in March.
J Christmas is a holiday in June.
K Christmas is a holiday in September.
L Christmas is a holiday in December.

D6

{(Labor Day, September), (Christmas, December)}

D7

In exercises H through K, you used the members of A × B to make replacements for a and b in "a is a holiday in b." A × B is the universe for the pair of variables a and b. You may use the symbol below at the right to show that you are working with an ordered pair of variables. D8 shows a short way of reading this symbol.

$$(a, b)$$

L Is the solution set of "a is a holiday in b" a **?** subset of the universe for (a, b)? Explain your answer.

Now you will study Cartesian sets in which each member is an ordered pair of numbers.

A How many variables are there in the condition expressed in D9?

We will use the symbol (x, y) to express the ordered pair of variables for $x > y$.

B What do you need before you can make replacements for x and y?

We will use the members of set X, tabulated in D10, as replacements for the first component of (x, y). We will use the members of set Y as replacements for the second component.

C D11 shows how each member of X may be matched with each member of Y. How many ordered pairs are formed?

D The ordered pairs that are formed when each member of X is matched with each member of Y are the members of the Cartesian set X × Y. The set X × Y is the universe for (x, y). Tabulate X × Y.

E When you use the first components of the members of the universe to make replacements for x in $x > y$ and the second components to make replacements for y, do you obtain the statements expressed in D12?

F Which statements expressed in D12 are true?

G Which ordered pairs in X × Y make true statements from $x > y$?

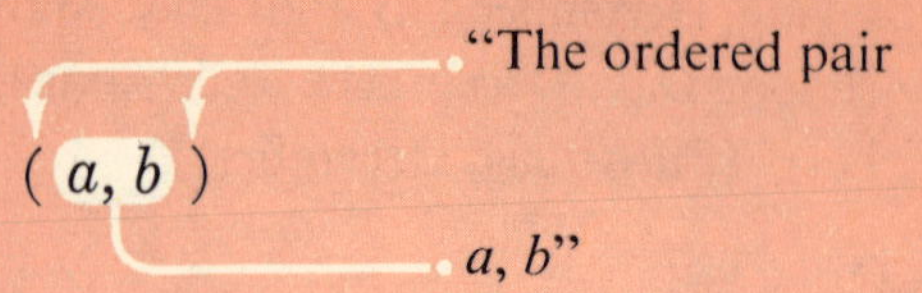

D8

$x > y.$

D9

X = {1, 2, 3, 4}.
Y = {1, 2, 3, 4, 5}.

D10

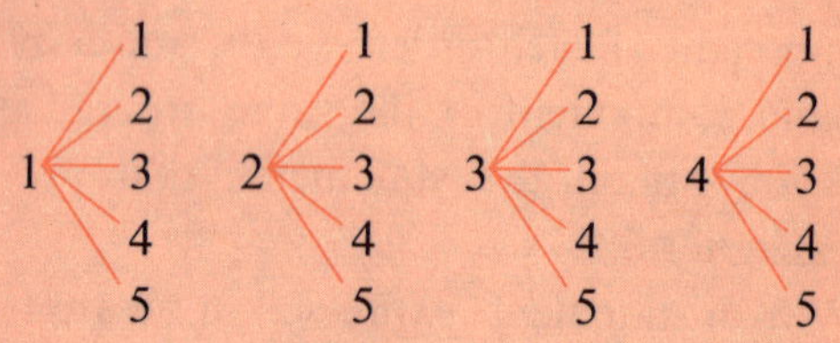

D11

Universe for (x, y) = X × Y.

$x > y.$

A 1 > 1.	**K** 3 > 1.
B 1 > 2.	**L** 3 > 2.
C 1 > 3.	**M** 3 > 3.
D 1 > 4.	**N** 3 > 4.
E 1 > 5.	**O** 3 > 5.
F 2 > 1.	**P** 4 > 1.
G 2 > 2.	**Q** 4 > 2.
H 2 > 3.	**R** 4 > 3.
I 2 > 4.	**S** 4 > 4.
J 2 > 5.	**T** 4 > 5.

D12

Universe for $(x, y) = S \times T$.
$S = \{1, 3, 5\}$.
$T = \{2, 4, 6\}$.
$y = x + 1$.

D13

$A = \{1, 2, 3\}$.

D14

$A \times A = \{(1, 1), (1, 2), (1, 3), (2, 1), (2, 2), (2, 3), (3, 1), (3, 2), (3, 3)\}$.

D15

Universe for $(m, n) = A \times A$.
$m < 2 + n$.

D16

H Tabulate the solution set of $x > y$.

I Is the solution set of $x > y$ a subset of the universe for (x, y)? Explain your answer.

J Now look at D13. How is the Cartesian set $S \times T$ obtained? Tabulate $S \times T$.

K What condition is expressed in D13? What is the universe for the variables?

L The members of what set will be used as replacements for x? The members of what set will be used as replacements for y?

M Write the sentences that express all the statements obtained when you make replacements for x and y in $y = x + 1$.

N Which of the sentences that you wrote express true statements?

O Tabulate the solution set of $y = x + 1$.

P Is the solution set a subset of $S \times T$?

Q ? Look again at D13. Suppose that $S \times T$ is the universe for (y, x) rather than for (x, y). The members of what set would be used as replacements for y? The members of what set would be used as replacements for x?

It is also possible to produce a Cartesian set from only one set of objects.

A ? Set A is tabulated in D14. Make a diagram to show how each member of A may be matched with itself and with each of the other members of A.

When each member of A is matched with itself and with each of the other members of A, ordered pairs are formed. These ordered pairs are the members of the Cartesian set $A \times A$. This set is tabulated in D15.

B $A \times A$ is the *Cartesian set of A*. For each ordered pair that is a member of $A \times A$, both components are members of the same set. What is this set?

C What condition is expressed in D16? What is the universe for (m, n)?

D Look again at D15. Is $(1, 3)$ a member of $A \times A$? Can you use $(1, 3)$ to make replacements for (m, n) for $m < 2 + n$?

E ? If you use $(1, 3)$, how do you know that you should replace m by 1 and n by 3?

F Think about the statement you obtain when you use $(1, 3)$ to make replacements in the condition. Is $1 < 2 + 3$ a true statement? Is $(1, 3)$ a solution of $m < 2 + n$?

G Use each member of $A \times A$ to make replacements for m and n. For each statement obtained, decide whether or not the statement is true. Then tabulate the solution set of $m < 2 + n$.

H Is the solution set of $m < 2 + n$ a subset of $A \times A$?

In this lesson you have formed sets of ordered pairs. You have used members of sets of ordered pairs to make replacements in conditions in two variables. You have also found the solution sets of the conditions.

On your own

1 Set A, tabulated below, is a set of rivers. Set B is a set of continents. Tabulate A × B.

A = {Amazon, Danube, Nile}.

B = {Africa, Asia, Europe, Australia}.

2 Sets M, P, and R are tabulated below. Tabulate M × P, P × R, and M × R.

M = {7, 11, 6, 4}.

P = {1, 100, 15, 10, 5}.

R = {1, 2}.

3 Is (100, 11) a member of M × P?

4 Tabulate P × M. Is (100, 11) a member of P × M?

5 Tabulate M × M. How many members are there in M × M?

6 G × H is tabulated below. Tabulate G. Tabulate H.

G × H = {(1, 2), (1, 4), (1, 6), (1, 8), (1, 10), (3, 2), (3, 4), (3, 6), (3, 8), (3, 10)}.

Which of the sets tabulated in exercises 7, 8, and 9 are subsets of G × H?

7 {(1, 2), (1, 8), (3, 2), (3, 4)}

8 {1, 2, 3, 4}

9 {(3, 8), (1, 8), (4, 3)}

G × H, tabulated in exercise 6, is the universe for (x, y) for the conditions expressed in exercises 10 through 17. Tabulate the solution set of each condition.

10 $x + 3 = y$.

11 $x < y$.

12 $x > y$.

13 $y > x + 2$.

14 $y < x + 1$.

15 $2x > y$.

16 $x + y = x + 4$.

17 $2x < 2y$.

18 Explain how {10, 1}, (10, 1), and {(10, 1)} differ.

19 Suppose that {(1, 1), (1, 2), (1, 3), (2, 1), (2, 2), (2, 3)} is the universe for the variables in $s > r$. What else must you know before you can find the solution set of $s > r$?

3 | 32 **Exploring ideas**

Graphs of sets of ordered pairs

You have studied sets of ordered pairs and found solution sets of conditions in two variables. Now you will learn to make graphs of universes and solution sets whose members are ordered pairs.

A Look at D1. To obtain statements from $x + 2 < y$, you must make replacements for two variables. What are the variables?

B Tabulate A × B. Then use each member of A × B to make replacements for x and y in $x + 2 < y$. Write the sentences that express the statements you obtain.

C Which of the sentences that you wrote express true statements?

D Tabulate the solution set of $x + 2 < y$. Is each solution a member of A × B? Is the solution set a subset of A × B?

Another way to represent the universe for (x, y) and the solution set of $x + 2 < y$ is to make a graph. First, pictures of two number lines are drawn, as shown in D2. Each of these number lines is an *axis* (ak′sis). Notice that the two axes (ak′sēz) are perpendicular. The horizontal number line is the *first axis*. The vertical number line is the *second axis*.

The first component of each ordered pair in A × B is associated with a point in the first axis. The second component of each ordered pair in A × B is associated with a point in the second axis.

E Look at D3. Each dot represents a point associated with a member of A × B. Is point D

Universe for $(x, y) = A \times B$.
$A = \{0, 1, 2, 3\}$.
$B = \{0, 1, 2, 3, 4\}$.
$x + 2 < y$.

D1

Universe for $(x, y) = A \times B$.

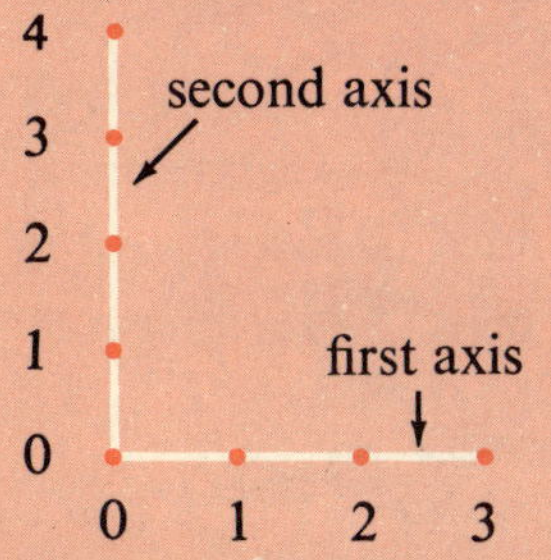

D2

Universe for $(x, y) = A \times B$.

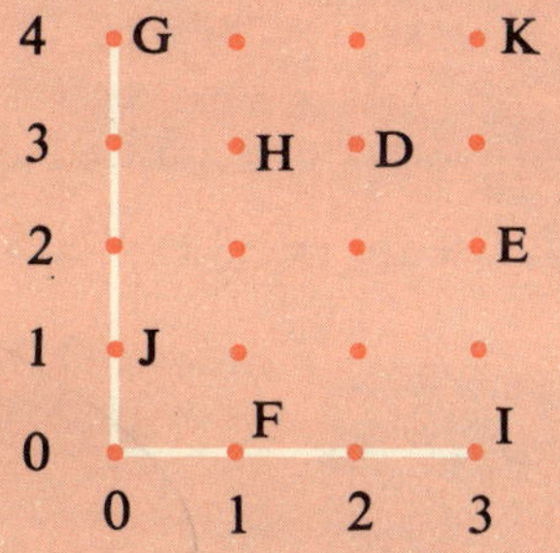

D3

Universe for $(x, y) = A \times B$.

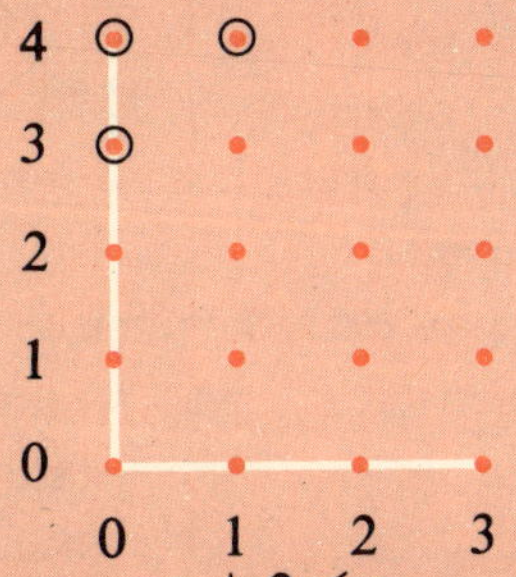

$x + 2 < y$.

D4

located directly above point 2 in the first axis? Is it located directly to the right of point 3 in the second axis? Point D is associated with (2, 3). Is (2, 3) a member of $A \times B$?

F Is point E located directly above point 3 in the first axis? Is it located directly to the right of point 2 in the second axis? With what ordered pair is point E associated? Is this ordered pair also a member of $A \times B$?

G Now look at the dot representing point F. Is the location of point F the same as the location of point 1 in the first axis? Is point F located directly to the right of point 0 in the second axis? What ordered pair is associated with point F?

H Look at the dot representing point G. Is point G located directly above point 0 in the first axis? Is the location of point G the same as the location of point 4 in the second axis? With what ordered pair is point G associated? Is this ordered pair a member of $A \times B$?

I For points H, I, J, and K, name the ordered pair associated with each point.

J Is each member of $A \times B$ associated with a point represented by a dot? Does each dot represent a point associated with a member of $A \times B$?

The set of dots that represent the points associated with the members of $A \times B$ is a graph of $A \times B$.

K How many members are there in $A \times B$? How many dots are in the graph of $A \times B$?

L Which dots in D4 form a graph of $A \times B$?

Now you are prepared to decide whether or not the encircled dots in D4 form a graph of the solution set of $x + 2 < y$.

M The solution set of $x + 2 < y$ is $\{(0, 3), (0, 4), (1, 4)\}$. Is each solution associated with a point whose dot is encircled? Does each encircled dot represent a point associated with a solution of $x + 2 < y$?

The encircled dots represent the points associated with the solutions of $x + 2 < y$. The set of encircled dots is a graph of the solution set of $x + 2 < y$.

N Is the graph of the solution set of $x + 2 < y$ **?** a subset of the graph of A × B? Explain your answer.

In the following exercises you will work with other conditions in two variables to give you more experience in using sets of ordered pairs.

A Look at D5. Tabulate A × A. Then use each member of A × A to make replacements for x and y in $2x > y$. For each statement obtained, decide whether or not the statement is true. Then tabulate the solution set of $2x > y$.

B Is the solution set a subset of the universe?

A graph can be used to represent the universe for (x, y) and the solution set of $2x > y$.

C Look at D6. The numbers that are replacements for x are associated with points in which axis? The numbers that are replacements for y are associated with points in which axis?

D Is each member of A × A associated with a point represented by a dot? Does each dot represent a point associated with a member of A × A?

E Does D6 show a graph of the universe?

Now you can decide whether or not the encircled dots in D6 form a graph of the solution set of $2x > y$. Use the solution set you tabulated for exercise A to help you decide.

F Is each solution of $2x > y$ associated with a point whose dot is encircled? Are there any encircled dots that do not represent points associated with solutions of $2x > y$?

G Does the set of encircled dots form a graph of the solution set of $2x > y$?

H D6 shows two graphs. The set of all dots is a graph of the universe. The set of encircled dots is a graph of the solution set of $2x > y$.

Universe for $(x, y) = A \times A$.
$A = \{0, 1, 2, 3\}$.
$2x > y$.

D5

Universe for $(x, y) = A \times A$.

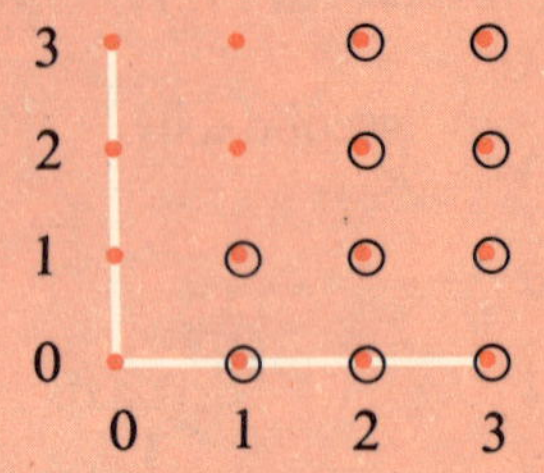

$2x > y$.

D6

Universe for $(x, y) = A \times A$.
$A = \{0, 1, 2, 3\}$.
$y + 3 = x$.

D7

Universe for $(x, y) = A \times A$.

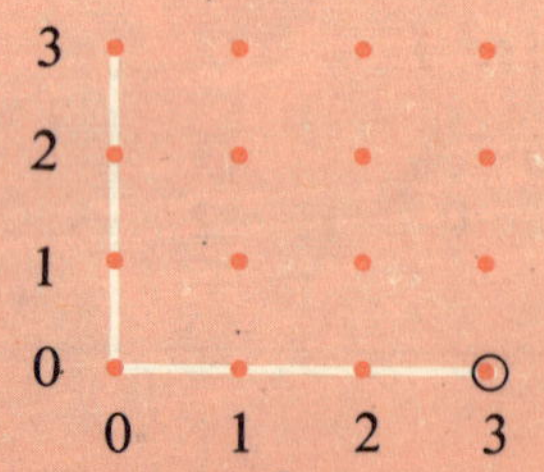

$y + 3 = x$.

D8

Is the graph of the solution set a subset of the graph of the universe?

I Look at D7. Use each member of A × A to make replacements for x and y in $y + 3 = x$. Decide whether or not each statement obtained is true.

J Tabulate the solution set of $y + 3 = x$. Is the solution set a subset of the universe?

K Is a graph of the universe for (x, y) shown in D8? Explain your answer.

L Does the set of encircled dots form a graph of the solution set of $y + 3 = x$? Explain your answer.

M Is the graph of the solution set of $y + 3 = x$ a subset of the graph of the universe?

You have learned to make a graph of a universe when the universe is a set of ordered pairs. You have also learned to make graphs of solution sets of conditions in two variables.

On your own

1 D9 shows a graph of a set of ordered pairs. First tabulate the set of ordered pairs that are associated with all the points represented by dots in the graph. Then tabulate the set of ordered pairs that are associated with the points represented by encircled dots.

2 For D10, use the instructions given for D9.

3 For D11, tabulate the set of ordered pairs associated with the points represented by dots.

Each set tabulated in exercises 4, 5, and 6 is a subset of the set you tabulated for exercise 3. For each exercise make a copy of the graph that is shown in D11. Then make a graph of the subset.

4 $\{(1, 3)\}$

5 $\{(0, 0), (0, 1), (0, 2), (1, 0), (1, 1), (1, 2), (2, 0), (2, 1), (2, 2)\}$

6 $\{(0, 4), (1, 4), (2, 4), (3, 4), (4, 4)\}$

7 Set A and set B are tabulated below. Tabulate $A \times B$.

$A = \{0, 1, 2, 3, 4\}$. $B = \{0, 1, 2, 3\}$.

8 Now use $A \times B$ as the universe for (x, y) for $x = y + 1$. Tabulate the solution set of $x = y + 1$. Same 10 = 11, 12 = 13.

9 Make a graph of the solution set of $x = y + 1$. Remember that the graph of the solution set of $x = y + 1$ is shown as a subset of the graph of the universe.

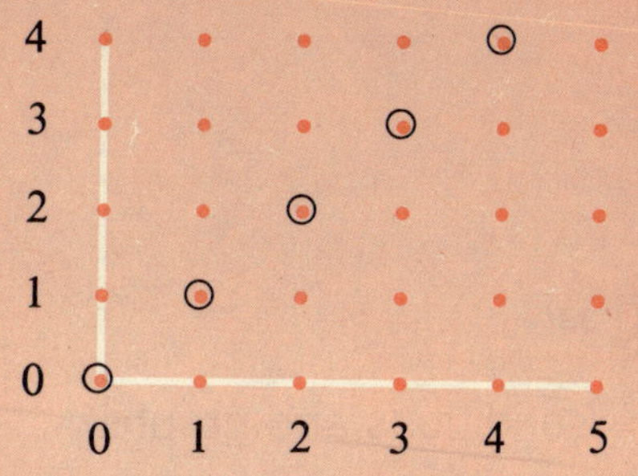

D9

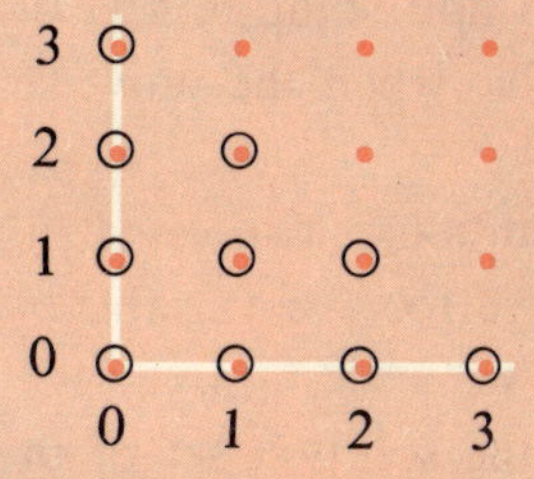

D10

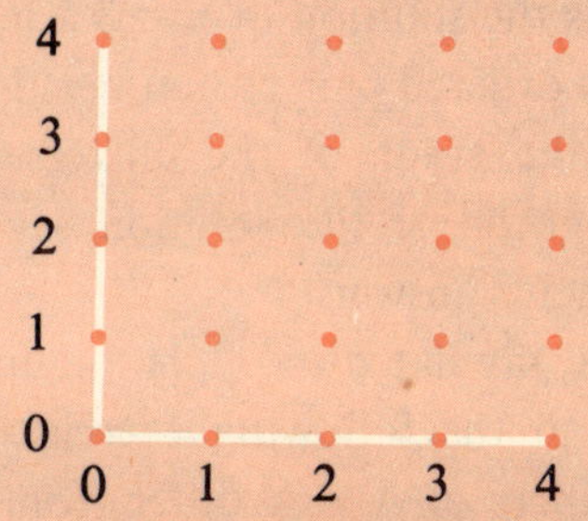

D11

For the conditions expressed in exercises 10 through 13, use the universe for (x, y) that is tabulated below. First tabulate the solution set of each condition. Then, for each condition, make graphs of the universe and the solution set.

Universe for $(x, y) = \{(0, 0), (0, 1), (0, 2), (0, 3), (1, 0), (1, 1), (1, 2), (1, 3), (2, 0), (2, 1), (2, 2), (2, 3), (3, 0), (3, 1), (3, 2), (3, 3), (4, 0), (4, 1), (4, 2), (4, 3)\}$.

10 $x = y$.

11 $x > y$.

12 $2y = x$.

13 $y + x < 5$.

$U = \{0, 1, 2, \ldots, 10\}$.

$x = 3$.

D1

$A = \{0, 1, 2, 3, 4\}$.

$A \times A = \{(0, 0), (0, 1), (0, 2), (0, 3), (0, 4), (1, 0), (1, 1), (1, 2), (1, 3), (1, 4), (2, 0), (2, 1), (2, 2), (2, 3), (2, 4), (3, 0), (3, 1), (3, 2), (3, 3), (3, 4), (4, 0), (4, 1), (4, 2), (4, 3), (4, 4)\}$.

$x = 3$.

D2

Universe for $(x, y) = A \times A$.

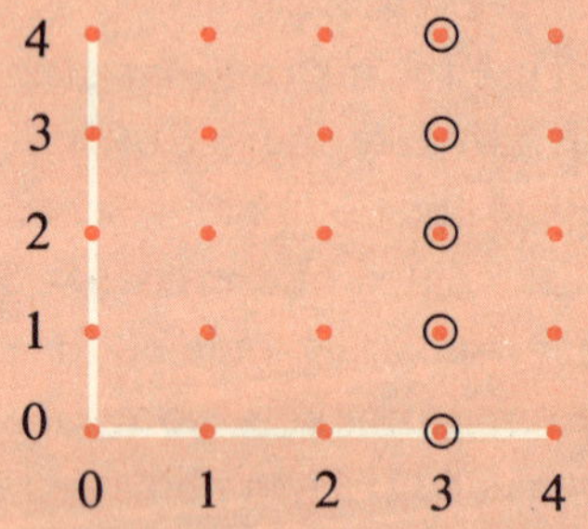

$x = 3$.

D3

3 | 33 **Exploring ideas**

Conditions and graphs

You have learned to use a set of ordered pairs as a universe. In this lesson you will learn how to find solution sets of conditions in one variable when the universe is a set of ordered pairs.

A What condition is expressed in D1? What is the universe for the variable? Is the universe a finite set?

B Tabulate the solution set of the condition expressed in D1. The solution set has how many members? Is the solution set a finite set?

C Why is the solution of $x = 3$ a number and ? not an ordered pair of numbers?

D Does the graph of the universe in D1 include a graph of the solution set of $x = 3$? Explain your answer.

E $A \times A$, tabulated in D2, is the universe you will use in the following exercises. How do the members of $A \times A$ differ from the members of the universe tabulated in D1?

When the universe is a set of ordered pairs, you can use any two different variables to refer to the members of the universe. In this lesson we will use (x, y) to refer to the members of the universe. This means that a Cartesian set is the universe for a pair of variables, x and y, in a condition, and that the first components are the replacements for x and the second components are the replacements for y.

F Even though the universe is a set of ordered pairs, you can find the solution set of a condition in only one variable. How many variables are there in $x = 3$?

G How do you know that x in $x = 3$ may be re- ? placed by the first component of each ordered pair in $A \times A$?

H Does $x = 3$ contain a variable that may be replaced by the second component of each member of $A \times A$?

I Look at D3. Which dots form a graph of $A \times A$?

J Do the encircled dots in D3 represent points associated with ordered pairs? What is the first component of each of these ordered pairs? Tabulate this set of ordered pairs.

 Finding solution sets of conditions in one variable when the universe is a set of ordered pairs; determining conditions from graphs of their solution sets

K Is the condition $x = 3$ satisfied by each of the ordered pairs contained in the set you tabulated for exercise J?

L Do any other ordered pairs in the universe satisfy the condition?

The set of ordered pairs that you tabulated for exercise J is the solution set of $x = 3$. The first component of each of these ordered pairs is 3. The condition does not make a requirement about the second component of each solution. Therefore, each ordered pair in the universe whose first component is 3 is a solution of $x = 3$.

M Which dots in D3 form a graph of the solution set of $x = 3$?

N Is the solution set of $x = 3$ a finite set? Is the solution set a subset of the universe? Explain your answers.

Next you will find the solution set of a condition for inequality in one variable. The universe is a set of ordered pairs.

A Look at D4. What is the universe for (x, y)? Tabulate the universe.

B What requirement does $y < 4$ make about the first component of each member of the solution set?

C What requirement does $y < 4$ make about the second component of each member of the solution set?

D Look at D5. Which dots form a graph of $A \times B$?

E Tabulate the set of ordered pairs associated with the points represented by encircled dots.

F Is $y < 4$ satisfied by each ordered pair in this set?

G Do any other ordered pairs in $A \times B$ satisfy $y < 4$?

H Is the set of ordered pairs you tabulated for exercise E the solution set of $y < 4$? Explain your answer.

Universe for $(x, y) = A \times B$.
$A = \{0, 1, 2, 3, 4\}$.
$B = \{0, 1, 2, 3, 4, 5\}$.
$y < 4$.

D4

Universe for $(x, y) = A \times B$.

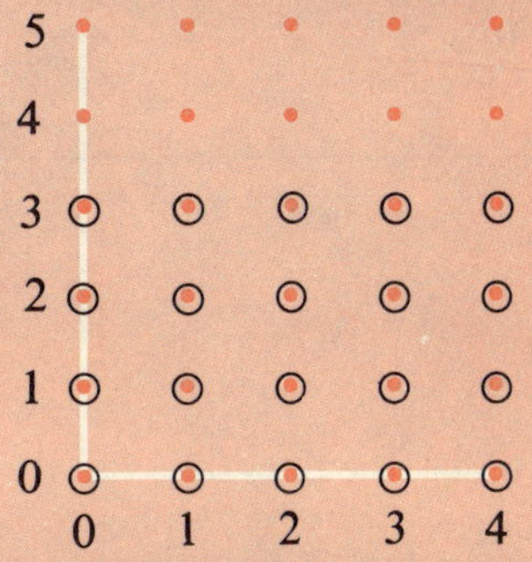

$y < 4$.

D5

Universe for $(x, y) = R \times R$.
$R = \{0, 1, 2, 3\}$.
$y + 3 > 4$.

D6

I Which dots in D5 form a graph of the solution set of $y < 4$? Is the solution set of $y < 4$ a subset of the universe?

J Look at D6. What condition is expressed? What is the universe for (x, y)?

K Make a graph of $R \times R$.

L Tabulate the solution set of $y + 3 > 4$. Remember that an ordered pair whose second component satisfies $y + 3 > 4$ is a solution of $y + 3 > 4$.

M Why is the solution set of $y + 3 > 4$ a set of ordered pairs?

N In the graph of $R \times R$ that you made for exercise K, make a graph of the solution set of $y + 3 > 4$.

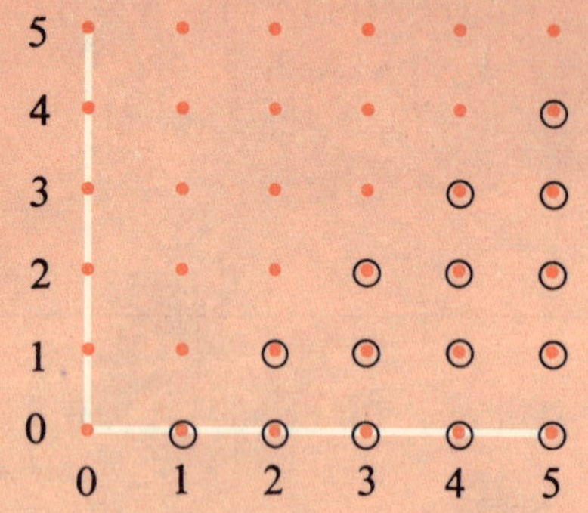

D7

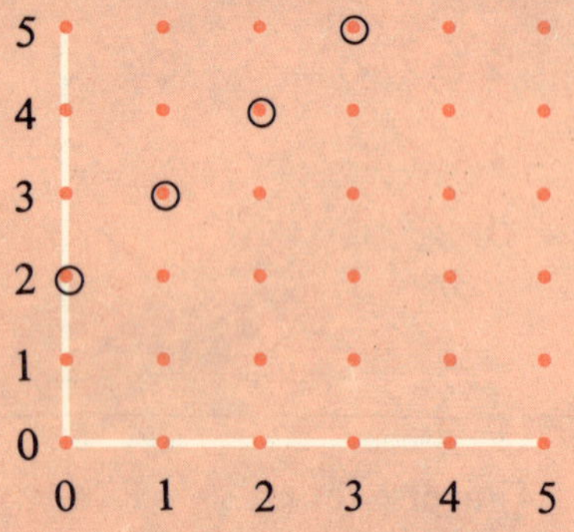

D8

Next you will see how you can obtain a condition when you are given a graph of its solution set.

A A graph of a universe for (x, y) consists of all the dots in D7. A graph of the solution set of a condition consists of the encircled dots. Tabulate this solution set.

B Think about the members of the solution set that you have tabulated. Is the first component of each member less than the second component? Is the first component of each member greater than the second component?

C ? Can the set you tabulated in exercise A be the solution set of $x < y$? Can it be the solution set of $x > y$? Explain your answers.

D A graph of a universe for (x, y) consists of all the dots in D8. A graph of the solution set of a condition consists of the encircled dots. Tabulate this solution set.

E What number can be added to the first component of each member so that the sum equals the second component?

F ? The set you tabulated in exercise D is the solution set of a condition. What is a condition that has this solution set?

In this lesson you have learned that when the universe is a set of ordered pairs, the solution set of a condition in one variable is also a set of ordered pairs. You have also learned how to obtain a condition by studying a graph of its solution set.

On your own

The universe for (x, y) for the conditions expressed in exercises 1 through 6 is tabulated below. Tabulate the solution set of each condition. For each condition, make a graph of the universe and a graph of the solution set.

Universe for $(x, y) = \{(0, 0), (0, 1), (0, 2), (0, 3), (0, 4), (0, 5), (1, 0), (1, 1), (1, 2), (1, 3), (1, 4), (1, 5), (2, 0), (2, 1), (2, 2), (2, 3), (2, 4), (2, 5), (3, 0), (3, 1), (3, 2), (3, 3), (3, 4), (3, 5), (4, 0), (4, 1), (4, 2), (4, 3), (4, 4), (4, 5)\}$.

1 $x = 2$. **3** $x > 2$. **5** $y + 3 < 6$.

2 $x < 2$. **4** $x = y$. **6** $y + 2 = x$.

The universe for (x, y) for the conditions expressed in exercises 7 through 12 is the same as the universe you used for the exercises above. Tabulate the solution set of each condition.

7 $x + 3 = 4$. **10** $y + 1 = 3$.

8 $y + 1 > 3$. **11** $x + 1 = 4$.

9 $x + 2 < 5$. **12** $x < y$.

13 D9 shows a graph of a set of ordered pairs. The dots form a graph of the universe for (x, y). A graph of the solution set of a condition consists of the encircled dots. Tabulate the solution set. Then write a sentence expressing a condition for which this set of ordered pairs is the solution set.

14 For D10, use the instructions given for D9.

15 For D11, use the instructions given for D9.

16 For D12, use the instructions given for D9.

17 For D13, use the instructions given for D9.

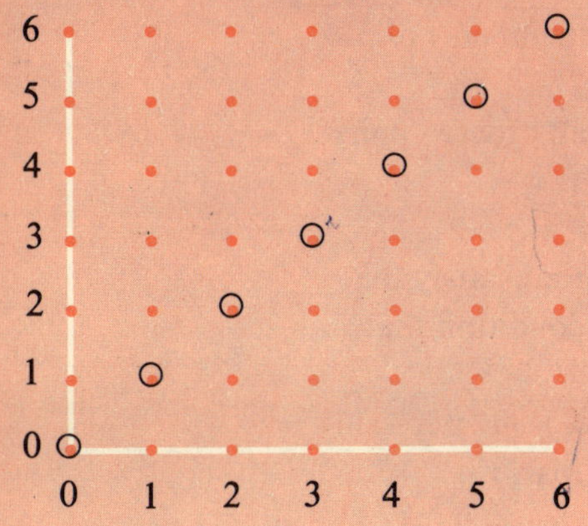

D9

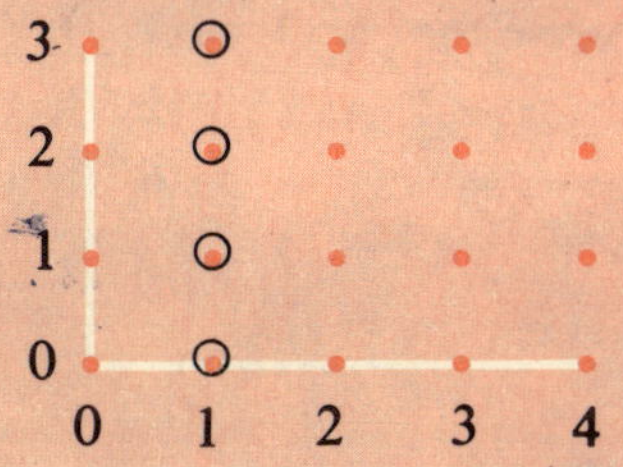

D10

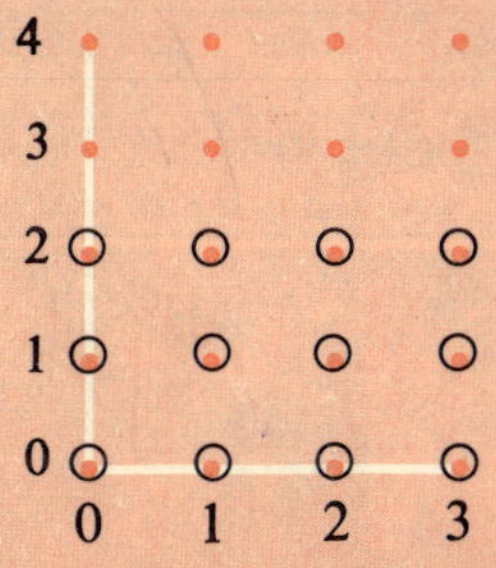

D11

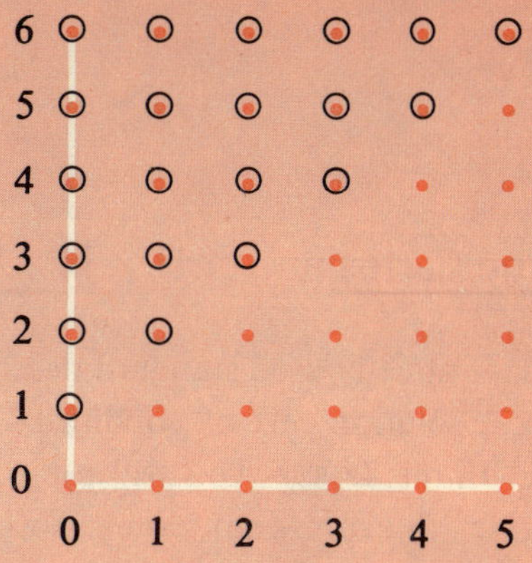

D12

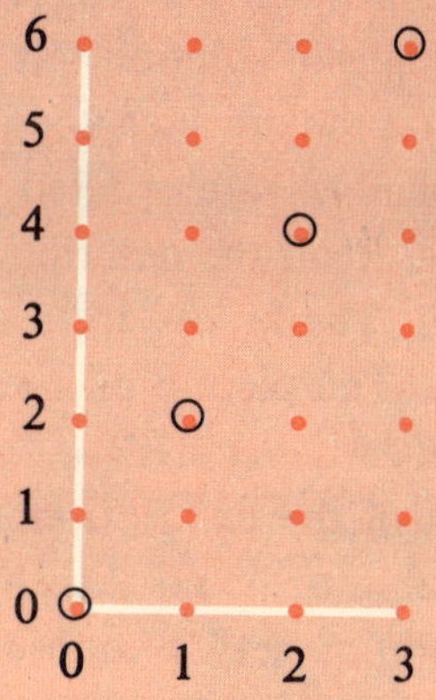

D13

KEEPING SKILFUL

Find the difference.

1 7136, 5929

2 6851, 5983

3 31408, 8267

4 12040, 92

5 50000, 36105

6 42367, 38298

Multiply

7 726 by 38.

8 905 by 41.

9 826 by 600.

10 315 by 287.

11 604 by 190.

12 271 by 305.

13 7872 by 96.

Divide

14 6490 by 27.

15 14212 by 34.

16 12816 by 178.

17 21720 by 235.

18 35534 by 109.

19 108373 by 519.

20 62400 by 400.

3 | 34 **Exploring ideas**

The Cartesian set N × N

You have already used standard descriptions to express solution sets of conditions in one variable. In this lesson, you will use standard descriptions to express solution sets of conditions in two variables. You will also learn about the Cartesian set of the set of natural numbers, and you will use this set as a universe in making graphs of solution sets.

A Assume that the universe you are using is a set whose members are ordered pairs of natural numbers. Read the description of a solution set in D1. The braces are used instead of what words? The picture of a vertical line is used instead of what words?

B What part of the description expresses the condition that must be satisfied by each member of the solution set? Suppose the universe is for (x, y). Does the sentence $x > y$ also express this condition?

D2 shows how to read a standard description of the solution set of $x > y$.

C What condition is satisfied by each member **?** of $\{(x, y) \mid x > y\}$? How do you know that $\{(x, y) \mid x > y\}$ is the solution set of $x > y$?

D Read each standard description in D3. What is the universe for the variables? What condition is satisfied by each member of A? Of B? Of C? Of D?

E Tabulate each of the sets described in D3.

F Read sentences A and B in D4. Does sentence A express a true statement? Does sentence B express a true statement? Explain your answers.

{all ordered pairs | the first component of each ordered pair is greater than the second component}

D1

"The set whose members are — $\{ (x, y) \mid x > y \}$

all ordered pairs x, y

that satisfy the condition that

x is greater than y"

D2

Universe for $(x, y) = \{(7, 7), (7, 2), (2, 7), (2, 2), (6, 7), (6, 2)\}$.

$A = \{(x, y) \mid x = y\}$.
$B = \{(x, y) \mid x = 2\}$.
$C = \{(x, y) \mid x > 8 - y\}$.
$D = \{(x, y) \mid y > 3\}$.

D3

Universe for $(x, y) = \{(7, 7), (7, 2), (2, 7), (2, 2), (6, 7), (6, 2)\}$.

A $\{(x, y) \mid x < y\} = \{(2, 7), (6, 7)\}$.
B $\{(x, y) \mid x = 5\} = \{\ \ \}$.

D4

 Using standard description to name the solution set of a condition when the universe is a set of ordered pairs; using the Cartesian set N × N as the universe for (x, y)

Now you will learn more about making graphs when the universe is a set of ordered pairs.

A Suppose that the universe for (x, y) is the set of all ordered pairs such that both components of each ordered pair are natural numbers. Which of the following are members of the universe?

(2, 3) ($\frac{1}{2}$, 6) (500, 3) (7, 7)

B Name the set that contains all the first components of the ordered pairs in the universe described in exercise A. Name the set that contains all the second components of the ordered pairs.

C Is N × N a name for the universe described ? in exercise A? Explain your answer.

D Is the Cartesian set N × N an infinite set? ? Explain your answer.

E In lesson 13 you learned how to make a graph of N. Now you will learn how to make a graph of N × N. You will use natural-number lines as the first and second axes. In D5, what do the three small dots to the right of the picture of the first axis tell you? What do the three small dots above the picture of the second axis tell you?

F Point A, represented in D5, is associated with (1, 4), which is a member of N × N. D6 shows how to write and read another name for point A. What is another name for each of points B through H, represented in D5?

G Now think about these eight members of N × N. Is each component of each member less than 6?

H The graph in D5 does not contain the dots that represent points (6, 0), (7, 0), and (8, 0). Does the graph contain the dots that represent points (0, 6), (0, 7), and (0, 8)?

I Suppose the picture of the first axis were extended to contain the dot representing point 8.

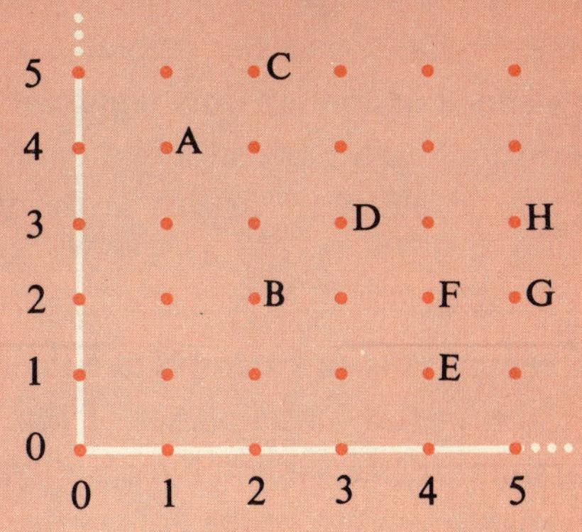

D5

D6

Could you then use dots to locate points (6, 0), (7, 0), and (8, 0)?

J Also suppose the picture of the second axis were extended to contain the dot representing point 8. Could you then use dots to locate points (0, 6), (0, 7), and (0, 8)?

K How many members of N × N have 0 as a second component? Imagine that you could locate all the points that are associated with the members of N × N that have 0 as a second component. In which axis would these points be located?

L How many members of N × N have 0 as a first component? Imagine that you could locate all the points that are associated with the members of N × N that have 0 as a first component. Where would these points be located?

M How many members of N × N have 1 as a first component? Describe the location of all the points associated with these members.

N How many members of N × N have 9 as a second component? Describe the location of all the points associated with these members.

O Look at D7. Imagine that the pictures of both the first axis and the second axis have been extended to contain dots representing all points through 100. For each point named, tell where you would place its dot in the graph: (0, 10), (1, 17), (9, 3), (20, 4), (5, 93), (6, 75), (100, 5), (99, 8).

Mathematicians call a graph like the one in D7 a graph of the Cartesian set of the set of natural numbers. It is a graph of $N \times N$.

D7 shows just a few of the dots in the graph of $N \times N$. Since $N \times N$ is an infinite set, the graph of $N \times N$ is an infinite set of dots. To obtain more dots in the graph, more dots could be put in the pictures of the axes.

When we make a graph of $N \times N$, we will place three small dots at the end of the picture of each axis. These dots indicate that the graph of $N \times N$ is an infinite set.

P Does D8 also show a graph of $N \times N$? How do you know?

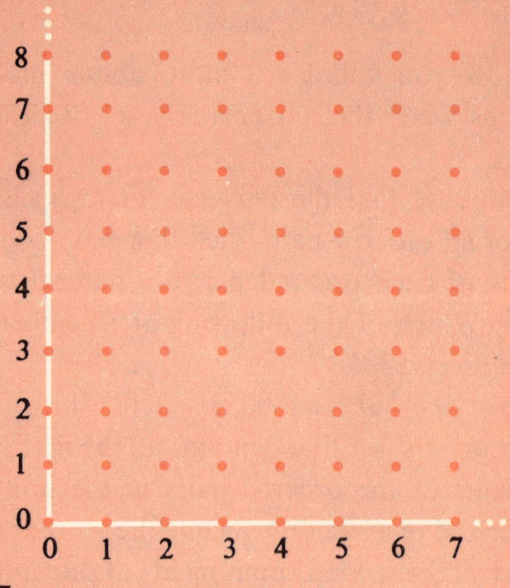

D7

Universe for $(x, y) = N \times N$.

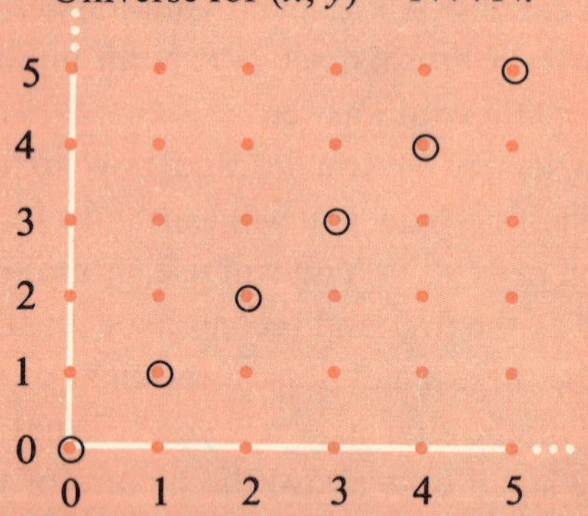

$\{(x, y) | y = x\}$
Incomplete graph

D8

Now you will see how you can use a graph of $N \times N$ in making a graph of the solution set of a condition.

A Read the standard description in D8. Is the set described the solution set of $y = x$?

B Can you make a graph of $\{(x, y) | y = x\}$ by using a graph of the universe? How do you know?

C Look at the encircled dots in the graph in D8. Name the ordered pairs associated with the points represented by these dots. Does each of these ordered pairs satisfy $y = x$?

D Is (98, 98) a solution of $y = x$? In the graph in D8, is there a dot that locates point (98, 98)? What would you have to do before you could place a dot to locate this point?

E Name five other members of $\{(x, y) | y = x\}$ whose points are not represented by dots in the graph in D8.

F The words "incomplete graph" tell you that the entire graph of the solution set of a condition is not shown. Why are the words "incomplete graph" used in D8? How do you know that the solution set of $y = x$ is an infinite set?

Now you will learn how to make graphs of the solution sets of $y > x$ and $y < x$. The universe for (x, y) is $N \times N$.

G Look at D9. The encircled dots are in the graph of $\{(x, y) | y = x\}$. Are any of these dots in the graph of $\{(x, y) | y > x\}$?

H Look at the dots that are below the encircled dots. Select any two of these dots and name the points they represent. Are the points you named associated with ordered pairs? Are these ordered pairs members of the solution set of $y > x$? Explain your answer.

I Should the graph of the solution set of $y > x$ contain any dots below the encircled dots?

J Look at the dots enclosed by squares. Are these dots in the graph of $\{(x, y) | y > x\}$? Explain your answer.

K Does (3, 100) satisfy $y > x$? Does (19, 47) satisfy $y > x$? How do you know that the solution set of $y > x$ is an infinite set?

L Does D9 include all possible dots in the graph of $\{(x, y) | y > x\}$? Why are the words "incomplete graph" used in D9?

M Study D10. How are the dots in the graph of the solution set of $y = x$ indicated? How are the dots in the graph of the solution set of $y < x$ indicated? How is the position of the dots in the graph of $\{(x, y) | y < x\}$ related to the position of the dots in the graph of $\{(x, y) | y = x\}$?

N Is the solution set of $y < x$ an infinite set? Why are the words "incomplete graph" used?

O Look at D11. Does the display show all the dots in the graph of $\{(x, y) | x + y = 4\}$? Is $\{(x, y) | x + y = 4\}$ an infinite set? A finite set?

P How could you use the graph of the solution set of $x + y = 4$ to make a graph of the solution set of $x + y < 4$? To make a graph of the solution set of $x + y > 4$?

Q Is the solution set of $x + y < 4$ a finite set? Is the solution set of $x + y > 4$ a finite set? Explain your answers.

Now you can use a standard description to express the solution set of a condition in two variables. You also can use a graph of N × N in making graphs of solution sets.

Universe for $(x, y) = N \times N$.

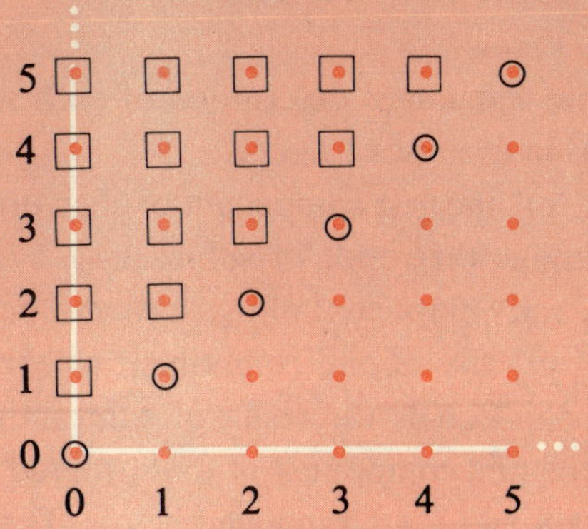

$\{(x, y) | y > x\}$

Incomplete graph

D9

Universe for $(x, y) = N \times N$.

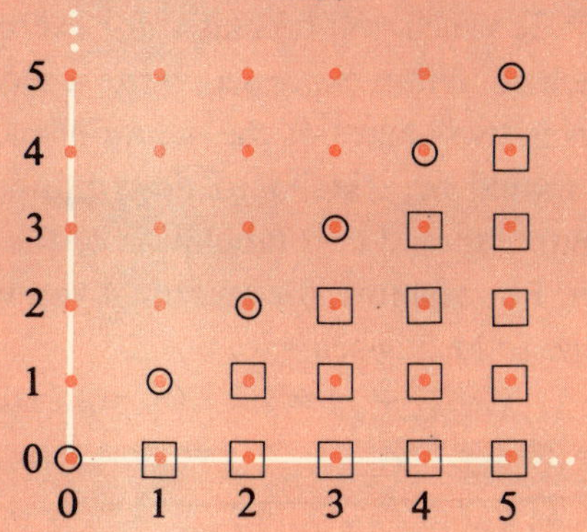

$\{(x, y) | y < x\}$

Incomplete graph

D10

Universe for $(x, y) = N \times N$.

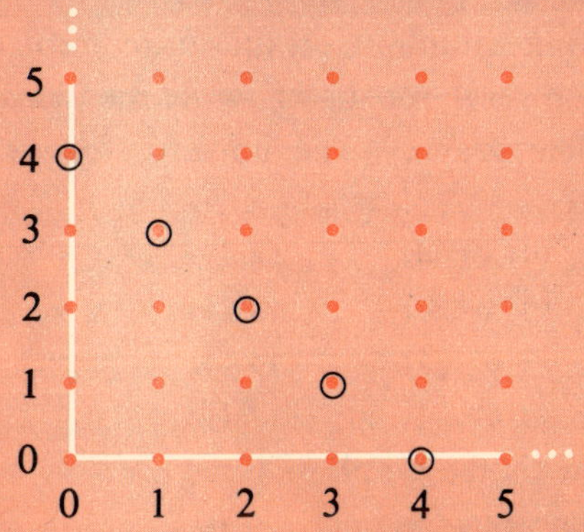

$\{(x, y) | x + y = 4\}$

D11

On your own

Write a standard description of each set described in exercises 1 and 2.

1 $\{(x, y) |$ the first component of each ordered pair equals the result of subtracting 14 from the second component of that ordered pair$\}$

2 $\{(x, y) |$ the second component of each ordered pair equals the result of subtracting 14 from the first component of that ordered pair$\}$

3 Sets S and T are tabulated below. Tabulate $S \times T$.

$S = \{5, 6, 7, 8, 9, 10\}$.

$T = \{20, 21\}$.

The universe for (x, y) in exercises 4 through 9 is $S \times T$, which you tabulated for exercise 3. For each condition expressed, write a sentence that gives two names of the solution set. One name should be a standard description. The other name should be a tabulation of the solution set. For example, for exercise 4 you would write the following sentence:

$\{(x, y) | x = 27 - y\} = \{(7, 20), (6, 21)\}$.

4 $x = 27 - y$.

5 $x > 27 - y$.

6 $x < 27 - y$.

7 $y = 20$.

8 $y - 12 = x$.

9 $3x < y + 9$.

For each of exercises 10 through 17, follow these instructions: First make a graph of $N \times N$. Then make a graph of the solution set described in the exercise. Tell whether this set is finite or infinite. If the entire graph of the solution set is not shown, write the words "incomplete graph." The universe for (x, y) is $N \times N$.

10 $\{(x, y) | x = 4\}$

11 $\{(x, y) | x < 4\}$

12 $\{(x, y) | y = 4\}$

13 $\{(x, y) | y > 4\}$

14 $\{(x, y) | x + y = 6\}$

15 $\{(x, y) | x + y > 6\}$

16 $\{(x, y) | y = 2 + x\}$

17 $\{(x, y) | y > 2 + x\}$

18 How is the graph of $\{(x, y) | x < 4\}$ related to the graph of $\{(x, y) | x = 4\}$?

19 How is the graph of $\{(x, y) | x + y > 6\}$ related to the graph of $\{(x, y) | x + y = 6\}$?

KEEPING SKILFUL

For exercises 1 through 10, tell whether each sentence expresses a condition or a statement.

1 $29 < 600 \div 24$.

2 $n = 861 + 79$.

3 $34 - s > 18$.

4 $6(15) > 6(14)$.

5 $3 + 1 = 7 - 3$.

6 $d = 19 + 32$.

7 $8 + 6 = 2(7)$.

8 $w > 24 + 9$.

9 $15 - 6 < 3 + 6$.

10 $m > 3m$.

11 Which sentences in exercises 1 through 10 express true statements? Which express false statements?

12 Tabulate the solution set of each condition expressed in exercises 1 through 10. $U = N$.

13 Set R and set S are tabulated below. Tabulate $R \times S$.

$R = \{0, 1, 2, 3\}$.

$S = \{0, 1, 2\}$.

For each condition expressed in exercises 14 through 21, the universe for (f, g) is set $R \times S$, which you tabulated for exercise 13. First tabulate the solution set of each condition. Then, for each condition, make a graph of the universe and of the solution set.

14 $f + g = 4$.

15 $f + g < 3$.

16 $f + 2 < 4$.

17 $f + g > 2$.

18 $7 - f > 5$.

19 $f + 1 = g$.

20 $f = g$.

21 $3 - g = f$.

For each of exercises 22 through 26, first tabulate sets K and L. Next tabulate $K \cap L$. Then tabulate $K \cup L$. $U = N$.

22 $K = \{c | 39 - c > 27\}$.
$L = \{c | 42 + c < 51\}$.

23 $K = \{v | 2103 - v = 1926\}$.
$L = \{v | v + 624 < 631\}$.

24 $K = \{d | d + 76 > 92\}$.
$L = \{d | 121 + d < 140\}$.

25 $K = \{b | b - 95 > 17\}$.
$L = \{b | 739 + b > 766\}$.

26 $K = \{m | 304 - m = 268\}$.
$L = \{m | m + 435 = 471\}$.

3 | 35 **Exploring ideas**

Charts and solution sets

Universe for $(x, y) = A \times A$.
$A = \{0, 1, 2, 3, 4, 5\}$.
$y = 5 - x$.

D1

Universe for $(x, y) = A \times A$.
$y = 5 - x$.

x	0	1	2	3	4	5
y	5					

D2

Universe for $(x, y) = B \times B$.
$B = \{0, 1, 2, 3, 4, 5, 6\}$.
$x + y = 4$.

x	0	1	2	3	4
y					

D3

You have learned to find solution sets of conditions in two variables by making replacements for each of the variables, and deciding whether or not each statement that you obtained was true. You have also learned how to make graphs of universes and of solution sets of conditions. Now you will find solution sets by first replacing one of the variables in the condition and then determining the replacement for the other variable.

A Look at D1. What condition is expressed? What is the universe for (x, y)? Is $A \times A$ a set of ordered pairs? Tabulate $A \times A$.

B Is $A \times A$ an infinite set? Is it a finite set?

C By completing the chart in D2, you will learn a convenient way to obtain the solution set of $y = 5 - x$. The ordered pairs named in the completed chart will be solutions of the condition. Is each number named in the row opposite the letter x the first component of at least one member of $A \times A$? Are these numbers the only numbers that can be used as replacements for x in $y = 5 - x$? How do you know?

D Replace x in $y = 5 - x$ by 0. What replacement for y satisfies $y = 5 - 0$?

E Look again at the chart in D2. Why is the numeral 5 placed in the row opposite the letter y and directly below the numeral 0?

F Is $(0, 5)$ a member of the solution set of $y = 5 - x$? How do you know?

G Copy the chart in D2. Use each of the other numbers named in the row opposite the letter x as a replacement for x in $y = 5 - x$. For each condition you obtain, find the replacement for y that satisfies the condition. Complete the chart by writing the name of each replacement for y.

H What are the six ordered pairs that you can obtain from your completed chart? Is each of these ordered pairs a member of $A \times A$? Are there any other members of $A \times A$ that satisfy $y = 5 - x$?

I Tabulate $\{(x, y) \mid y = 5 - x\}$.

Notice that each first component of the members of $A \times A$ is a first component of a solution of $y = 5 - x$. Now you will see that each first component of the members of the universe is not always a first component of a solution.

J Look at D3. What is the universe for (x, y)? Is $B \times B$ an infinite set? Is it a finite set?

K Replace x in $x+y=4$ by 5. Do you obtain $5+y=4$? Is there a member of B that satisfies $5+y=4$?

L Why do you not use either 5 or 6 as a replacement for x in $x+y=4$?

M Look at the chart in D3. Why are the numbers named in the row opposite the letter x the only numbers that you use as replacements for x in $x+y=4$?

N Copy the chart in D3. Use each number named in the top row as a replacement for x in $x+y=4$. For each condition you obtain, find the replacement for y that satisfies the condition. Then complete the chart.

O How many ordered pairs can you obtain from the chart? Is each of these ordered pairs a member of $B \times B$? Are there any other members of $B \times B$ that satisfy $x+y=4$?

P Tabulate $\{(x, y) \mid x+y=4\}$.

Q Make a graph of $\{(x, y) \mid x+y=4\}$.

You have used charts to help you determine the solutions of conditions for equality. Now you will use a chart to help you determine the solutions of a condition for inequality.

A What condition for inequality is expressed in D4? What is the universe for (x, y)?

B Use 4 as a replacement for x in $x+y<4$. What condition do you obtain? Are there any members of B that satisfy $4+y<4$?

C Why do you not use a number greater than 3 as a replacement for x in $x+y<4$?

D Replace x in $x+y<4$ by 0. What condition do you obtain? Is 0 the first component of more than one ordered pair that satisfies $x+y<4$? Explain your answer.

E What members of B satisfy $0+y<4$? Where are these members named in the chart in D4?

F Now replace x by 1. Does any member of B that is greater than 2 satisfy $1+y<4$?

Universe for $(x, y) = B \times B$.
$B = \{0, 1, 2, 3, 4, 5, 6\}$.
$x+y=4$.

x	0	1	2	3	4
y					

D3

Universe for $(x, y) = B \times B$.
$B = \{0, 1, 2, 3, 4, 5, 6\}$.
$x+y<4$.

x	0	1	2	3
y	0			
	1			
	2			
	3			

D4

G What members of B satisfy $1+y<4$? Where will you write the names of these members in your chart?

H Copy and complete the chart in D4.

I From the chart, you obtain ten ordered pairs that satisfy $x+y<4$. What universe does each of these ordered pairs belong to?

J Tabulate $\{(x, y) \mid x+y<4\}$.

K Make a graph of $\{(x, y) \mid x+y<4\}$.

So far in this lesson, each universe you have used has been a finite Cartesian set. In the following exercises, you will use the Cartesian set $N \times N$ as the universe.

A What condition is expressed in D5? What numbers can be used as replacements for r in $s=2r+1$?

B Is the set of numbers that can be used as replacements for r an infinite set?

C When you replace r by 50, you obtain $s = 2(50) + 1$. What member of N satisfies this condition?

You know that each member of N can be used as a replacement for r. Since it is impossible to put the name of each number that can be used as a replacement for r in a chart, use only the names of the numbers from 0 through 4 in your chart.

D Make and complete a chart for $s = 2r + 1$.

E Tabulate the set of ordered pairs that you obtain from your chart. Is each member of this set a solution of $s = 2r + 1$?

F ? Are the members of the set you tabulated for exercise E the only members of $\{(r, s) \mid s = 2r + 1\}$? Explain your answer. Remember that the universe for (r, s) is $N \times N$.

G What condition is expressed in D6?

H Make a chart that names some of the solutions of $s < 2r + 1$. Use only the numbers from 0 through 4 as replacements for r.

I Tabulate the set of ordered pairs that you obtain from your chart. Is this set the solution set of $s < 2r + 1$? Explain your answer.

Universe for $(r, s) = N \times N$.
$s = 2r + 1$.

D5

Universe for $(r, s) = N \times N$.
$s < 2r + 1$.

D6

Universe for $(r, s) = N \times N$.
$s > 2r + 1$.

D7

J Is $\{(r, s) \mid s < 2r + 1\}$ a finite set? Is it an infinite set?

K Make a graph of $N \times N$ that contains all the dots that represent points associated with the ordered pairs you tabulated for both exercises E and I. Encircle the dots in the graph of $\{(r, s) \mid s = 2r + 1\}$. Use squares to enclose the dots in the graph of $\{(r, s) \mid s < 2r + 1\}$.

L ? What condition is expressed in D7? Make a chart to help you determine some of the members of $\{(r, s) \mid s > 2r + 1\}$. Use the numbers from 0 through 4 as replacements for r. Do not find any members of $\{(r, s) \mid s > 2r + 1\}$ in which the second components are greater than 10.

M Are the ordered pairs that you obtain from your chart the only ordered pairs that satisfy $s > 2r + 1$?

Now you know how to make and use charts to help you determine the solutions of conditions in two variables.

On your own

For each condition expressed in exercises 1 through 6, the universe for (x, y) is $D \times D$. $D = \{0, 1, 2, 3, 4, 5, 6, 7, 8\}$. For each condition, make a chart to help you determine the members of the solution set. Then tabulate the solution set. As replacements for x, use only those members of D that are first components of members of the solution set. For exercise 2, for example, you should not use 5 as a replacement for x because $3(5) = 15$, and 15 is not in the universe for y. There is no member of D that satisfies $3(5) = y$.

1 $y = 8 - x$.
2 $3x = y$.
3 $y = x + 1$.
4 $y + x < 3$.
5 $x + 4 = y$.
6 $y = x + 5$.

For each condition expressed in exercises 7 through 11, the universe for (r, s) is $N \times N$. Each chart names a few of the possible replacements for one of the variables. Copy each chart and write in the missing numerals.

7

$s + 17 = r.$						
r						
s	0	1	2	25	93	104

8

$s = 4r + 2.$									
r	0	3	4	6	12	17	95	118	213
s									

9

$4r - 2 > s.$				
r	1	2	3	4
s				

10

$3s + r = 35.$								
r								
s	1	2	4	6	8	9	10	11

11

$r + s < 8.$				
r	0	2	4	6
s				

For each condition expressed in exercises 12 through 17, the universe for (x, y) is N × N. For each exercise, make a chart to help you determine some of the members of the solution set. Use the numbers from 0 through 6 as replacements for x. Tabulate the set of ordered pairs that you obtain from your chart.

12 $x = y - 7.$ **15** $7 - x > y.$
13 $y = x + 2.$ **16** $21 - 3x = y.$
14 $2x + 3 = y.$ **17** $y - 2 = x.$

For each of exercises 12, 15, and 17, make a graph of the solution set of the condition expressed in the exercise. Encircle only the dots that represent points associated with the ordered pairs you can obtain from your charts.

KEEPING SKILFUL

For exercises 1 through 6, round each of the numbers named to the next greater thousand, to the next lesser hundred, and to the next greater ten.

1 3276 **3** 6892 **5** 36,993
2 4721 **4** 19,929 **6** 5550

Find the sum.

7 368, 705, 296
8 4823, 1960, 382
9 6510, 7396, 982, 4968
10 7727, 88, 9276, 338
11 36805, 72412, 65120
12 210, 87654, 2341, 72
13 16315, 7024, 62657, 9824

Multiply
14 324 by 65.
15 805 by 94.
16 214 by 465.
17 617 by 840.
18 809 by 321.
19 354 by 605.

Divide
20 3668 by 57.
21 9360 by 36.
22 18098 by 94.
23 11890 by 245.
24 21384 by 132.
25 26546 by 241.

For each of exercises 26 through 33, tabulate the solution set of the condition. U = N.

26 $87 + c < 95 \wedge 103 - c > 98.$
27 $w > 288 \div 24 \wedge w + 34 < 53.$
28 $2463 - f = 1987.$
29 $32 - d > 23 \wedge d + 24 > 30.$
30 $s < 34(6) \wedge 27 - s > 9.$
31 $m + m > 8.$
32 $n - 14 > 16 \wedge 47 - n > 14.$
33 $b + 324 > 419 \wedge b > 59 + 67.$

For each of exercises 34 through 39, tabulate the set named. Sets J, K, and L are tabulated below.

J = {(0, 1) (1, 2), (2, 3), (3, 4)}.
K = {(3, 4)}.
L = {(1, 0), (1, 2), (3, 2), (2, 3)}.

34 L ∪ J **36** K ∩ J **38** J ∩ L
35 K ∩ L **37** J ∪ K **39** K ∩ K

3 36 **Exploring ideas**

Compound conditions in two variables

You have studied compound conditions in one variable. In this lesson you will study compound conditions in two variables and find the solution sets of these conditions.

A Look at D1. What is the universe for (x, y)?

B Does the open sentence in D1 express a compound condition? Explain your answer. How many variables are there in this condition?

C How do you know that the solution set **?** of $x + y = 6 \wedge y = 2x$ is a set of ordered pairs?

D How do you know that each solution of the compound condition must satisfy both $x + y = 6$ and $y = 2x$?

> REMINDER
> Each solution of a compound condition that has two simple conditions and the connective "and" must satisfy both simple conditions.
> *See lesson 24, page 90.*

First you will use a graph of the solution set of $x + y = 6$ and a graph of the solution set of $y = 2x$ to find a graph of $\{(x, y) | x + y = 6 \wedge y = 2x\}$.

E Look at D2. How are the dots in the graph of $\{(x, y) | x + y = 6\}$ indicated? How are the dots in the graph of $\{(x, y) | y = 2x\}$ indicated?

F Which dot is in the graph of both the solution set of $x + y = 6$ and the solution set of $y = 2x$? What ordered pair is associated with the point represented by this dot?

G Does (2, 4) satisfy both $x + y = 6$ and $y = 2x$? Is (2, 4) the only ordered pair that satisfies both $x + y = 6$ and $y = 2x$?

H Tabulate $\{(x, y) | x + y = 6 \wedge y = 2x\}$.

Now you will study the intersection of the solution sets of two simple conditions in two variables.

> REMINDER
> The intersection of two sets is the set that contains only those objects that belong to both sets.
> *See lesson 22, page 83.*

Universe for $(x, y) = N \times N$.
$x + y = 6 \wedge y = 2x$.

D1

Universe for $(x, y) = N \times N$.

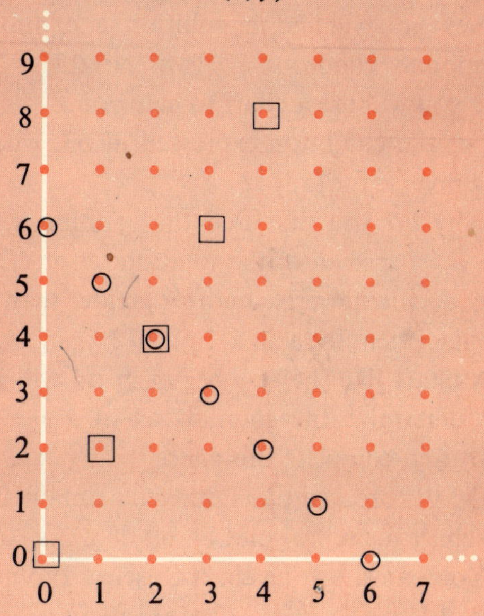

$\{(x, y) | x + y = 6 \wedge y = 2x\}$

D2

I Tabulate the intersection of the solution sets of $x+y=6$ and $y=2x$. Is this the same set as the set you tabulated for exercise H?

J Does the following sentence express a true ? statement? $\{(x, y) \mid x+y=6 \wedge y=2x\} = \{(x, y) \mid x+y=6\} \cap \{(x, y) \mid y=2x\}$.

Next you will find the solution set of another compound condition in two variables. This time you will use a chart to help you.

K For the condition expressed in D3, what is the universe for (x, y)?

L Why do you first find the solution set of $x+y<7$ instead of the solution set of $y>x$? Why do you not use a number greater than 6 as a replacement for x in $x+y<7$?

M A chart like the one begun in D4 will help you determine the solution set of $x+y<7$. Copy and complete this chart.

N Do the ordered pairs that you obtain from the chart form the solution set of $x+y<7$?

You can use your chart to select the members of $\{(x, y) \mid x+y<7\}$ that satisfy $y>x$.

O What does the condition $y>x$ require? Which members of $\{(x, y) \mid x+y<7\}$ satisfy $y>x$? Does each of these ordered pairs satisfy both $x+y<7$ and $y>x$?

P Tabulate $\{(x, y) \mid x+y<7 \wedge y>x\}$. Is this set a finite set?

Q Why is $\{(x, y) \mid x+y<7\} \cap \{(x, y) \mid y>x\}$? the same set as the set you tabulated for exercise P?

Sometimes one of the simple conditions in a compound condition has only one variable. Exercises A through M will help you find the solution set of such a compound condition.

A Look at D5. What is the universe for (x, y)?

B Which simple condition in $x+y<8 \wedge x+1=4$ contains only one variable? Why do you first find the solution set of $x+1=4$ instead of the solution set of $x+y<8$?

Universe for $(x, y) = N \times N$.
$x+y<7 \wedge y>x$.

D3

Universe for $(x, y) = N \times N$.
$x+y<7$.

x	0	1	2	3	4	5	6
y	0						
	1						
	2						
	3						
	4						
	5						
	6						

D4

Universe for $(x, y) = N \times N$.
$x+y<8 \wedge x+1=4$.

D5

Universe for $(x, y) = N \times N$.

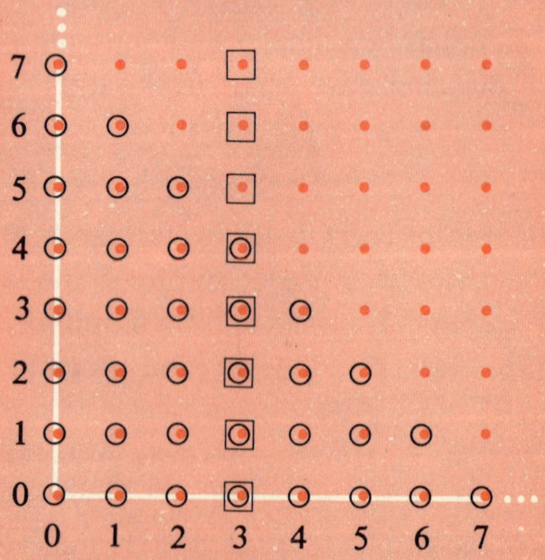

D6 $\{(x, y) \mid x+y<8 \wedge x+1=4\}$

C Is $x + 1 = 4$ satisfied by each ordered pair in $N \times N$ whose first component is 3? Is the solution set of $x + 1 = 4$ an infinite set? **?**

Next you must decide which ordered pairs that satisfy $x + 1 = 4$ also satisfy $x + y < 8$.

D Replace x in $x + y < 8$ by 3. Which members of N satisfy $3 + y < 8$?

E Which ordered pairs in $N \times N$ have a first component of 3 and a second component that satisfies $3 + y < 8$? Are these the only ordered pairs in $N \times N$ that satisfy the compound condition?

F Tabulate $\{(x, y) \mid x + y < 8 \wedge x + 1 = 4\}$. Is this the same set as $\{(x, y) \mid x + y < 8\} \cap \{(x, y) \mid x + 1 = 4\}$?

G The graphs of $\{(x, y) \mid x + y < 8\}$ and $\{(x, y) \mid x + 1 = 4\}$ are shown in D6. In which graph are the dots encircled? Is this graph incomplete? In which graph are the dots enclosed by squares? Is this graph incomplete?

H How is the graph of $\{(x, y) \mid x + y < 8 \wedge x + 1 = 4\}$ indicated? Is this graph incomplete?

I Look at D7. Which simple condition in $y + 2 > x \wedge y + 1 < 7$ has only one variable?

J Is $y + 1 < 7$ satisfied by each ordered pair in $N \times N$ whose second component is a number from 0 through 5? **?**

K You can use a chart like the one begun in D8 to help you decide which ordered pairs that satisfy $y + 1 < 7$ also satisfy $y + 2 > x$. Why does the chart first show the names of the replacements for y, instead of for x? Why do you use only the numbers from 0 through 5 as replacements for y? Copy and complete the chart.

L Does each ordered pair that you obtain from your chart satisfy $y + 2 > x \wedge y + 1 < 7$?

M Tabulate $\{(x, y) \mid y + 2 > x \wedge y + 1 < 7\}$.

Universe for $(x, y) = N \times N$.
$y + 2 > x \wedge y + 1 < 7$.

D7

Universe for $(x, y) = N \times N$.
$y + 2 > x$.

y	0	1	2	3	4	5
x						

D8

Universe for $(x, y) = N \times N$.
$x + y < 6 \wedge x + y = 7$.

D9

Universe for $(x, y) = N \times N$.
$x = y \wedge x + y > 1$.

D10

So far in this lesson the solution sets of the compound conditions have had one or more members, but they have not been infinite sets. The solution set of a compound condition may also be an infinite set or the empty set.

N Look at D9. What does the first simple condition, $x + y < 6$, require? What does the second simple condition, $x + y = 7$, require?

O Is it possible for the sum of two numbers to be both less than 6 and equal to 7?

P Tabulate $\{(x, y) \mid x + y < 6 \wedge x + y = 7\}$.

Q Look at D10. Does each ordered pair whose first component is the same as its second component satisfy $x = y$? Is $\{(x, y) \mid x = y\}$ an infinite set?

R Does (0, 0) satisfy $x+y>1$? Does (1, 1) satisfy $x+y>1$?

S Is $x=y \wedge x+y>1$ satisfied by each ordered pair whose components are the same and also greater than 0?

T Is $\{(x, y) | x=y \wedge x+y>1\}$ an infinite set?

Now you know how to use charts and graphs to help determine solution sets of compound conditions in two variables.

On your own

For each of exercises 1 through 4, make a graph of N × N and graphs of the solution sets of both simple conditions. Include only as many dots as you need to determine whether the solution set of the compound condition is a finite or an infinite set. If the solution set is infinite, label your graph "incomplete graph." If the solution set is a finite set, tabulate it. The universe for $(x, y) = N \times N$.

1 $x+y=5 \wedge y=x+1$.

2 $x>4 \wedge y>3$.

3 $x+y>3 \wedge x+3=y$.

4 $x+y<4 \wedge x+y>1$.

For each of the compound conditions expressed in exercises 5 through 17, tabulate the solution set. The universe for $(x, y) = N \times N$.

5 $x+y<5 \wedge 2x+y=7$.

6 $x+y=325 \wedge x+42=205$.

7 $125-x=y \wedge y-25=52$.

8 $2x-16=y \wedge x-1=7$.

9 $x-y=17 \wedge x-12=9$.

10 $2x+y<5 \wedge x+1<8$.

11 $y-x=751 \wedge y+15=801$.

12 $x=13+y \wedge y<7$.

13 $x-y<6 \wedge x+3=39$.

14 $x+y<8 \wedge y>2x$.

15 $x+y=16 \wedge 2x=y$.

16 $140-x=y \wedge x+3=21$.

17 $x-y=32 \wedge y+4<7$.

CHECKING UP

Use lessons 30 through 36 if you need to restudy the ideas expressed in these tests.

Test 34

Using sets A and B, tabulated below, tabulate each set named in exercises 1 through 6.

$A=\{2, 4, 7\}$. $B=\{3, 4\}$.

1 A × B **2** B × A **3** A × A **4** B × B

5 $\{(x, y) | 2y>x+3\}$. The universe for (x, y) is A × B.

6 $\{(x, y) | x<y\}$. The universe for (x, y) is B × A.

Test 35

7 The encircled dots in the display below form a graph of a set of ordered pairs. Tabulate this set.

8 The dots enclosed by squares also form a graph of a set of ordered pairs. Tabulate this set.

For exercises 9, 10, and 11, the universe for $(x, y) = N \times N$.

9 Make a chart to help you determine the members of the solution set of $7-x=y \wedge x<8$.

10 Tabulate $\{(x, y) | 7-x=y \wedge x<8\}$.

11 Make a graph of N × N. Encircle the dots in the graph of $\{(x, y) | 7-x=y \wedge x<8\}$.

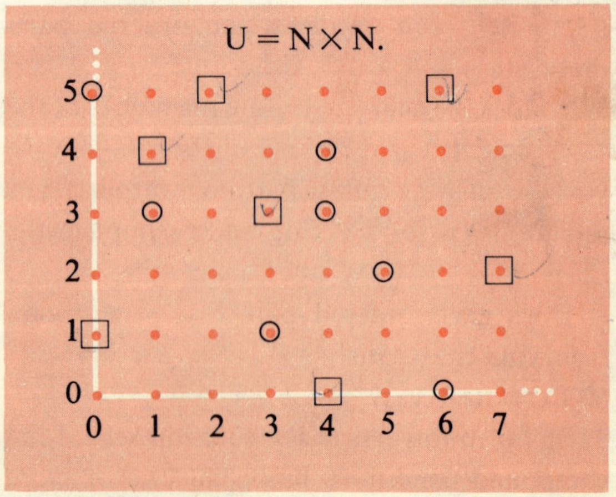

3 37 Exploring problems

Simple conditions for problems

You have learned how to find solution sets of conditions in two variables. In this lesson you will learn how to solve problems by using simple conditions in two variables.

Read the problem in D1. First you will develop the condition for the problem. $U = N \times N$.

A Do you know how many fish George caught? Use x as a variable for the number of fish George could have caught.

x

B Do you know how many fish Steve caught? Use y as a variable for the number of fish Steve could have caught.

y

C Why is $x + y$, and not $x - y$, used in the condition? What does $x + y$ refer to?

$x + y$

D Why is the idea of "less than" used in the condition? How many variables are there in the condition?

$x + y < 5.$

E Now you can find the solution set of the condition. What is the universe for (x, y)? Will the solution set be a set of ordered pairs?

F How do you know that George caught fewer than 5 fish? What numbers do you use as replacements for x in $x + y < 5$?

G Look at the chart in D2. The numbers named opposite the letter x are the numbers you use as replacements for x in $x + y < 5$. Why do you not use 5 as a replacement for x?

H Copy and complete the chart in D2.

George and Steve went fishing. Together, they caught fewer than 5 fish. How many fish could each of the boys have caught?

D1

Universe for $(x, y) = N \times N$.
$x + y < 5$.

x	0	1	2	3	4
y					

D2

I Tabulate $\{(x, y) \mid x + y < 5\}$.

J What does the first component of each member of the solution set refer to? What does the second component of each member refer to?

Since you know the ordered pairs that satisfy the condition for the problem in D1, you can now answer the question asked in the problem. You use the solutions of $x + y < 5$ to get the answers to the problem.

If George caught 0 fish, Steve could have caught from 0 through 4 fish.

If George caught 1 fish, Steve could have caught from 0 through 3 fish.

K What are the other answers to the problem in D1?

L You can verify the answer you obtain from (0, 0) by answering the following question: If George caught 0 fish and Steve caught 0 fish, could George and Steve together have caught fewer than 5 fish?

M Verify the answers you obtain from (1, 3), (2, 2), (3, 1), and (4, 0).

Read the problem in D3. You will first develop the condition for the problem. $U = C \times C$. Remember that $C = \{1, 2, 3, \ldots\}$. The ordered pairs that are members of $C \times C$ do not have 0 as a first or a second component.

A Is 8 the number of stamps that Judy bought? 8

B Do you know how many stamps Judy used? Use m as a variable for the number of stamps she could have used. m

C Why is $8 - m$, and not $8 + m$, used in the condition? $8 - m$

D Do you know how many stamps Judy had left? Use n as a variable for the number of stamps that she could have had left. n

E Why is the idea of equality used in the condition? $8 - m = n.$

F Now you can find the solution set of $8 - m = n$. What is the universe for (m, n)?

G What is the greatest number of postage stamps Judy could have used? What is the least number of postage stamps Judy could have used?

H Why do you not use 0 as a replacement for m in the condition? Why do you not use 8 as a replacement for m?

I What numbers do you use as replacements for m in $8 - m = n$?

J Copy and complete the chart in D4.

K Tabulate $\{(m, n) \mid 8 - m = n\}$.

L What does the first component of each member of the solution set refer to? What does the second component of each member refer to?

M What are the answers to the problem in D3? Remember to use each solution of $8 - m = n$ to get an answer.

Judy bought 8 postage stamps. She used some, but not all, of these stamps. How many stamps could she have used, and how many stamps could she have had left?

D3

Universe for $(m, n) = C \times C$.
$8 - m = n$.

m	1	2	3	4	5	6	7
n							

D4

Now you know how to solve problems by using simple conditions in two variables.

On your own

For each problem, first write a sentence that expresses the condition for the problem. Use whatever letters you wish as names for the variables. Tell what each variable refers to in the problem. Then make a chart to help you determine the ordered pairs that satisfy the condition. Finally, tabulate the solution set and answer the problem. The universe is given for each problem.

1 Dave and Ted built 5 model boats. How many boats could each of the boys have built? $U = N \times N$.

2 Ernie had 9 fishhooks. He gave some, but not all, of them to Tom. He kept the others for himself. How many fishhooks could he have given to Tom, and how many could he have kept for himself? $U = C \times C$.

3 Martha bought fewer than 6 lemons and limes. How many lemons and how many limes could she have bought? $U = C \times C$.

4 Mr. Phillips picked 4 bushels of apples. He sold some, but not all, of the 4 bushels. How many bushels of apples could he have sold, and how many could he have had left? $U = C \times C$.

5 Together, Louise and Connie made fewer than 7 posters. How many posters could each of the girls have made? $U = C \times C$.

6 Jane had 6 tickets to sell. She sold as many of them as she could and returned the others. How many tickets could she have sold, and how many tickets could she have returned? $U = N \times N$.

7 During the summer, Larry works at a grocery store on Fridays and Saturdays. He works a total of 8 hours during these two days. How many hours can he work on each of these days? $U = C \times C$.

8 Mrs. Ray took 7 pies to a bake sale. Some, but not all, of the pies were cherry, and the others were lemon. How many pies of each kind could she have taken to the bake sale? $U = C \times C$.

9 Harold had 10¢. He spent some, but not all, of this money. How much money could he have spent, and how much could he have had left? $U = C \times C$.

3 | 38 **Exploring problems**

Compound conditions for problems

You have solved problems by using simple conditions in two variables. In this lesson you will learn to solve problems by using compound conditions in two variables.

Read the problem in D1. The exercises that follow will help you develop the compound condition for the problem. $U = N \times N$.

Finding answers to problems involving compound conditions in which one simple condition has two variables and the other condition has one variable

Together, Helen and Sue have 22 phonograph records. If Helen had 3 more, she would have 12 records. How many records does each of the girls have?

D1

A Do you know how many records Helen has? Use r as a variable for the number of records Helen has.

B Do you know how many records Sue has? Use s as a variable for the number of records Sue has.

r

s

C Why is $r + s$, and not $r - s$, used in the condition? What does $r + s$ refer to?

$r + s$

D Why is the idea of equality used in the condition? Does the sentence at the right above express one of the simple conditions for the problem?

$r + s = 22.$

E Why is $r + 3$, and not $s + 3$, used in the other simple condition?

$r + 3$

F Why is the idea of equality used in the condition? Does the sentence at the right above express the other simple condition for the problem?

$r + 3 = 12.$

G Does the sentence below express the compound condition for the problem?

$$r + s = 22 \wedge r + 3 = 12.$$

Now you can find the solution set of the compound condition. Remember that each member of this set must satisfy each of the simple conditions.

H What is the universe for (r, s)?

I What replacement for r satisfies $r + 3 = 12$?

J Is 9 the first component of each solution of $r + s = 22 \wedge r + 3 = 12$? How do you know?

K Use 9 as a replacement for r in $r+s=22$. What number satisfies $9+s=22$?

L Tabulate $\{(r, s) | r+s=22 \wedge r+3=12\}$.

M To what does the first component of the solution of the compound condition refer? To what does the second component refer?

Since you know the solution of the compound condition for the problem, you can use this solution to get the answer to the problem.

Helen has 9 records, and Sue has 13 records.

N You can verify this answer by answering the following questions: If Helen has 9 records and Sue has 13 records, do Helen and Sue together have 22 records? If Helen had 3 records more than the 9 she has, would she have 12 records?

Read the problem in D2. First you will develop the compound condition for the problem. $U = C \times C$.

A Do you know Karen's age now? Use x as a variable for the number of years Karen's age is now. x

B Do you know Jean's age now? Use y as a variable for the number of years Jean's age is now. y

C Why is the idea of "greater than" used in the condition? Does the sentence at the right express one of the simple conditions for the problem? $x>y$.

D Why is $x-5$, and not $x+5$, used in the other simple condition? What does $x-5$ refer to? $x-5$

E Why is the idea of equality used in the condition? Does the sentence at the right below express the other simple condition for the problem? $x-5=9$.

F Does the sentence at the right express the compound condition for the problem? $x>y \wedge x-5=9$.

Karen is older than Jean. Five years ago Karen was 9 years old. How old is Karen now? How old can Jean be now?

D2

On Saturday, Tom and Ed painted fewer than 24 screens. Tom painted 7 screens in the morning and 6 screens in the afternoon. How many screens could Ed have painted on Saturday?

D3

G Now you can find the solution set of the compound condition. What is the universe for (x, y)?

H What replacement for x satisfies $x-5=9$?

I How do you know that 14 is the first component of each solution of $x>y \wedge x-5=9$?

J Use 14 as a replacement for x in $x>y$. The second components of the ordered pairs you are to find must satisfy $14>y$. What members of C satisfy $14>y$?

K Tabulate $\{(x, y) | x>y \wedge x-5=9\}$.

L To what does the first component of each solution of the compound condition refer? To what does the second component of each solution refer?

You can use the solutions of the compound condition to get the answers to the problem.

Karen is 14 years old, and Jean can be from 1 through 13 years old.

Read the problem in D3. You will develop the condition for this problem. $U = C \times C$.

A Use w as a variable for the number of screens that Tom painted. Use z as a variable for the number of screens that Ed could have painted. What is the universe for (w, z)?

B You know that Tom and Ed painted fewer than 24 screens on Saturday. Is $w + z < 24$ one of the simple conditions for the problem?

C You also know that Tom painted 7 screens in the morning and 6 screens in the afternoon. Is $w = 7 + 6$ also a simple condition for the problem?

D What is the compound condition for the problem in D3?

E What replacement for w satisfies $w = 7 + 6$?

F What is the first component of each member of $\{(w, z) | w + z < 24 \wedge w = 7 + 6\}$?

G Use 13 as a replacement for w in $w + z < 24$. The second components of the ordered pairs you are to find must satisfy $13 + z < 24$. What members of C satisfy $13 + z < 24$?

H Tabulate $\{(w, z) | w + z < 24 \wedge w = 7 + 6\}$.

I To what does the first component of each solution of the compound condition refer? To what does the second component of each solution refer?

J Read the problem in D3 again. Notice that you are asked to find only the number of screens that Ed could have painted. Which components of the solutions of the compound condition do you use to get the answers to the problem?

Now you can answer the question asked in the problem.

Ed could have painted from 1 through 10 screens on Saturday.

Now you know how to solve problems by using compound conditions in two variables.

On your own

For each problem, first write a sentence that expresses the compound condition for the problem. Use whatever letters you wish as names for the variables. Tell what each variable refers to. Then tabulate the solution set of the compound condition and use the solutions to get the answers to the problem. The universe is given for each problem.

1 Mrs. King paid $455 for a new stove and freezer. If she had paid $49 less for the stove, she would have paid $139 for it. How many dollars did she pay for each of the appliances? $U = N \times N$.

2 Together, Larry and Tom have fewer than 15 fossils. Tom has more than 10. How many fossils can each of the boys have? $U = C \times C$.

3 Jane is older than Helen. In 9 years, Jane will be 21 years old. How old is Jane now? How old can Helen be now? $U = C \times C$.

4 During a football game, Jay scored more points than Don. Jay scored 6 points during the first half of the game and 7 points during the second half. How many points could Don have scored during the game? $U = N \times N$.

5 Betty spent 11 days in Alberta and Saskatchewan. She spent more than 6 days in Alberta. How many days could she have spent in each of these provinces? $U = C \times C$

6 Mrs. Ross made 6 more aprons than potholders. After she gave 8 of the aprons away, she had 5 aprons left. How many aprons and how many potholders did she make? $U = N \times N$.

7 Fewer than 8 students received a grade of A on an English examination. More than 3 boys received a grade of A. How many boys and how many girls could have received a grade of A on this examination? $U = N \times N$.

8 Together, Sandy and Ruth made 48 sandwiches. Ruth made 9 peanut butter sandwiches and 13 cheese sandwiches. Sandy made the other sandwiches. How many did Sandy make? $U = N \times N$.

9 In two days Beth read a 150-page book. The second day she read fewer than 7 pages. How many pages could she have read on each of the two days? $U = C \times C$.

10 Lake Michigan is 307 miles long. Lake Michigan is 101 miles longer than Lake Huron. Lake Huron is 144 miles shorter than Lake Superior. What is the length of Lake Huron? Of Lake Superior? $U = N \times N$.

11 One year American tourists spent a total of $2,640,000,000 in the foreign countries that they visited. They spent $380,000,000 in Canada and $365,000,000 in Mexico. How many dollars were spent by American tourists in countries other than Canada and Mexico? $U = N \times N$.

KEEPING SKILFUL

Make one sketch for exercises 1 through 8.

1 Make a sketch of $\overleftrightarrow{RS}$.

2 Make a sketch of $\overleftrightarrow{MN}$ that intersects $\overleftrightarrow{RS}$ in point Q.

3 Name the sides and vertex of each angle formed by $\overleftrightarrow{MN}$ and $\overleftrightarrow{RS}$.

4 Name the common vertex of $\angle RQN$ and $\angle RQM$. Name the common side of these two angles.

5 Describe the union of $\overrightarrow{QM}$ and $\overrightarrow{QN}$.

6 Name four linear pairs of angles.

7 What is a supplement of $\angle RQN$? What is a supplement of $\angle RQM$?

8 Describe the union of $\overrightarrow{QR}$ and $\overrightarrow{QS}$.

Make one sketch for exercises 9 through 14.

9 Make a sketch of a triangle determined by noncollinear points B, C, and D.

10 $\triangle CBD$ is the union of what segments?

11 Locate point K in the interior of $\angle BCD$ and in the exterior of $\triangle CBD$.

12 Locate point F in the interior of $\angle CDB$ and in the interior of $\angle CBD$.

13 Locate point G in the interior of $\angle CDB$ and between C and B.

14 Locate point W in the interior of $\angle CBD$ and the exterior of $\angle BCD$.

3 | 39 Exploring problems

Compound conditions for more complex problems

In this lesson you will learn to solve problems that are different from those you have had so far. You will use compound conditions in which each simple condition has two variables.

Read the problem in D1. The exercises that follow will help you develop the compound condition for the problem. $U = N \times N$.

A Do you know how many trees Earl planted? Use x as a variable for the number of trees Earl planted.

B Do you know how many trees Earl's father planted? Use y as a variable for the number of trees Earl's father planted. x y

C Why is $x + y$, and not $x - y$, used in the condition? What does $x + y$ refer to? $x + y$

D Why is the idea of equality used in the condition? Does the sentence at the right above express one of the simple conditions for the problem? $x + y = 7.$

E Why is $x + 3$, and not $y + 3$, used in the other simple condition for the problem? $x + 3$

F Does the sentence at the right above express the other simple condition for the problem? What does y refer to? $x + 3 = y.$

G Does the sentence at the right express the compound condition for the problem? $x + y = 7 \wedge x + 3 = y.$

Earl and his father planted 7 trees in all. If Earl had planted 3 more trees, he would have planted the same number as his father. How many trees did each of them plant?

D1

Universe for $(x, y) = N \times N$.
$x + y = 7$.

x	0	1	2	3	4	5	6	7
y								

D2

There are fewer than 9 students in the cast of the spring play. The number of boys in the cast is greater than the number of girls. How many boys and how many girls can be in the cast?

D3

Now you can find the solution set of the compound condition.

H What is the universe for (x, y)?

I Look at D2. You can use a chart like this to help determine the ordered pairs that are solutions of $x + y = 7$. Why are the numbers from 0 through 7 the only numbers that are used as replacements for x in $x + y = 7$?

J Copy and complete the chart in D2.

K Tabulate $\{(x, y) | x + y = 7\}$.

Now you can find the solutions of $x + y = 7$ that are also solutions of $x + 3 = y$.

L Which member of the set you tabulated in exercise K has a second component that is 3 more than the first component?

M Tabulate $\{(x, y) | x + y = 7 \wedge x + 3 = y\}$.

N To what does the first component of the solution of the compound condition refer? To what does the second component refer?

Since you know the solution of the compound condition for the problem, you can use this solution to answer the question asked in the problem.

Earl planted 2 trees, and his father planted 5 trees.

O You can verify the answer you get from (2, 5) by answering the following questions: If Earl planted 2 trees and his father planted 5 trees, did they plant 7 trees in all? If Earl had planted 3 more trees, would he have planted the same number as his father?

Read the problem in D3. First you will develop the compound condition for the problem. $U = N \times N$.

A Do you know how many boys are members of the cast? Use m as a variable for the number of boys who are in the cast. m

B Do you know how many girls are members of the cast? n
Use n as a variable for the number of girls who are in the cast.

C Why is $m + n$, and not $m - n$, used in the condition? $m + n$

D Why is the idea of "less than" used in the condition? Does the sentence at the right express one of the simple conditions for the problem? $m + n < 9.$

E Why is $m > n$, and not $n > m$, the other simple condition for the problem? $m > n.$

F Does the sentence at the right express the compound condition for the problem? $m + n < 9 \wedge m > n.$

Now you can find the solution set of the compound condition.

G What is the universe for (m, n)?

H Look at D4. You can use a chart like this to help determine the ordered pairs that are solutions of $m+n<9$. Why are the numbers from 0 through 8 the only numbers that are used as replacements for m in $m+n<9$?

I Use the number 0 as a replacement for m in $m+n<9$. What replacements for n satisfy $0+n<9$?

J Copy and complete the chart in D4.

With the help of your chart, you can find the solutions of $m+n<9$ that are also solutions of $m>n$.

K Which of the ordered pairs expressed in your chart have first components that are greater than their second components?

L Tabulate $\{(m, n) | m+n<9 \wedge m>n\}$.

M To what does the first component of each solution of the compound condition refer? To what does the second component refer?

You can use the solutions of the compound condition to get the answers to the problem.

If the number of boys in the cast is 1, the number of girls in the cast is 0.

If there are 2 boys in the cast, there is either 0 or 1 girl in the cast.

If there are 3 boys in the cast, there are 0, 1, or 2 girls in the cast.

N What are the other answers to the problem?

Universe for $(m, n) = N \times N$.
$m+n<9$.

m	0	1	2	3	4	5	6	7	8
n									

D4

During the school baseball season, Bob and Jack together hit fewer than 8 home runs. If Bob had hit 5 fewer home runs, he would have hit the same number of home runs as Jack. How many home runs could each of the boys have hit?

D5

Read the problem in D5. You will develop the compound condition for this problem. $U = N \times N$.

A Do you know how many home runs Bob hit? Use a as a variable for the number of home runs that Bob hit. a

B Do you know how many home runs Jack hit? Use b as a variable for the number of home runs that Jack hit. b

C Does the sentence below at the right express one of the simple conditions for the problem? Why is $a+b$, and not $a-b$, used in the condition? Why is the idea of "less than" used in the condition? $a+b<8$.

D Why is $a-5$, and not $b-5$, used in the other simple condition for the problem? $a-5$

E Does the sentence at the right below express the other simple condition for the problem? What does b refer to? $a-5=b$.

F Does the sentence at the right express the compound condition for the problem? $a+b<8 \wedge a-5=b$.

Now you can find the solution set of the compound condition.

G What is the universe for (a, b)?

Universe for $(a, b) = N \times N$.
$a + b < 8$.

a	0	1	2	3	4	5	6	7
b								

D6

H You can use a chart like the one in D6 to help determine the ordered pairs that are members of the solution set of $a + b < 8$. Why are the numbers from 0 through 7 the only numbers that are used as replacements for a in $a + b < 8$?

I Use the number 0 as a replacement for a in $a + b < 8$. What replacements for b satisfy $0 + b < 8$?

J Copy and complete the chart in D6.

K How do you know that each ordered pair **?** that satisfies the compound condition must have a first component that is equal to, or greater than, 5?

L Tabulate $\{(a, b) \mid a + b < 8 \wedge a - 5 = b\}$.

M To what does the first component of each solution of the compound condition refer? To what does the second component refer?

N Give the answers to the problem in D5.

Now you know how to solve problems that involve compound conditions in two variables.

On your own

For each problem, write a sentence that expresses the compound condition for the problem. To express the variables, use any letters you wish. Tell what each variable refers to in the problem. Then tabulate the solution set of the compound condition and use the solutions to get the answers to the problem. The universe is given for each problem.

1 Lucy answered all 8 questions on a test. She had more correct than incorrect answers. How many correct and how many incorrect answers could she have had? $U = N \times N$.

2 Sarah spent less than 5¢ for an eraser and a pencil. She spent less for the pencil than for the eraser. How many cents could she have spent for each item? $U = C \times C$.

3 Nova Scotia has 4 more senators in the Canadian Senate than Newfoundland has. Together, these two provinces have 16 senators. How many senators does each of these provinces have? $U = N \times N$.

4 Mr. Hayes bought fewer than 15 postage stamps. He bought the same number of 4-cent stamps as 5-cent stamps. How many stamps of each kind could he have bought? $U = C \times C$.

5 In an election for class treasurer, Dale received 11 more votes than Harvey. Together, the boys received 21 votes. How many votes did each of the boys receive? $U = N \times N$.

6 Jane and Alice sold fewer than 9 boxes of candy in all. If Alice had sold 4 fewer boxes, she would have sold the same number as Jane. How many boxes of candy could each of the girls have sold? $U = N \times N$.

7 Babe Ruth hit 9 more home runs during the 1918 baseball season than during the 1917 season. He hit only 13 home runs during these two seasons. How many home runs did he hit during each of the two seasons? $U = N \times N$.

8 Henry and Jim each sold the same number of newspapers. Together, they sold fewer than 21 papers. How many papers could each of the boys have sold? $U = C \times C$.

9 During a professional football game, the Ottawa Rough Riders and the Edmonton Eskimos scored a total of 22 points. The Rough Riders scored 10 more points than the Eskimos. How many points did each of the teams score? $U = N \times N$.

SPECIAL CHALLENGE

Think about {a, b, c}. The subsets of this set are { }, {a}, {b}, {c}, {a, b}, {a, c}, {b, c}, and {a, b, c}. Notice that the empty set and the set itself are both subsets of {a, b, c}. In later lessons you will learn why the empty set is a subset of every set.

A How many subsets does a set with three members have?

B Tabulate all the subsets of {a, b}. Remember to include the empty set and the set itself. How many subsets does a set with two members have?

C Tabulate all the subsets of {a, b, c, d}. How many subsets does a set with four members have?

D Tabulate all the subsets of {a, b, c, d, e}. How many subsets does a set with five members have?

E How many subsets do you think each of the following sets will have? A set with six members. A set with seven members. A set with ten members.

For exercises F and G, use what you know about the intersection of sets to help you.

F Nine Canadian football teams compete for the Grey Cup. Three sports writers picked the following teams to win pre-season games on July 28.

{Edmonton, Regina, Ottawa, Hamilton}
{Winnipeg, Ottawa, Montreal, Edmonton}
{Hamilton, Edmonton, Vancouver, Montreal}

No writer picked Toronto to win. Calgary did not play on July 28. Determine the league teams that played each other on that day.

G There are six points and four lines. Each point is contained in two and only two lines. Each pair of lines has one and only one member in common. Make a sketch to represent these six points and four lines.

3 | 40 **Exploring problems**

Conditions for abstract problems

In lessons 37, 38, and 39, you used ordered pairs to obtain answers to problems about persons and things. In this lesson, you will learn that when problems concern numbers only, you can use ordered pairs as answers to the problems. $U = N \times N$.

A Read the problem in D1. Use x as a variable for the first number. Use y as a variable for the second number. Is $x + y = 7$ the condition for the problem?

B Tabulate $\{(x, y) \mid x + y = 7\}$. Each solution of the condition is an answer to the problem.

C Is the sum of 0 and 7 the number 7? Is (0, 7) an answer to the problem? What are the other answers?

D Read the problem in D2. Use x as a variable for the first number. Use y as a variable for the second number. Is $x + y = 8$ one of the simple conditions for the problem? Is $y < 2x$ the other simple condition?

E Does the sentence in D3 express the compound condition for the problem in D2?

F Tabulate $\{(x, y) \mid x + y = 8\}$.

G What does the condition $y < 2x$ require? Which members of the set that you tabulated for exercise F satisfy $y < 2x$?

H Tabulate $\{(x, y) \mid x + y = 8 \wedge y < 2x\}$.

I Is each solution of $x + y = 8 \wedge y < 2x$ an answer to the problem in D2?

J Read the problem in D4. Use x as a variable for the first number. Use y as a variable for the second number.

The sum of two numbers is 7. What can the numbers be?

D1

The sum of two numbers is 8. The second number is less than the product of 2 and the first number. What can the numbers be?

D2

$$x + y = 8 \wedge y < 2x.$$

D3

A first number is less than a second number. When 3 is subtracted from the first number, the difference is 5. What can the numbers be?

D4

$$x < y \wedge x - 3 = 5.$$

D5

The sum of two numbers is 10. The first number is equal to the product of 3 and the second number. What are the numbers?

D6

$$m + n = 10 \wedge m = 3n.$$

D7

K Does the sentence in D5 express the compound condition for the problem?

L What replacement for x satisfies the simple condition $x - 3 = 5$?

M How do you know that 8 is the first component of each solution of $x < y \wedge x - 3 = 5$?

N What does the condition $x < y$ require?

O Are (8, 9) and (8, 123) solutions of $x < y \wedge x - 3 = 5$? How do you know that the solution set of $x < y \wedge x - 3 = 5$ is an infinite set?

P Is each ordered pair named in exercise O an answer to the problem in D4? Give three other answers to the problem.

Q Give the standard description of the solution set of the condition for the problem.

R Read the problem in D6. Use m as a variable for the first number. Use n as a variable for the second number.

S Does the sentence in D7 express the compound condition for the problem?

T Tabulate $\{(m, n) \mid m + n = 10\}$.

U Do any of the ordered pairs that you named in exercise T have a first component that is equal to the product of 3 and the second component? Are there any ordered pairs in $N \times N$ that satisfy $m + n = 10 \wedge m = 3n$?

V Tabulate $\{(m, n) \mid m + n = 10 \wedge m = 3n\}$.

W Are there any members of the universe that are answers to the problem in D6?

Now you know how to solve problems that are about numbers only.

On your own

For each problem, first write a sentence that expresses the condition for the problem. If the solution set of the condition is finite, tabulate the solution set. If the solution set is infinite, write a standard description of the solution set. Use a as a variable for the first number. Use b as a variable for the second number. The universe for $(a, b) = N \times N$.

1 The sum of two numbers is 15. What can the numbers be?

2 The sum of two numbers is less than 20. The first number is equal to the second number. What can the numbers be?

3 The sum of two numbers is 78. Fifteen less than the first number is 26. What are the numbers?

4 The sum of two numbers is 10. The first number is greater than the second number. What can the numbers be?

5 When a first number is subtracted from a second number, the difference is 43. Fifty-eight more than the first number is 321. What are the numbers?

6 A first number is 5 more than a second number. The first number is also 2 less than 8. What are the numbers?

7 When 7 is subtracted from a first number, the difference is 4. The first number is equal to the product of 3 and the second number. What are the numbers?

8 When a number less than 4 is added to a second number, each sum is less than 5. What can the numbers be?

9 When a number greater than the product of 9 and 4 is added to a second number, each sum is greater than 40. What can the numbers be?

10 When a second number is subtracted from a first number, the difference is 9. The sum of the two numbers is 21. What are the numbers?

11 A first number is less than a second number. The second number is 8 less than 13. What can the numbers be?

12 A first number is equal to the quotient of 645 and 129. When a second number is subtracted from the first number, each difference is greater than 6. What can the numbers be?

13 The sum of two numbers is 21. The second number is equal to the product of 2 and the first number. What are the numbers?

APPLYING MATHEMATICS

In this lesson you will solve problems similar to the ones you have studied so far in this book. For each of problems 1 through 20, first write a sentence that expresses the condition for the problem. Use any letters you wish as names for the variables. Tell what each variable refers to in the problem. Then tabulate the solution set of the condition and give the answer to the problem. The universe is given for each problem.

1 A car dealer had more than 17 new cars to sell. He sold 8 of these cars and then had fewer than 12 new cars left to sell. How many new cars could he have had to begin with? U = N.

2 Nine students belong to the science club at Woodworth School. How many boys and how many girls can be members of this club? U = C × C.

3 After Mr. Foster wrote a check for $186, he had $418 left in his checking account. How many dollars did Mr. Foster have in his checking account before he wrote the check for $186? U = N.

4 Carol is 5 years younger than Ann. In 14 years, Carol will be 21 years old. How old is each of the girls now? U = N × N.

5 Altogether, Mary bought fewer than 5 yards of silk cloth and cotton cloth. How many yards of each kind of cloth could she have bought? U = C × C.

6 One day, Bill and his father together plowed fewer than 28 acres of land. Bill plowed 6 acres in the morning and 5 acres in the afternoon. How many acres could Bill's father have plowed that day? U = C × C.

7 Rachel collects foreign dolls. She has more than 12 of them now. If she had 5 fewer dolls, she would have fewer than 11 in all. How many dolls can Rachel have now? U = N.

8 There are as many boys as girls on the staff of the school paper. There are fewer than 23 students on the staff. How many girls and how many boys can be on the staff? U = C × C.

9 One Saturday, Mr. Baker sold 7 men's suits and overcoats. He sold fewer overcoats than suits. How many of each could he have sold? U = C × C.

10 Together, Andy and Peter sold 22 magazines. Andy sold 8 more magazines than Peter. How many magazines did each of the boys sell? U = N × N.

11 Jim had 427 stamps in his collection. After he sold some of them, he still had more than 369 stamps. How many stamps could he have sold? U = C.

12 Nine years from now, Beverly will be more than 22 years old. Six years ago, she was less than 10 years old. How old can Beverly be now? U = N.

13 Sound travels at different speeds in different materials. In air, the speed of sound is about 1088 feet per second; in hard wood, it is about 12,620 feet per second. Sound travels about how many feet per second faster in hard wood than in air? U = N.

14 Susan had 91¢. She spent 12¢ for a comb and 25¢ for some ribbon. How many cents did she have left after she bought the comb and ribbon? U = N × N.

15 If Judy had 15 more phonograph records, she would have more than 37 records. If she had 12 fewer records, she would have fewer than 15 records. How many phonograph records can Judy have now? U = N.

16 According to a recent survey, two of the largest cities in the world were Tokyo and London. The population of Tokyo was 9,311,774, and the population of London was 8,222,340. What was the total population of these two cities at the time of the survey? U = N.

17 Elizabeth has finished more experiments for science class than Nancy has. When Elizabeth finishes 8 more, she will have finished 21 experiments. How many experiments has Elizabeth finished? How many can Nancy have finished? U = N × N.

18 There were 71,719 persons who entered Canada as immigrants in 1946. In 1956, there were 93,138 more people who entered Canada as immigrants than in 1946. How many people entered Canada as immigrants in 1956? U = N.

19 After John bought 13 new stamps, he still had fewer than 145 stamps. If he had bought 35 new stamps, he would have had more than 161 stamps. How many stamps could John have had to begin with? U = N.

20 The area of Waterton Lakes National Park is 203 sq. mi. Kootenay National Park is 340 sq. mi. larger than Waterton Lakes park and 468 sq. mi. larger than Elk Island National Park. What are the areas of Kootenay and Elk Island parks? U = N × N.

For each of problems 21 through 25, first write a sentence that expresses the condition for the problem. Then tabulate the solution set of the condition.

21 The sum of two numbers is 9. What can the numbers be? U = N × N.

22 What numbers are greater than the product of 466 and 238? U = N.

23 What numbers greater than 78 can be added to 75 so that each sum is less than 160? U = N.

24 The sum of two numbers is less than 17. The first number is equal to the product of 2 and the second number. What can the numbers be? U = N × N.

25 When the first of two numbers is subtracted from the second, the difference is 5. The first number is less than 16. What can the numbers be? U = N × N.

CHECKING UP

The small numeral within parentheses tells what page to turn to for help if you need it.

Test 36

For exercises 1 through 6, write "T" for each sentence that expresses a true statement. Write "F" for each sentence that expresses a false statement.

1 (2, 5) and (5, 2) are the same ordered pair. (123)

2 If the universe for (x, y) is $N \times N$, then the solution set of $x + 2 = 7$ is a set of ordered pairs. (134)

3 If $A = \{1, 3, 9\}$, and $B = \{9, 1, 3\}$, then $A \times B = B \times A$. (129)

4 If C has 3 members, and D has 4 members, then $C \times D$ has 7 members. (127)

5 Each member of $\{(x, y) \mid x = 2y \wedge x + y = 42\}$ satisfies $x = 2y$. (147)

6 If the universe for (x, y) is $N \times N$, then the solution set of $x < 5$ is a finite set. (138)

7 $A = \{0, 1, 2\}$. Tabulate $A \times A$. (129)

8 $B = \{2, 4\}$, and $C = \{1, 3, 5, 7\}$. Tabulate $C \times B$. (126)

The graph in D1 is a complete graph of $X \times Y$. Use the graph for exercises 9 through 14.

9 Tabulate set X. (130)

10 Tabulate set Y. (130)

11 Point A is associated with what ordered pair? (131)

12 Which letter names the point associated with (4, 1)? (131)

13 Which letter names the point associated with (2, 3)? (131)

14 The encircled dots form the graph of the solution set of a condition that has x and y as variables. The universe for (x, y) is $X \times Y$. Tabulate the solution set of this condition. (132)

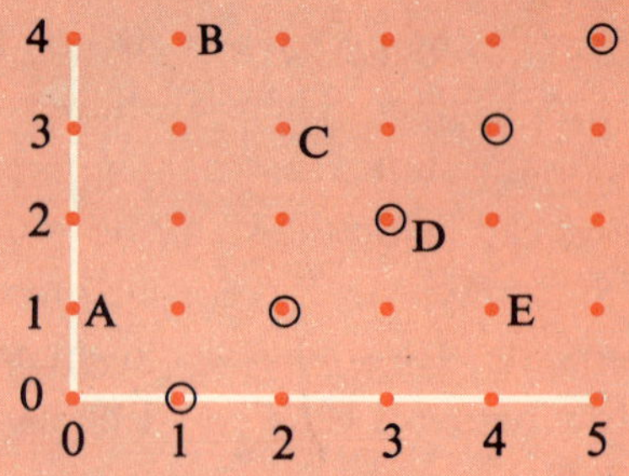

D1

Universe for $(x, y) = N \times N$.

$x + y < 6$.

x	0	1	2	3	4	5
y						

D2

Test 37

For each of exercises 15 through 18, the universe for (a, b) is $R \times S$. $R = \{0, 1, 2, 3\}$. $S = \{0, 1, 2\}$.

15 Write a standard description of the solution set of $b = a + 1$. (138)

16 Tabulate the solution set of $b = a + 1$. (132)

17 Make a graph of $R \times S$. (130)

18 In your graph, encircle each dot that represents a point associated with a solution of $b = a + 1$. (132)

19 Copy and complete the chart in D2. Then tabulate the solution set of the condition expressed in D2. The universe for (x, y) is $N \times N$. (148)

For each of the compound conditions expressed in exercises 20 through 24, tabulate the solution set. The universe for (x, y) is $N \times N$.

20 $x < 5 \wedge y = x + 5$. (147)

21 $x + y = 9 \wedge y = 2x$. (147)

22 $2y + 3 > 3x \wedge y + 5 < 9$. (147)

23 $y + x = 5 \wedge x + y > 8$. (147)

24 $4x + 2 = y \wedge 8 + x < 15$. (147)

Test 38

For each problem, write a sentence that expresses the condition for the problem. Use any letters you wish as names for the variables. Tabulate the solution set of the condition and then give the answer to the problem. The universe is given for each problem.

25 Mary and Donna together ate 4 sandwiches for lunch. How many sandwiches could each of the girls have eaten? $U = C \times C$. (151)

26 Together, Barbara and Kathy took 18 cupcakes to a bake sale. Barbara took 4 more cupcakes than Kathy. How many cupcakes did each of the girls take to the bake sale? $U = N \times N$. (156)

27 Eight inches of snow fell during January and February. Less than 5 inches of snow fell during February. How many inches of snow could have fallen during each of these months? $U = C \times C$. (153)

28 During a softball game, Henry had more hits than Steve. Together, the two boys had 6 hits. How many hits could each of the boys have had? $U = N \times N$. (156)

29 A farmer has 32 more steers than hogs. If he had 47 more steers, he would have 172. How many steers and how many hogs does the farmer have? $U = N \times N$. (153)

30 The sum of two numbers is less than 12. The second number is twice the first number. What can the numbers be? $U = N \times N$. (160)

31 When the first of two numbers is subtracted from the second number, the difference is 7. Two more than the first number is 11. What are the numbers? $U = N \times N$. (160)

32 The sum of two numbers is less than 5. What can the numbers be? $U = N \times N$. (160)

33 When the first of two numbers is subtracted from the second number, the difference is 9. The first number is less than 7. What can the numbers be? $U = N \times N$. (160)

CHECKING UP

The small numeral within parentheses tells what page to turn to for help if you have trouble with an exercise.

Test 39

For exercises 1 through 7, write "T" for each exercise in which a true statement is expressed. Write "F" for each exercise in which a false statement is expressed.

1 If $\overline{LM} \cong \overline{NM}$ and $\overline{KJ} > \overline{LM}$, then $\overline{NM} > \overline{KJ}$. (43)

2 The sentence $17 + r \neq 32$ expresses a condition for inequality. (21)

3 The set whose members are all the natural numbers greater than 20 is a finite set. (23)

4 If $U = N$, then a true statement is obtained for each replacement of x in $x + 1 < 2x$. (24)

5 If $U = N$, then $5 + 7 = 12$ can be obtained from $x + x = 12$. (21)

6 $\angle RST$ includes ray ST and ray RS. (105)

7 $\{X \mid \overline{CX} \cong \overline{CD}\}$ is a standard description of a circle with center C and radius CD. (47)

What words or symbols best complete exercises 8 through 13?

8 The solution set of $x > 4 \wedge x < 8$ is the ____ of the solution sets of $x > 4$ and $x < 8$. (92)

9 If ℓ_1 is parallel to ℓ_2, then $\ell_1 \cap \ell_2$ is ____. (101)

10 If points B and C are contained in plane BCD, then ____ is the intersection of $\overleftrightarrow{BC}$ and plane BCD. (101)

11 Point B is in the interior of $\triangle GHI$. Point C is in the exterior of $\triangle GHI$. There is exactly one member in $\overline{BC}$ ____ $\triangle GHI$. (114)

12 Point K is between points J and L. $\overline{JK} \cup \overline{KL} =$ ____. (87)

13 If plane RST and plane QRS are not the same plane, then plane RST $\cap$ plane QRS = ____. (100)

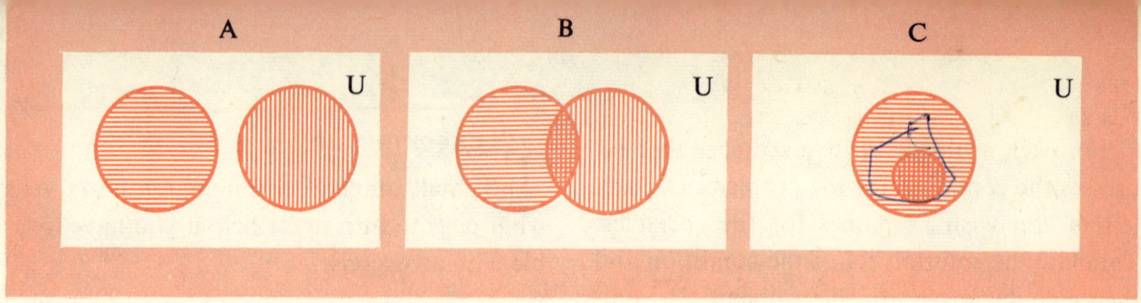

Test 40

Six sets are described below. Use these descriptions to decide which of Venn diagrams A, B, or C in the display above represents the set named in each of exercises 14 through 22. The universe is the set of all plane geometric figures. (84, 89)

Set D is the set of all simple closed curves.
Set E is the set of all simple polygons.
Set F is the set of all right triangles.
Set G is the set of all isosceles triangles.
Set H is the set of all equilateral triangles.
Set I is the set of all circles.

14 $D \cap E$ **17** $H \cap F$ **20** $E \cup I$
15 $I \cap F$ **18** $E \cup H$ **21** $I \cap D$
16 $G \cap E$ **19** $G \cap F$ **22** $G \cup H$

Test 41

For each of the conditions expressed in exercises 23 through 26, make a graph of the universe. Then encircle each dot that represents a point associated with a member of the solution set. $U = \{0, 1, 2, 3, 4, 5, 6, 7, 8, 9, 10\}$.

23 $5 + x = 9$. (52) **25** $b + 2 < 6$. (52)
24 $10 - w \neq 3$. (52) **26** $12 - x > 5$. (52)

For each compound condition tabulate the solution set. The universe for $(x, y) = N \times N$.

27 $x + 5 = 55 \wedge x - y = 42$. (147)
28 $x + y = 10 \wedge x + y < 10$. (147)
29 $x + y < 7 \wedge y < 2x$. (147)
30 $y < 3 + x \wedge x < 4$. (147)

Test 42

For each problem, write a sentence that expresses the condition, tabulate its solution set, and give the answer to the problem.

31 A committee in Highcrest School wrote a new school constitution that contained 2670 words. This was 875 more words than the old constitution contained. How many words did the old constitution contain? $U = N$. (68)

32 There are 5 children in the Hughes' family. How many boys and how many girls can be in this family? $U = N \times N$. (151)

33 The Pep Club had fewer than 32 pennants. After the club bought 18 pennants, it had more than 40. How many pennants could the club have had to begin with? $U = N$. (94)

34 Bill scored 21 points in a table tennis game. Fewer than 38 points were scored in the game. How many points could Bill's opponent have scored? $U = N$. (73)

35 Chuck and Will caddied 15 times in all at The Pines Golf Club. Will caddied more than 9 times. How many times could each of the boys have caddied at The Pines? $U = C \times C$. (153)

36 Fewer than 20 students are in Mrs. Turner's class. There are 8 more boys than girls in this class. How many boys and how many girls could be in this class? $U = C \times C$. (156)

Test 43

Multiply	Divide
37 64 by 19. (55)	**44** 216 by 24. (58)
38 507 by 98. (55)	**45** 962 by 13. (58)
39 813 by 45. (55)	**46** 1935 by 45. (58)
40 729 by 560. (55)	**47** 2584 by 76. (58)
41 609 by 304. (55)	**48** 57152 by 19. (58)
42 521 by 128. (55)	**49** 71120 by 508. (59)
43 937 by 467. (55)	**50** 89975 by 295. (59)

Unit 4

Conditions involving rate pairs

4 41 **Exploring ideas**

Equivalent ordered pairs

In this unit you are going to use conditions to solve rate problems. First you must learn about ordered pairs that are related to each other in a special way.

If 3 pencils are sold for 12 cents, you can say that these pencils are sold at the rate of 3 pencils for 12 cents, or 3 pencils per 12 cents.

A You can represent this rate by using an ordered pair of numbers. Think of (3, 12) as representing the rate at which the pencils are sold.

3 pencils
per 12 cents
(3, 12)

Which component of (3, 12) refers to the number of pencils?

B Which component refers to the number of cents needed to buy the pencils? The black markers at the left represent the pencils. The red markers represent the cents.

C There are other ordered pairs that represent the rate at which these pencils are sold. The markers that represent the 3 pencils and the 12 cents have been separated into 3 equal groups.

1 pencil
per 4 cents
(1, 4)

Will the 4 cents in each group buy the 1 pencil in that group?

D Can you say that the pencils are sold at the rate of 1 pencil per 4 cents?

E Does (1, 4) also represent the rate at which the pencils are sold?

2 pencils
per 8 cents
(2, 8)

F Think of two of the groups just described. Does (2, 8) also represent the rate at which the pencils are sold?

G Suppose that you buy more than 3 pencils at the same rate. Can you buy 6 pencils for 24 cents?

H Can you represent the rate by using (6, 24)?

I Name five more ordered pairs that represent the rate at which the pencils are sold. Use the markers to help you.

J Set A, tabulated in D1, is a set of some of ? the ordered pairs that represent the rate at which the pencils are sold. Does set A contain all the ordered pairs that represent the rate at which the pencils are sold? Explain your answer.

Each member of set A represents the same rate. The exercises that follow will help you understand how a set like A differs from the other sets of ordered pairs that you have studied.

K Look at D2. First we will select any two members of A. Suppose that we select (1, 4) and (2, 8). D2 shows that you are to find the product of the first component of (1, 4) and the second component of (2, 8). What is this product? You also are to find the product of the first component of (2, 8) and the second component of (1, 4). What is this product?

L Is the product of 1 and 8 the same number as the product of 2 and 4? Is $1 \times 8 = 2 \times 4$ a true statement?

M Next we will select two other members of A. Suppose that we select (3, 12) and (4, 16). Look at D3. Is 3×16 the product of the first component of (3, 12) and the second component of (4, 16)? 4×12 is the product of which components of (3, 12) and (4, 16)?

$$A = \{(1, 4), (2, 8), (3, 12), (4, 16)\}.$$

D1

1×8

(1, 4) (2, 8)

2×4

$$1 \times 8 = 2 \times 4.$$

D2

3×16

(3, 12) (4, 16)

4×12

$$3 \times 16 = 4 \times 12.$$

D3

e quiv a lent ordered pairs (i kwiv′ə lənt). Ordered pairs that are related as follows: In (a, b) and (c, d) suppose that a, b, c, and d are replaced by any members of C. If a true statement is obtained from $a \times d = c \times b$, then (a, b) is equivalent to (c, d). Also, if (a, b) is equivalent to (c, d), then a true statement is obtained from $a \times d = c \times b$.

N Is the product of 3 and 16 the same number as the product of 4 and 12? Is $3 \times 16 = 4 \times 12$ a true statement?

O In exercises K through N, you first worked with (1, 4) and (2, 8) and then with (3, 12) and (4, 16). In each case, you found two products. Which components did you multiply to find each of these two products? Were these products equal? In any two ordered pairs, if these two products are equal, the ordered pairs are *equivalent ordered pairs*.

P Look again at D2 and D3. How do you know that (1, 4) and (2, 8) are equivalent ordered pairs? How do you know that (3, 12) and (4, 16) are equivalent ordered pairs?

Q Are (2, 8) and (3, 12) equivalent ordered pairs? Explain your answer.

Each exercise below names two ordered pairs. For each exercise, decide if the ordered pairs are equivalent.

R (55, 22), (5, 2)	**V** (1, 7), (7, 42)
S (9, 12), (54, 72)	**W** (63, 45), (7, 5)
T (5, 9), (35, 54)	**X** (27, 9), (9, 1)
U (2, 3), (20, 30)	**Y** (4, 13), (24, 78)

The work that follows will help you develop the definition of equivalent ordered pairs.

A Think of two ordered pairs of variables, (a, b) and (c, d). The universe for each of the variables is C. Can you tell if these ordered pairs are equivalent? Explain your answer.

B Look at D4. Which components are used to obtain $a \times d$? How is $c \times b$ obtained?

C Look at D5. What is the universe for each of the variables? What replacements have been made for the variables in (a, b)? In (c, d)?

D How is the statement $2 \times 9 = 3 \times 6$ obtained? Is $2 \times 9 = 3 \times 6$ a true statement? How do you know that (2, 6) and (3, 9) are equivalent ordered pairs?

Any two ordered pairs, (a, b) and (c, d), are equivalent only if, upon replacement of each variable, a true statement is obtained from $a \times d = c \times b$. Notice that the two products must be equal before the two ordered pairs can be equivalent.

E What replacements must be made for a, b, c, and d to obtain (1, 4) and (4, 16) from (a, b) and (c, d)? With the same replacements, what statement is obtained from $a \times d = c \times b$? Is this a true statement? Is (1, 4) equivalent to (4, 16)?

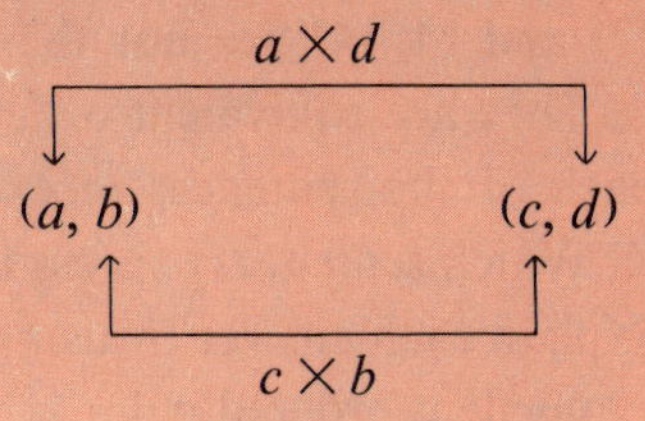

$$a \times d = c \times b.$$

D4

U = C.

$(a, b) \quad (c, d)$

$(2, 6) \quad (3, 9)$

$$a \times d = c \times b.$$

$$2 \times 9 = 3 \times 6.$$

D5

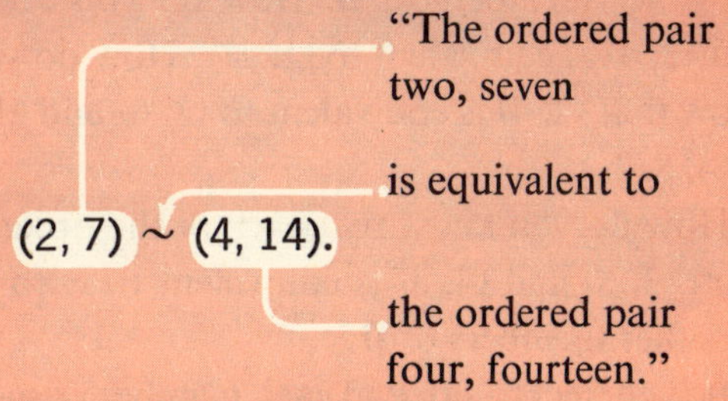

D6

F Is (2, 5) equivalent to (4, 7)? Explain your answer.

G Is (2, 7) equivalent to (10, 35)? Is (10, 35) equivalent to (2, 7)?

The symbol at the right below is used to express the idea of equivalence. D6 shows how to write and read a sentence that includes the symbol for equivalence. $\sim$

Notice that "equivalence" and "equality" are not used in the same way. You know that (2, 7) is equivalent to (4, 14) because $2 \times 14 = 4 \times 7$. However, (2, 7) is not *equal* to (4, 14) because (2, 7) and (4, 14) are not the same ordered pair. They are equivalent ordered pairs.

Read each of the sentences in exercises H through K. Which sentences express true statements? Explain each answer by using the definition of equivalent ordered pairs.

H $(3, 9) \sim (4, 10)$. **J** $(3, 9) \sim (1, 3)$.

I $(1, 7) \sim (9, 63)$. **K** $(1, 7) \sim (7, 1)$.

L Look at D7. How many members are there in set B? You are going to decide if each member of B is equivalent to each of the other members of B.

M First decide if (1, 2) is equivalent to each of the other members of B. Is $(1, 2) \sim (2, 4)$? Is $(1, 2) \sim (3, 6)$? Is $(1, 2) \sim (4, 8)$? Use the definition of equivalent ordered pairs to explain your answers.

N Next decide if (2, 4) is equivalent to each of the other members of B. How do you know that (2, 4) is equivalent to (1, 2)? How do you know that (2, 4) is equivalent to (3, 6) and also to (4, 8)?

O How do you know that each of the ordered pairs (3, 6) and (4, 8) is equivalent to each of the other members of B?

P Is it correct to say that each member of set B is equivalent to each of the other members of set B?

Q Is each member of B equivalent to itself?
? Explain your answer.

In some sets of ordered pairs, each member is equivalent to each of the other members. Such a set of ordered pairs is a *proportional relation.* Set B, tabulated in D7, is a proportional relation.

pro por tion al re la tion (prə pôr′shən əl ri lā′shən). A set of ordered pairs in which each member is equivalent to each of the other members. {(3, 1), (6, 2), (9, 3)} is a proportional relation.

$$B = \{(1, 2),\ (2, 4),\ (3, 6),\ (4, 8)\}.$$

D7

$2 \times 6 = 12.$ $6 \div 2 = 3.$

$(6, 8) \sim (12, 16).$ $(6, 8) \sim (3, 4).$

$2 \times 8 = 16.$ $8 \div 2 = 4.$

D8

R Set $M = \{(7, 2), (14, 4), (21, 6), (28, 8)\}$. Is (7, 2) equivalent to (14, 4)? To (21, 6)? To (28, 8)?

S Is M a proportional relation? Explain your answer.

T $G = \{(1, 1), (1, 2), (2, 1), (2, 2)\}$. Is G a proportional relation? Explain your answer.

You have learned how to use the definition of equivalent ordered pairs to decide if two ordered pairs are equivalent. Now you will learn one way to find ordered pairs equivalent to a given ordered pair.

A First you will see how (12, 16) and (3, 4) can be obtained from (6, 8). Is $(12, 16) \sim (6, 8)$? Is $(3, 4) \sim (6, 8)$?

B Look at D8. By what number can you multiply the first component of (6, 8) to obtain the first component of (12, 16)?

C How can the second component of (12, 16) be obtained from the second component of (6, 8)?

D By what number can you multiply each component of (6, 8) to obtain (12, 16)?

E Look again at D8. By what number can you divide the first component of (6, 8) to obtain the first component of (3, 4)?

F How can the second component of (3, 4) be obtained from the second component of (6, 8)?

G By what number can you divide each component of (6, 8) to obtain (3, 4)?

H Are (3, 4) and (12, 16) equivalent? Explain your answer.

Six ordered pairs that are equivalent to (6, 8) are named below. Tell how you can obtain each ordered pair from (6, 8).

I (18, 24)	K (66, 88)	M (12, 16)
J (42, 56)	L (48, 64)	N (72, 96)

O If you multiply each component of (6, 8) **?** by the same counting number, will each ordered pair that you obtain be equivalent to (6, 8)?

Six ordered pairs that are equivalent to (120, 160) are named below. Tell how you can obtain each ordered pair from (120, 160).

P (12, 16)	R (3, 4)	T (30, 40)
Q (6, 8)	S (15, 20)	U (60, 80)

In the preceding exercises, you have been given ordered pairs and have used multiplication or division to find ordered pairs equivalent to them. Now you will be given an ordered pair and one component of an equivalent ordered pair. You will find the other component.

A Look at D9. The given ordered pair is (5, 8). The first component of an ordered pair equivalent to (5, 8) is 30. The second component of the pair is y. What is the universe for y?

B How can you obtain the first component of (30, y) from the first component of (5, 8)?

C How can you obtain the replacement for y from the second component of (5, 8)? What is the replacement for y?

D Is $(5, 8) \sim (30, 48)$?

E Look at D10. The second component of an ordered pair equivalent to (10, 24) is 12. The first component of the pair is x.

F How can you obtain the second component of (x, 12) from the second component of (10, 24)?

$$U = C.$$
$$(5, 8) \sim (30, y).$$
$$6 \times 5 = 30.$$
$$6 \times 8 = y.$$

D9

$$U = C.$$
$$(10, 24) \sim (x, 12).$$
$$24 \div 2 = 12.$$
$$10 \div 2 = x.$$

D10

G How can you obtain the replacement for x from the first component of (10, 24)? What is the replacement for x?

H Is $(10, 24) \sim (5, 12)$ a true statement?

Six ordered pairs are named below. For each ordered pair, what replacement should you make for the variable to obtain an ordered pair that is equivalent to (16, 24)? U = C.

I (x, 6)	K (48, y)	M (8, y)
J (32, y)	L (x, 96)	N (x, 3)

O For each ordered pair named in exercises I through N, how did you obtain the replacement for the variable?

In this lesson you have learned about equivalent ordered pairs and proportional relations. You have also learned how to find ordered pairs that are equivalent to a given ordered pair.

On your own

1 Suppose that you can buy 5 pieces of candy for 8 cents. Which ordered pairs named below represent the rate at which the candy is sold?

a (10, 8)	c (10, 16)	e (5, 8)
b (45, 72)	d (15, 20)	f (20, 32)

2 Explain why (5, 8) and (10, 16) are equivalent ordered pairs.

3 Explain why (10, 16) and (45, 72) are equivalent ordered pairs.

4 Explain why (5, 8) and (10, 8) are not equivalent ordered pairs.

Set A is tabulated below. For each of exercises 5 through 13, decide which member of A is equivalent to the ordered pair named. Then write a sentence using the symbol for equivalence.

A = {(1, 2), (2, 1), (2, 3), (3, 2), (3, 4), (4, 3), (4, 5), (5, 4)}.

5 (4, 6)	8 (3, 6)	11 (12, 9)
6 (6, 4)	9 (10, 8)	12 (9, 6)
7 (6, 3)	10 (8, 10)	13 (6, 8)

For each of exercises 14 through 19, tell whether or not the set tabulated is a proportional relation. Explain each of your answers.

14 {(60, 3), (3, 60)}

15 {(70, 5), (28, 2), (14, 1)}

16 {(7, 1), (63, 9), (35, 5)}

17 {(125, 70), (250, 140)}

18 {(100, 7), (200, 7)}

19 {(8, 24), (37, 121), (62, 185)}

20 How can you obtain (25, 15) from (5, 3)? Explain why (25, 15) and (5, 3) are equivalent ordered pairs.

21 How can you obtain (25, 15) from (50, 30)? Explain why (25, 15) and (50, 30) are equivalent ordered pairs.

For each ordered pair named in exercises 22 through 27, what replacement should you make for the variable to obtain an ordered pair that is equivalent to (2, 3)? U = C.

22 $(8, y)$	24 $(x, 15)$	26 $(x, 39)$
23 $(100, y)$	25 $(14, y)$	27 $(x, 51)$

For each ordered pair named in exercises 28 through 33, what replacement should you make for the variable to obtain an ordered pair that is equivalent to (40, 48)? U = C.

28 $(10, y)$	30 $(x, 12)$	32 $(x, 24)$
29 $(x, 6)$	31 $(20, y)$	33 $(5, y)$

KEEPING SKILFUL

For exercises 1 through 10, tell whether each sentence is an open sentence or a closed sentence.

1 $9 \neq 7 + 3$.	6 $m > 4m$.
2 $s = s + 1$.	7 $11 = n + 4$.
3 $d + 3 < 10$.	8 $8(2) > 15$.
4 $13 = 26 \div 2$.	9 $c \neq 5 + 6$.
5 $r = 23(9)$.	10 $15 - 7 = 8$.

11 For each closed sentence in exercises 1 through 10, tell which it expresses, an equation or an inequality.

12 For each open sentence in exercises 1 through 10, tell which it expresses, a condition for equality or a condition for inequality.

13 J = {0, 2, 4}. K = {1, 3, 5, 7}. Tabulate J × K.

For exercises 14 through 19, the universe is J × K, which you tabulated for exercise 13.

14 Tabulate the subset of J × K in which each member has a first component less than 3.

15 Tabulate the subset of J × K in which the sum of the components of each member is equal to 7.

16 Tabulate $\{(x,y) | x + y > 6\}$.

17 Tabulate $\{(x,y) | x < y\}$.

18 Tabulate $\{(x,y) | y > x + 3\}$.

19 Tabulate $\{(x,y) | x = y - 1\}$.

Tabulate each set described below. For exercises 20 through 27, U = N. For exercises 28 through 32, U = N × N.

20 $\{c \mid c = 29(14)\}$	24 $\{w \mid w > 109 - 11\}$
21 $\{n \mid n < 18 + 13\}$	25 $\{t \mid t + 1 \neq t\}$
22 $\{r \mid 52 = 91 - r\}$	26 $\{m \mid 63 + m = 90\}$
23 $\{s \mid 32 - s > 15\}$	27 $\{d \mid d < 42 - 29\}$

28 $\{(c, d) \mid c + d = 403 \wedge c + 72 = 213\}$

29 $\{(r, s) \mid 326 + s = 517 \wedge r + s < 200\}$

30 $\{(x, y) \mid x + y < 9 \wedge x + 2 = y\}$

31 $\{(m, n) \mid n - 49 = 172 \wedge m - n = 83\}$

32 $\{(r, s) \mid r > s \wedge r < 261 \div 87\}$

4 | 42 **Exploring ideas**

Rate pairs and ratios

In the last lesson you learned that a proportional relation is a set of ordered pairs in which each ordered pair is equivalent to each of the other ordered pairs in the set. In this lesson you will learn about special kinds of ordered pairs called rate pairs. You will use standard descriptions to describe proportional relations.

A Read the tabulation in D1. Is the set a proportional relation? Explain your answer.

You know that each member of a proportional relation is equivalent to each of the other members. Each ordered pair that is a member of a proportional relation is a *rate pair*.

B Are the members of the set tabulated in D1 rate pairs? How do you know?

Rate pairs are ordered pairs that are used to solve rate and comparison problems. There are various ways in which to express a rate pair. D2 shows four ways to express the same rate pair. You should read the first symbol as "one to two" because in this case (1, 2) expresses a rate pair. You also read the other three symbols "one to two."

Each name below expresses a rate pair. Read each name.

C 6:5 **D** 4/15 **E** $\frac{6}{9}$ **F** (100, 106) **G** 7/21

Although different kinds of symbols can be used in expressing a rate pair, it is convenient to use the same kind of symbol all the time. In this book, we will agree to use a symbol like the one at the right in expressing a rate pair.

1/2

{(1, 15), (2, 30), (3, 45), (4, 60), (5, 75)}

D1

(1, 2) 1:2 $\frac{1}{2}$ 1/2

D2

rate pair (rāt). A member of a proportional relation. Each member of {(1, 2), (2, 4), (3, 6)} is a rate pair.

ra ti o (rā′shē o or rā′shō). A name of a rate pair. The symbols 1/4, 2/3, and 9/5 are ratios.

A name of a rate pair is a *ratio*.

H In the ratio 1/2, where is the name of the first component of the rate pair placed? Where is the name of the second component of this rate pair placed?

Now that you have a special symbol for expressing rate pairs, use this symbol to express each member of a proportional relation.

I Tabulate the set whose members are expressed below by writing the names of the members in the form 1/15, 2/30, and so on.

(1, 15), (2, 30), (3, 45), (4, 60), (5, 75)

In this book, rate pairs will be used to represent many kinds of rates. In problems about rates, you may see expressions like these: "20 persons *per* square mile," "4 cans *for* 89¢," "30 miles *per* hour," "100 yards *in* 10 seconds," "3 cups of sugar *to* 1 cup of water." But when you read a ratio that expresses a rate pair, we will agree that you can always use the word "to." By this agreement, you and your classmates will always read the mathematical symbol for a rate pair in the same way.

$1/15 \sim 2/30.$

"One to fifteen

is equivalent to

two to thirty."

D3

A $(1, 15) \sim (2, 30).$ — 1×30 (arrows from 1 to 30), 2×15 (arrows from 2 to 15)

B $1/15 \sim 2/30.$ — 1×30 (arrows from 1 to 30), 2×15 (arrows from 2 to 15)

$$1 \times 30 = 2 \times 15.$$

D4

A $6/27 \sim 2/9.$

B $5/9 \sim 15/21.$

C $3/5 \sim 12/20.$

D $10/1 \sim 50/5.$

E $2/13 \sim 3/13.$

F $7/9 \sim 28/36.$

D5

J If you write the ratios in the sentence $(1, 15) \sim (2, 30)$ in the form 1/15 and 2/30, do you obtain the sentence in D3? To read this sentence, study D3.

K Look at D4. What do the arrows in A indicate?

L The arrows in B also indicate what numbers must be multiplied before you can tell if the sentence in B expresses a true statement. Are 1/15 and 2/30 equivalent rate pairs?

M Does the sentence $1/15 \sim 2/30$ express the same true statement as the sentence $(1, 15) \sim (2, 30)$?

N Read the sentences in D5. Tell what ratios each sentence contains.

O Which of the sentences in D5 express true statements? How do you know?

You already know how to tabulate finite proportional relations. Now you will learn how to express infinite proportional relations.

A Study D6. Are the rate pairs expressed equivalent rate pairs? How do you know?

B Are the rate pairs expressed in D6 all possible rate pairs that are equivalent to 4/7?

C Could you write all the ratios that express rate pairs equivalent to 4/7? Explain your answer.

D Study D7. It shows how to write and read the tabulation of a proportional relation that includes all rate pairs equivalent to 4/7.

E Is 16/28 a member of the proportional relation tabulated in D7? Is 24/42 a member? Is 200/350 a member? Name five other members.

F Is the set of all rate pairs equivalent to 4/7 a finite set? An infinite set? A set of rate pairs like the set tabulated in D7 is an *infinite proportional relation.*

G ? When you tabulate an infinite proportional relation, why is it unnecessary to list more than one member?

H Is $4/7 \sim 8/14$ a true statement? How do you know that {8/14, . . .} contains 4/7?

4/7, 8/14, 12/21, 16/28, 20/35

D6

{ 4/7, . . . }

"The set whose members are

the rate pair 4/7 and all rate pairs equivalent to 4/7"

D7

I Is each member of {8/14, . . .} equivalent to
? 4/7? Is {8/14, . . .} the same proportional relation as {4/7, . . .}? Is {100/175, . . .} the same proportional relation as {4/7, . . .}? Explain your answers.

Now you will use a standard description to express an infinite proportional relation.

J Study D8. Suppose that x is a variable for the first component of each rate pair that is equivalent to 4/7, and that y is a variable for the second component. Then (x, y) is an ordered pair of variables for each rate pair that is equivalent to 4/7. What is the universe for (x, y)?

K Is $x/y \sim 4/7$ satisfied by 4/7? By 8/14? By 60/105? Does each member of {4/7, . . .} satisfy $x/y \sim 4/7$?

L How do you know that the solution set of $x/y \sim 4/7$ is an infinite set? Is the solution set of $x/y \sim 4/7$ a proportional relation?

The proportional relation determined by $x/y \sim 4/7$ may be named by a standard description. D9 shows how to write and read this standard description.

M Is $\{(x, y) \mid x/y \sim 8/14\}$ the same propor-
? tional relation as $\{(x, y) \mid x/y \sim 4/7\}$?

Read each standard description given below.

N $\{(x, y) \mid x/y \sim 7/15\}$ **P** $\{(r, s) \mid r/s \sim 1/100\}$

O $\{(x, y) \mid x/y \sim 10/1\}$ **Q** $\{(m, n) \mid m/n \sim n/m\}$

D10 includes a graph of C × C and also of the proportional relation that is described in D10. Notice that a graph of C × C does not contain a dot for the point (0, 0). This is because 0 is not a member of C.

R Name the ordered pairs associated with points represented by encircled dots. Are these ordered pairs members of $\{(x, y) \mid x/y \sim 1/3\}$?

S Is the graph of $\{(x, y) \mid x/y \sim 1/3\}$ an incomplete graph? Name three other members of the proportional relation whose points are not represented by dots in the graph in D10.

Universe for $(x, y) = \text{C} \times \text{C}$.
$x/y \sim 4/7$.

D8

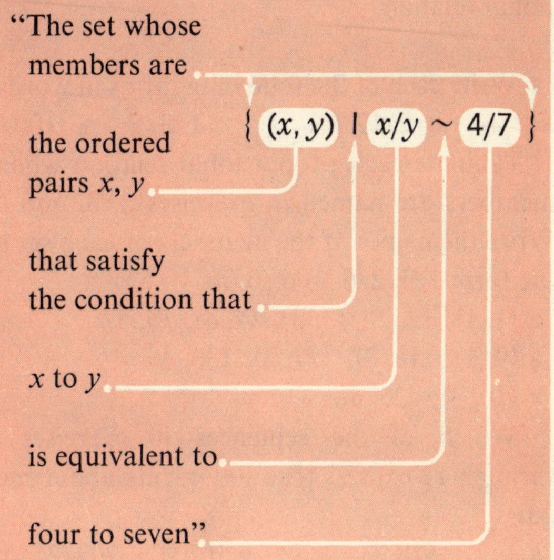

D9

Universe for $(x, y) = \text{C} \times \text{C}$.

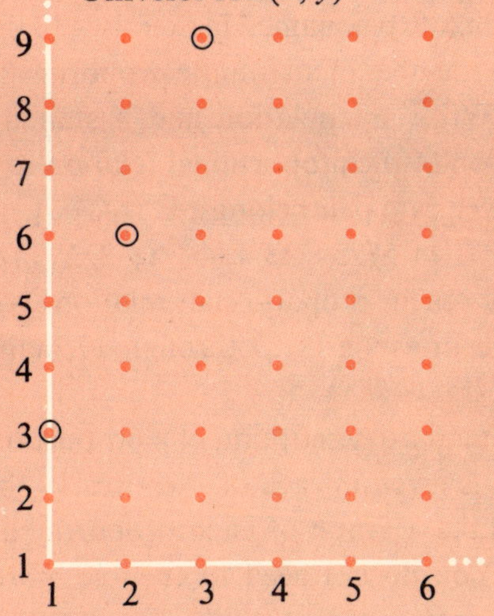

$\{(x, y) \mid x/y \sim 1/3\}$
Incomplete graph

D10

In this lesson you have learned that a rate pair is a member of a proportional relation and that a ratio is a name of a rate pair. You have also learned how to express an infinite proportional relation and how to make a graph of a proportional relation.

On your own

1 Write each of the following ratios in words:

a 1/6 **b** 2/12 **c** 3/1 **d** 8/5 **e** 100/1

Tabulate each proportional relation whose members are named in exercises 2, 3, and 4. Write the names of the members of each set in the form 1/3, 2/6, and so on.

2 (1, 1), (2, 2), (3, 3), (4, 4), (5, 5)

3 (9, 1), (18, 2), (27, 3), (36, 4)

4 (10, 3), (20, 6)

Which of the sentences in exercises 5 through 12 express true statements about rate pairs?

5 $1/2 \sim 6/8$.

6 $21/35 \sim 24/40$.

7 $9/1 \sim 99/11$.

8 $10/4 \sim 15/6$.

9 $101/1 \sim 202/2$.

10 $1/3 \sim 9/27$.

11 $7/5 \sim 35/30$.

12 $25/4 \sim 100/8$.

Each rate pair named in exercises 13 through 17 is a member of an infinite proportional relation. Write a tabulation and a standard description of the proportional relation to which the given rate pair belongs. $U = C \times C$.

13 3/8 **14** 5/25 **15** 1/4 **16** 2/2 **17** 4/17

18 For each proportional relation you described in exercises 13 through 17, name five members.

A standard description of a proportional relation is given in each of exercises 19 through 22. Make a graph of each proportional relation. You do not need to encircle more than three dots in each graph. The universe for $(x, y) = C \times C$.

19 $\{(x, y) \mid x/y \sim 3/2\}$

20 $\{(x, y) \mid x/y \sim 4/2\}$

21 $\{(x, y) \mid x/y \sim 2/5\}$

22 $\{(x, y) \mid x/y \sim 6/9\}$

4 43 **Exploring ideas**

Solution sets of conditions for equivalence

In this lesson you will use the definition of equivalent ordered pairs to determine missing components of rate pairs.

A Read the problem in D1. Sixteen plants cost how many dollars? Can you represent this rate by the rate pair 16/8? What does the first component of 16/8 refer to? What does the second component of 16/8 refer to?

B ? You do not yet know how many dollars 4 of the plants cost. First, you must find a rate pair that is equivalent to 16/8. How do you know that 4 is the first component of the rate pair you are to find?

C Does the open sentence in D2 express a condition for the problem? Notice that x is used as the second component of the rate pair that you are to find. For what is x a variable?

A condition like $16/8 \sim 4/x$ is a *condition for equivalence*. A condition for equivalence includes the idea of equivalence. You obtain a

Sixteen plants cost 8 dollars. At this rate, 4 of the plants cost how many dollars?

D1

$U = C$.

$16/8 \sim 4/x$.

D2

Using the definition of equivalent ordered pairs to determine missing components of rate pairs statement from a condition for equivalence by replacing the variable in the condition by a member of the universe. The condition $16/8 \sim 4/x$ requires you to find the replacement for x that makes $16/8$ and $4/x$ equivalent rate pairs.

You can use the definition of equivalent ordered pairs to find a replacement for the variable that satisfies a condition like $16/8 \sim 4/x$. You are permitted to use the definition of equivalent ordered pairs when you work with rate pairs because rate pairs are ordered pairs.

D Study D3. What do the arrows indicate? How was the condition $16x = 32$ obtained from $16/8 \sim 4/x$?

E Will the replacement for x that satisfies $16x = 32$ also satisfy $16/8 \sim 4/x$?

Now you must find the solution set of $16x = 32$. You can think of 16 times x, or $16x$, as 16 equal groups. Then you also must think of 32 as 16 equal groups. You need to find the number in each of the 16 groups. Markers will help you find this number.

These markers represent a group of 32 objects. The 32 markers are to be divided into 16 equal groups.

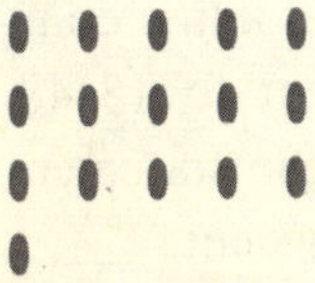

Notice how each new group has been started. One marker has been put in each of the 16 groups.

Another marker has been put in each of the groups. All 32 markers have been used. There are 2 markers in each group. To find the number of members in 16 equal groups, you can divide 32 by 16.

$16 \times x$

$16/8 \sim 4/x.$

4×8

$16x = 32.$

D3

$U = C.$

$8/16 \sim x/4.$

$32 = x(16).$

$32 = 16x.$

D4

F To find the replacement for x that satisfies $16x = 32$, you divide 32 by what number?

G In $16x = 32$, replace x by 2. Do you obtain $16(2) = 32$? Is $16(2) = 32$?

H Is $16/8 \sim 4/2$ a true statement?

I Are $16/8$ and $4/2$ members of the same proportional relation?

Now you know that the rate pairs $16/8$ and $4/2$ represent the same rate. You also know that the rate pair $4/2$ represents the rate of 4 plants for 2 dollars. Therefore, you can say:

4 of the plants cost 2 dollars.

J Read the problem in D1 again. This time use the rate pair $8/16$ to represent the rate. What does the first component refer to? What does the second component refer to?

K To find how many dollars 4 of the plants cost, you need to find another rate pair that is equivalent to $8/16$. Why will you use 4 as the second component of the new rate pair?

L Look at D4. Does $8/16 \sim x/4$ express a condition for the problem? Why is x used as the first component of the new rate pair? For what is x a variable?

You obtain $32 = x(16)$ from $8/16 \sim x/4$ by finding the product of 8 and 4 and the product of x and 16. The product of 8 and 4 is 8×4, or 32.

M $x(16)$ is the product of x and 16. Is $16x$ also the product of x and 16?

In working with conditions for equivalence such as $a/b \sim c/d$, you find the product of a and d and the product of c and b. The product of a and d is ad or da. The product of c and b is cb or bc.

N Explain how you find the solution set of $32 = 16x$. Tabulate $\{x \mid 32 = 16x\}$.

O First tabulate $\{x \mid 8/16 \sim x/4\}$. Then tabu-
? late $\{x \mid 16/8 \sim 4/x\}$. Does the sentence $\{x \mid 8/16 \sim x/4\} = \{x \mid 16/8 \sim 4/x\}$ express a true statement?

P If the first component of the first rate pair refers to a number of plants, then the first component of the second rate pair must refer to what?

Q If 16 plants cost 8 dollars, how many dollars did 4 of the plants cost?

R The solution set of $8/16 \sim x/4$ is the same as the solution set of $16/8 \sim 4/x$. May you use either of these conditions for the problem in D1?

The problem in D1 was solved by finding the solution set of a condition for equivalence. Now you will learn more about finding solution sets of conditions for equivalence.

A Look at D5. How is $480 = 15x$ obtained from $48/15 \sim x/10$?

The condition $15x = 480$ can also be obtained from $48/15 \sim x/10$. The solution set of $15x = 480$ is the same as the solution set of $480 = 15x$. First you will find the replacement for x that satisfies $15x = 480$.

B $15x = 480$ indicates that there are 15 groups, each containing a number represented by x. What is the total number in all 15 groups? What computation is needed to find the number in each group?

C What replacement for x satisfies $15x = 480$?

D Tabulate $\{x \mid 15x = 480\}$.

E Tabulate $\{x \mid 48/15 \sim x/10\}$. Why is this solution set the same as the solution set you tabulated for exercise D?

F Name the rate pair that has a second component of 10 and is equivalent to 48/15.

G Now name the rate pair that has a first com-
? ponent of 10 and is equivalent to 15/48. Write a sentence that expresses the statement that these two rate pairs are equivalent.

H Read the open sentence in D6. How do you obtain $17x = 4284$ from $x/63 \sim 68/17$? How do you find the solution set of $17x = 4284$?

I Tabulate $\{x \mid x/63 \sim 68/17\}$.

J Name the rate pair that has a second component of 63 and is equivalent to 68/17.

K Name the rate pair that has a first component of 63 and is equivalent to 17/68.

Sixteen plants cost 8 dollars. At this rate, 4 of the plants cost how many dollars?

D1

U = C.
$48/15 \sim x/10.$
$480 = 15x.$
$15x = 480.$

D5

U = C.
$x/63 \sim 68/17.$

D6

Now you know how to find the solution set of a condition for equivalence by using the definition of equivalent ordered pairs.

On your own

Use the definition of equivalent ordered pairs to help find the solution of each condition expressed below. Tabulate the solution set of each condition. U = C.

1 $25/10 \sim 15/x$.
2 $x/3 \sim 10/5$.
3 $7/21 \sim x/3$.
4 $9/15 \sim x/50$.
5 $1/2 \sim x/100$.
6 $13/26 \sim 5/x$.
7 $x/90 \sim 21/14$.
8 $x/1 \sim 55/11$.
9 $50/x \sim 1/5$.
10 $x/9 \sim 40/12$.
11 $1/3 \sim 8/x$.
12 $x/16 \sim 7/4$.
13 $13/9 \sim x/18$.
14 $x/25 \sim 40/100$.
15 $15/18 \sim 50/x$.
16 $4/9 \sim x/99$.
17 $x/26 \sim 6/39$.
18 $12/x \sim 15/40$.
19 $2/30 \sim x/75$.
20 $12/30 \sim 16/x$.
21 $14/x \sim 1/6$.
22 $x/85 \sim 12/10$.
23 $25/150 \sim 15/x$.
24 $72/x \sim 30/5$.

KEEPING SKILFUL

Find the sum.

1 112, 340, 5621, 569
2 3468, 1923, 4082, 601, 1977
3 12574, 81930, 64521
4 67689, 88677, 3594, 38624
5 36241, 132, 9876, 429, 29748

Find the difference.

6 9214, 5927
7 7345, 6216
8 2001, 798
9 82345, 17689
10 30026, 23472
11 92845, 41572

Multiply

12 32745 by 7.
13 49 by 68.
14 139 by 19.
15 451 by 367.
16 294 by 819.
17 635 by 708.

Divide

18 3684 by 38.
19 7805 by 45.
20 25572 by 36.
21 13592 by 321.
22 41965 by 235.
23 155480 by 598.

CHECKING UP

If you have trouble with these two tests, you should refer to lessons 41, 42, and 43.

Test 44

1 Write a ratio for a rate pair that represents the rate of 6 miles per hour.

2 Write a ratio for a rate pair that represents the rate of 2 apples for 7 cents.

3 Write a ratio for a rate pair that represents the rate of 3 eggs to 2 cups of milk.

Replacements for x, y, m, and n are named in exercises 4 through 7. For each exercise, write the sentence that expresses the statement you obtain when you use these replacements in $x/y \sim m/n$.

	x	y	m	n
4	3	7	12	24
5	2	9	4	18
6	5	8	10	80
7	4	6	16	24

8 Which of the sentences that you wrote for exercises 4 through 7 express true statements?

9 Now write the sentences that express the statements you obtain when you use the replacements named above in $xn = my$.

10 Which of the sentences that you wrote for exercise 9 express true statements?

Test 45

In each of exercises 11 through 14, one rate pair named is not equivalent to the other rate pairs named. Which pair is it?

11 2/5, 4/10, 6/12, 8/20
12 60/90, 30/60, 30/45, 2/3
13 8/14, 4/7, 12/28, 24/42, 16/28
14 6/4, 12/8, 9/6, 15/9, 3/2

15 Name the rate pair that is equivalent to 2/5 and has a first component of 6.

16 Name the rate pair that is equivalent to 15/9 and has a second component of 21.

17 Tabulate $\{x \mid x/12 \sim 132/22\}$. U = C.

18 Tabulate $\{x \mid 45/x \sim 72/168\}$. U = C.

19 Tabulate $\{x \mid x/40 \sim 15/100\}$. U = C.

4 44 **Exploring problems**

Problems involving conditions for equivalence

You know that a rate pair is a member of a proportional relation. You also know how to find a rate pair that is equivalent to a given rate pair. You will use this knowledge to find solutions of conditions for problems.

Read the problem in D1. The exercises that follow will help you develop a compound condition for the problem. U = C × C.

A For each 6 blocks that Jerry walks, Tim walks 8 blocks. Use 6 as the first component of a rate pair that represents this comparison. Use 8 as the second component. To what does the 8 refer?

6/8

B You know one rate pair that represents the comparison. You want to find rate pairs equivalent to 6/8. Use x as a variable for the number of blocks that Jerry walks. Why do you use x as a variable for the first component of each rate pair you are to find?

x

C Use y as a variable for the second component. What does y refer to?

y

D Why do you use x/y, and not y/x, to represent each rate pair equivalent to 6/8?

x/y

E Does the sentence at the right express a simple condition for the problem? What does the condition require about each rate pair you are to find?

$6/8 \sim x/y$.

Jerry and Tim compared their walking speeds. They found that Jerry walks 6 blocks while Tim walks 8 blocks. When Jerry has walked 24 blocks, how many blocks will Tim have walked?

D1

{3/4, . . .}

D2

F Study the tabulation of a proportional relation in D2. Is this set an infinite set? Name six rate pairs that are members of this set. Is each rate pair that you named a member of $\{(x, y) | 6/8 \sim x/y\}$? Explain your answer.

G What comparison does each member of the solution set of $6/8 \sim x/y$ represent?

H Read the problem in D1 again. What are you asked to find?

I How do you know that the rate pair you are to find must satisfy $x = 24$?

$x = 24$.

J Does the sentence at the right express a compound condition for the problem?

$6/8 \sim x/y \wedge x = 24$.

K Now you can find $\{(x, y) | 6/8 \sim x/y \wedge x = 24\}$. What is the first component of the rate pair that satisfies $6/8 \sim x/y \wedge x = 24$? Explain your answer.

REMINDER

Each solution of a compound condition that involves "and" must satisfy each of the simple conditions that make up the compound condition.

See lesson 24, page 90.

L What rate pair satisfies $6/8 \sim x/y$ and has 24 as a first component?

M Tabulate $\{(x, y) | 6/8 \sim x/y \wedge x = 24\}$.

N How many rate pairs are in the set you tabulated for exercise M? What does the first component of the member of the solution set refer to? What does the second component refer to?

Since you know the solution of the compound condition for the problem in D1, you can use the solution to get the answer to the problem.

When Jerry has walked 24 blocks, Tim will have walked 32 blocks.

O Verify the answer. You have found that when Jerry has walked 24 blocks, Tim will have walked 32 blocks. Does 24/32 represent the same comparison as 6/8?

To solve the problem in D1, you developed a compound condition for the problem. From the solution set of the simple condition $6/8 \sim x/y$, you obtained some of the rate pairs equivalent to 6/8. You used the other simple condition, $x = 24$, to select the rate pair that gave you the answer to the problem. There is another way to find the answer to the problem in D1. This way, in which you use a simple condition instead of a compound condition, is explained in exercises P through T.

P You know that 24 is the first component of the rate pair whose second component you are to find. If you replace x by 24 in $6/8 \sim x/y$, do you obtain $6/8 \sim 24/y$?

Q Is $6/8 \sim 24/y$ a condition for the problem in D1?

R How can the condition $6y = 192$ be obtained from $6/8 \sim 24/y$?

S What number satisfies $6y = 192$? The universe for y is C.

T Does the number that satisfies $6y = 192$ also satisfy $6/8 \sim 24/y$? Explain your answer.

At an automatic car wash, 20 cars can be washed in 60 minutes. At this rate, how many cars can be washed in 15 minutes?

D3

Now you can give the answer to the problem.

When Jerry has walked 24 blocks, Tim will have walked 32 blocks.

Problems like the one in D1 always give you the numbers that are the components of one rate pair and the number that is one component of an equivalent rate pair. You are to find the number that is the other component of this equivalent rate pair.

Read the problem in D3. You will develop a simple condition for this problem. U = C.

A Does the rate pair named below at the right represent the rate at which cars can be washed? What does the first component of the rate pair refer to? What does the second component refer to?

20/60

B What are you asked to find? How do you know that 15 is the second component of the rate pair whose first component you are to find? For what is w a variable?

$w/15$

C Does the sentence below at the right express a simple condition for the problem? What does this condition tell you about $w/15$?

$20/60 \sim w/15.$

D Explain how $300 = 60w$ can be obtained from $20/60 \sim w/15$.

E What number satisfies $300 = 60w$?

F Does the number that satisfies $300 = 60w$ also satisfy $20/60 \sim w/15$?

Now you can give the answer to the problem in D3.

5 cars can be washed in 15 minutes.

G Verify the answer. 5 cars can be washed in 15 minutes. Does $5/15$ represent the same rate as $20/60$?

Read the problem in D3 again. You can develop another condition for this problem. U = C.

H Why does the rate pair named below at the right also represent the rate at which cars can be washed? What does the first component of this rate pair refer to? What does the second component refer to?

$60/20$

I Is 15 the first component of the rate pair whose second component you are to find? Explain your answer. For what is w a variable?

$15/w$

J Does the sentence at the right below express a condition for the problem? What does the condition tell you about $15/w$?

$60/20 \sim 15/w.$

K Tabulate $\{w \mid 60/20 \sim 15/w\}$. What does the member of the solution set refer to?

L Why can you use either $20/60 \sim w/15$ or **?** $60/20 \sim 15/w$ as a condition for the problem in D3?

Read the problem in D4. You will develop a simple condition for this problem. U = C.

A Jim paid 18 cents for each package of paper. Does the rate pair named at the right below represent this rate? What does the first component of the rate pair refer to? What does the second component refer to?

$18/1$

B What are you asked to find in the problem? How do you know that 3 is the second component of the rate pair you are to find? For what is x a variable?

$x/3$

At an automatic car wash, 20 cars can be washed in 60 minutes. At this rate, how many cars can be washed in 15 minutes?

D3

Jim bought 3 packages of notebook paper. He paid 18 cents for each package. How many cents in all did Jim pay for the 3 packages of paper?

D4

In an election for class secretary, Janet received 39 votes, and Sue received 13 votes. Janet received how many times as many votes as Sue?

D5

C Does the sentence below at the right express a simple condition for the problem?

$18/1 \sim x/3.$

D Tabulate $\{x \mid 18/1 \sim x/3\}$.

Now you can give the answer to the problem.

Jim paid 54 cents for the 3 packages of paper.

E Does $54/3$ represent the same rate as $18/1$?

Read the problem in D5. U = C.

F You know that Janet received 39 votes and that Sue received 13 votes. Does the rate pair named at the right represent this comparison? What does the first component of the rate pair refer to? What does the second component refer to?

$39/13$

G You are asked to find how many times as many votes Janet received as Sue. This means that you must find how many votes Janet

Two inches on a map represent a distance of 35 miles. How many miles are represented by 4 inches on this map?

$$4/s \sim 2/35.$$

D6

received for each vote that Sue received. Use x as a variable for the number of votes that Janet received. Why do you use $x/1$, and not $1/x$?

$x/1$

H Does the sentence below at the right express a condition for the problem? What does the condition tell you about $x/1$?

$39/13 \sim x/1.$

I Tabulate $\{x \mid 39/13 \sim x/1\}$.

You can use the solution to get the answer to the problem.

Janet received 3 votes for each 1 vote that Sue received. Thus, Janet received three times as many votes as Sue.

Read the problem in D6. A sentence that expresses a condition for the problem is also given. $U = C$.

J In $4/s \sim 2/35$, what does the first component of $2/35$ refer to? What does the second component of $2/35$ refer to? For what is s a variable?

K Tabulate $\{s \mid 4/s \sim 2/35\}$.

L Give the answer to the problem.

M For the problem in D6, you can also use **?** the condition $s/4 \sim 35/2$, the condition $2/35 \sim 4/s$, or the condition $35/2 \sim s/4$. Explain why you can do this.

In this lesson you have learned to write sentences that express conditions for rate and comparison problems. You have also used solutions of conditions for equivalence to get the answers to problems.

On your own

For each problem, first write a sentence that expresses a condition for the problem. You may use any letter as a name for the variable. Then tabulate the solution set and give the answer to the problem. $U = C$.

1 Most of the known planets in our solar system have one or more satellites, or moons. Jupiter has 6 times as many satellites as Mars. Jupiter has 12 satellites. How many satellites does Mars have?

2 What is the cost of 5 cans of soup, if 3 cans of this soup cost 54¢?

3 Allen received 98 votes in a student council election. For each 2 votes that Allen received, Roger received 3 votes. How many votes did Roger receive in the election?

4 Last year the Gibson Auto Company sold 72 used cars. The company sold 8 used cars for each 6 new cars that they sold. How many new cars did the company sell last year?

5 Lois has 95 coins from England and 19 coins from France in her collection of foreign coins. She has how many times as many English coins as French coins?

6 Jerry was paid \$6 for delivering 24 grocery orders. At this rate, how many dollars would he be paid for delivering 16 orders?

7 The heat energy of food is measured in calories. There are 4 times as many calories in a piece of mince pie as in a glass of milk. There are 170 calories in a glass of milk. How many calories are there in a piece of mince pie?

8 Mrs. Adams bought 18 ears of sweet corn priced at 6 ears for 29¢. How many cents did she pay for the sweet corn?

9 In the Canadian Senate in September, 1958, Ontario had 12 senators for every 2 that Prince Edward Island had. Ontario had 24 senators. How many did Prince Edward Island have?

10 Last year Bob scored 192 points during the basketball season. For each 8 points that Bob scored, John scored 7 points. How many points did John score?

11 The distance between two cities is represented by 9 inches on a road map. Two inches on the map represent an actual distance of 28 miles. What is the actual distance between the two cities?

12 The population density of a land area is the average number of persons per square mile. The population density of Canada is approximately 4 persons. The land area of Canada is 3,560,238 square miles. Approximately how many persons live in Canada?

13 The population density of Australia is about 3 persons. About 8,925,000 persons live in Australia. The land area of Australia is about how many square miles?

14 An office building that was 76 feet high above the ground was demolished. Another office building that was 228 feet high above the ground was built in its place. The height of the new building was how many times the height of the old building?

15 Alice saves $4 out of each $9 that she earns. If she continues to save at this rate, how many dollars will she have saved when she has earned $216?

16 There were 16 times as many motor vehicles in Canada in 1935 as there were in 1914. In 1914, there were 74,246 motor vehicles. How many motor vehicles were there in Canada in 1935?

17 A certain printing press can print 237,500 newspapers in 5 hours. At this rate, the press can print how many newspapers in 3 hours?

18 In 1956, the population density of Saskatchewan was 4 persons. About 880,000 persons lived in Saskatchewan in 1956. The area of Saskatchewan is about how many square miles?

APPLYING MATHEMATICS

The problems in this lesson include terms often used in business. You will use the solutions of conditions for equivalence to get the answers to these problems.

For each problem, write a sentence expressing a condition for the problem. Then tabulate the solution set of the condition and give the answer to the problem. U = C.

1 Persons who have checking accounts are usually charged a small amount for each check that they write. This amount is called a *service charge*. If a bank charges 8¢ per check, what is the service charge for 12 checks?

2 During one month Mrs. Harris wrote 13 checks on a local bank. The total service charge was 91¢. What was the service charge per check?

3 The City Bank charges $6 per year for each $100 that it lends. The charge for the use of money is called *interest*. If Mr. Peters borrows $700, how much interest must he pay the bank at the end of one year?

4 Miss Owens borrowed $980 from the Merchants' National Bank and paid $49 interest at the end of one year. How much interest per year did she pay for each $100 that she borrowed?

5 A store reduced the price of a sofa $3 for each $75 of the regular price. When a regular price is reduced, the amount of the reduction is called the *discount*. The regular price of the sofa was $375. The discount amounted to how many dollars?

6 Mrs. Carter received a $20 discount on a television set that was regularly priced at $250. How many dollars' discount did she receive for each $100 of the regular price?

7 Mr. Baker, a salesman, receives $16 for each $80 worth of merchandise he sells. The amount he is paid is called his *commission*. How much commission would Mr. Baker be paid if he sold $560 worth of merchandise?

8 Mr. Thompson receives a commission of $24 for each $240 worth of merchandise that he sells. At this rate, how many dollars' worth of merchandise does he have to sell to earn a commission of $144?

9 After deductions for taxes and insurance are made from Mr. Hill's monthly salary, he receives a check for $436. The amount of the check is his *take-home pay*. What is Mr. Hill's yearly take-home pay?

10 Mrs. Smith's take-home pay amounts to $4 out of each $5 she earns. The amount of her yearly take-home pay is $5276. What is the amount of her yearly salary?

11 During the summer Tom works in a sporting goods store. One week he sold $288 worth of merchandise and was paid a commission of $16. At this rate, how many dollars' worth of merchandise did he have to sell to earn one dollar of commission?

12 Jay bought a camera on sale and received a discount of $2 for each $10 of the regular price. The amount of the discount he received was $8. What was the regular price of the camera?

13 The Copper City National Bank charges $5 interest per year for each $100 it lends. Mr. Harper borrowed some money from this bank and paid $33 interest at the end of one year. How many dollars had Mr. Harper borrowed?

14 Mr. Martin's yearly salary is $8472. What is his monthly salary?

15 Mr. Johnson receives a commission of $18 for each $200 worth of merchandise that he sells. How many dollars' worth of merchandise did he sell if his commission was $261?

16 Mr. Morgan borrowed $1280 from his bank and paid $64 interest at the end of one year. How much interest did his bank charge per year for each $100 he borrowed?

17 Miss Moore's monthly salary is $360. Her monthly take-home pay is $288. Her take-home pay amounts to how many dollars for each $10 of her salary?

18 Betty received a discount of $20 on a phonograph that was regularly priced at $200. For each $10 of the regular price, how many dollars' discount did she receive?

19 Virginia works in a department store. She receives a commission of $3 for each $45 worth of merchandise she sells. At this rate, what will her commission be if she sells $405 worth of merchandise?

KEEPING SKILFUL

For exercises 1 through 4, the universe for (m, n) is tabulated below. For each condition, tabulate the solution set and make graphs of the universe and the solution set.

Universe for $(m, n) = \{(0, 0), (0, 1), (0, 2), (0, 3), (0, 4), (1, 0), (1, 1), (1, 2), (1, 3), (1, 4), (2, 0), (2, 1), (2, 2), (2, 3), (2, 4), (3, 0), (3, 1), (3, 2), (3, 3), (3, 4)\}$.

1 $m + n > 3$. **3** $m + 1 = n$.

2 $n + 1 = 4$. **4** $m + 3 < 5$.

Tabulate the solution set of each condition expressed in exercises 5 through 12. $U = N$.

5 $28r = 1008$. **9** $279(426) = h$.

6 $16(205) = s$. **10** $f = 23(1264)$.

7 $507 \div 39 > t$. **11** $43g = 16598$.

8 $168w = 42672$. **12** $w > 76(92)$.

Tabulate the solution set of each condition expressed below. $U = N \times N$.

13 $x + y < 9 \wedge 5x = 30$.

14 $2x > y \wedge x + y = 18$.

15 $x + 5 = y \wedge x + 13 < 22$.

16 $15x = 345 \wedge x - 18 > y$.

17 $x + 4 > y \wedge x + y = 12$.

4 45 **Exploring ideas**

Per cent

You know that rate pairs are used to solve rate and comparison problems. In this lesson you will learn about a special kind of rate pair that has 100 as a second component.

A During a money-raising drive, the students in five rooms in Morgan School decided upon their goals. The picture in D1 represents the goals and the results of the drive. For each room, the stack of silver dollars at the left represents the number of dollars the students in the room actually raised. The stack of silver dollars at the right represents the goal. How much money did each room raise? What was its goal?

B You can use a rate pair to represent the comparison of the money raised by each room with the goal for that room. The rate pairs named in D2 represent these comparisons. To what does the first component of each rate pair refer? To what does the second component refer? Use D1 to help you answer these questions.

Use the rate pairs named in D2 to help you answer the questions in exercises C, D, and E.

C Which room raised more money than its **?** goal? Would you say that this room did better with respect to its goal than each of the other four rooms? Explain your answer.

D How do you know that Room 101 did better than Room 105?

E Why is it hard to decide whether Room 103 or Room 105 did better?

It is easier to compare the performances of the different rooms when all the comparisons are represented by rate pairs that have the same second components. These second components can be any counting number. However, comparisons are often represented by rate pairs in which the second components are 100.

To help you compare the performances of the five rooms, you can use rate pairs that are equivalent to the rate pairs named in D2 and that have second components of 100.

F Room 101 raised \$22 of its goal of \$25. Does 22/25 represent this comparison? Imagine that the goal had been \$100 and that the room did just as well toward reaching this goal. You can use the first condition expressed in D3 to help you find how many dollars the room would have had to raise. For what is n a variable?

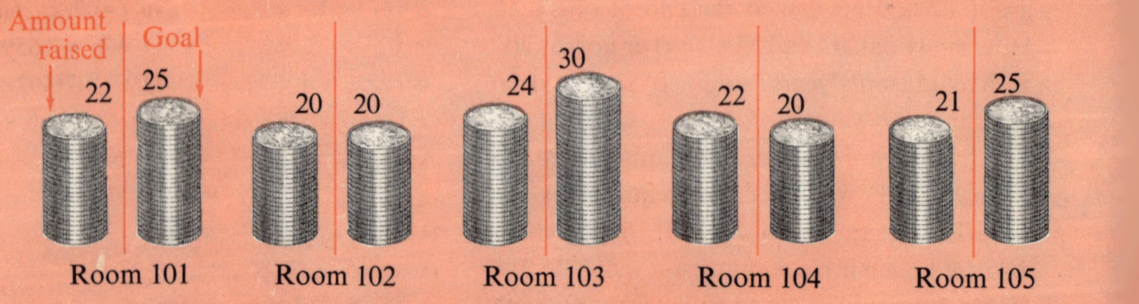

D1

Room 101	22/25
Room 102	20/20
Room 103	24/30
Room 104	22/20
Room 105	21/25

D2

U = C.

Room 101	$22/25 \sim n/100$.
Room 102	$20/20 \sim n/100$.
Room 103	$24/30 \sim n/100$.
Room 104	$22/20 \sim n/100$.
Room 105	$21/25 \sim n/100$.

D3

Room 101	$22/25 \sim 88/100$.
Room 102	$20/20 \sim 100/100$.
Room 103	$24/30 \sim 80/100$.
Room 104	$22/20 \sim 110/100$.
Room 105	$21/25 \sim 84/100$.

D4

G Suppose that each of the other rooms had set a goal of $100 and had done as well in reaching the $100 goal as it did in reaching the actual goal. Could you use the conditions expressed in D3 to help you find the amounts they would have had to raise? For what is *n* a variable in each condition?

H How can you find the replacement for *n* that satisfies each condition?

I Now look at D4. Does each of the sentences express a true statement?

J ? Does each statement expressed in D4 contain a rate pair whose second component is 100? Explain why it is now easier to decide which room did best, which room did second best, and so on.

K List the names of the five rooms in the order of their performance. Start with the name of the room that did best.

A rate pair that represents a comparison and has a second component of 100 is a *per cent*.

L Look again at D4. Is the rate pair 22/25 a per cent? Is the rate pair 88/100 a per cent?

M Is 88 per cent the same rate pair as 88/100?

The symbol at the right below is often used to express a rate pair that represents a comparison and that has a second component of 100. This symbol is the *per cent sign*. D5 shows how to write and read a ratio using the per cent sign.

%

N Read each ratio: 88%, 100%, 80%, 110%.

O Look at D6. For each room, is the rate pair named in column B equivalent to the rate pair named in column A?

P For each room, is the rate pair named in column C the same as the rate pair named in column B?

88 % — "Eighty-eight per cent"

D5

	A	B	C
Room 101	22/25	88/100	88%
Room 102	20/20	100/100	100%
Room 103	24/30	80/100	80%
Room 104	22/20	110/100	110%
Room 105	21/25	84/100	84%

D6

per cent (pər sent′). A rate pair that represents a comparison and that has a second component of 100.

Q If you were to list the per cents expressed in column C in order, beginning with the name of the least, you would start with 80%. What would be the greatest per cent named in your list?

Notice how easy it is to compare per cents. Since the second component of each per cent is 100, you can use just the first components to decide if a given per cent is greater than or less than another per cent.

R What is the first component of 80%? Of 81%? Is 80% less than 81%? Is 81% greater than 80%?

S Look again at column C in D6. Which of the rate pairs named has a first component greater than 100?

T Sometimes it is convenient to say that a rate pair is "greater than 100%." This means that the first component of the rate pair is greater than 100, and the second component is 100. What does it mean to say that a rate pair is 100%?

For each rate pair expressed below, tell whether it is greater than 100%, less than 100%, or equal to 100%.

U 95% **W** 100% **Y** 115%

V 137% **X** 45% **Z** 53%

Now you will work with other rate pairs that can be thought of as per cents. Look at D7. The chart shows Susan's performance on five mathematics tests.

A Write a ratio that expresses the rate pair for each test listed in D7. The first component of each rate pair should refer to the number of questions Susan answered correctly. The second component should refer to the number of questions on each test.

B For each of the five rate pairs you named in exercise A, find an equivalent rate pair that has a second component of 100.

	A	B	C
Room 101	22/25	88/100	88%
Room 102	20/20	100/100	100%
Room 103	24/30	80/100	80%
Room 104	22/20	110/100	110%
Room 105	21/25	84/100	84%

D6

	Number of questions answered correctly	Number of questions on test
Test 1	18	20
Test 2	12	15
Test 3	36	40
Test 4	28	28
Test 5	47	50

D7

C Now express each rate pair by using the per cent sign.

D You gave Susan's grade on each test as a per cent. Did Susan receive any grade greater than 100%? Would such a grade have been possible? Explain your answer.

E On which test did Susan do best? On which test did she do least well? Which rate pairs did you use to make these decisions? Which components did you use in making your decisions?

In this lesson you have learned that a per cent is a rate pair that represents a comparison and that has a second component of 100.

On your own

Express the rate pairs named in exercises 1 through 9 by using the per cent sign.

1 78/100	**4** 10/100	**7** 99/100
2 125/100	**5** 200/100	**8** 100/100
3 1/100	**6** 9/100	**9** 66/100

Write another name for each of the rate pairs expressed in exercises 10 through 18.

10 120%	**13** 71%	**16** 1000%
11 2%	**14** 5%	**17** 98%
12 500%	**15** 90%	**18** 43%

For each rate pair named in exercises 19 through 27, find an equivalent rate pair that has a second component of 100. Then express each rate pair by using the per cent sign.

19 4/5	**22** 90/30	**25** 10/1000
20 9/50	**23** 75/150	**26** 1000/10
21 32/64	**24** 96/32	**27** 5/4

At the beginning of the school year, several clubs in Logan School held membership drives. The chart in D8 shows how many new members each club hoped to have, and how many new members it actually did have at the end of the drive.

28 For each club listed in D8, write a ratio expressing the rate pair that compares the actual number of new members with the goal. The first component of the rate pair should refer to the number of new members obtained, and the second component should refer to the goal.

29 For each rate pair that you expressed for exercise 28, find an equivalent rate pair that has a second component of 100. Then express each rate pair by using the per cent sign.

30 Which per cents that you named for exercise 29 are greater than 100%? Less than 100%? Equal to 100%?

31 Which club did best in the membership drive? Which club did least well?

32 List the names of the clubs in the order of their performance. Start with the one that did best. Also express the per cent for each club.

33 If the Space Club had obtained 3 more members, would it have done better than the Pep Club? Explain your answer.

	New members	Membership goal
Camera Club	35	35
Drama Club	23	25
Glee Club	32	40
Mathematics Club	33	30
Pep Club	63	50
Space Club	18	15

D8

SPECIAL CHALLENGE

Each exercise below describes the intersection of two sets. If possible, make a sketch to represent the intersection. If a sketch cannot be made to represent the intersection, explain why it is impossible.

A The intersection of a segment and a triangle is the empty set.

B The intersection of a segment and a simple closed curve is a set with four members.

C The intersection of a line and a circle is a set with three members.

D The intersection of a triangle and a simple closed curve is a set with eight members.

E Points A and B are in the interior of a simple closed curve. The intersection of segment AB and the simple closed curve is a set with five members.

F The intersection of two planes is a set with one member.

G The intersection of a plane and a segment is an infinite set.

H The intersection of three planes is a set with one member.

I The intersection of a circle and a triangle is a set with five members.

4 46 **Exploring problems**

Problems involving per cents

You have learned that per cents are rate pairs that represent comparisons and that have second components of 100. In this lesson you will solve comparison problems by using what you have learned about per cents. U = C.

Read the problem in D1. You will develop the condition for the problem.

A The rate pair named at the right below represents the comparison of the number of students who live more than five blocks from Lee School with the number of students enrolled. What does the first component of the rate pair refer to? What does the second component refer to?

540/720

B The question in the problem asks you to find what per cent 540 is of 720. This means that you are to find how many students out of each 100 students enrolled live more than five blocks from school. How do you know that 100 is the second component of the rate pair whose first component you are to find? This rate pair is expressed at the right. For what is x a variable?

$x/100$

C What does the condition expressed below tell you about the rate pair whose first component you are to find?

$540/720 \sim x/100.$

D How do you obtain $54000 = 720x$ from $540/720 \sim x/100$?

540 of the 720 students enrolled at Lee School live more than five blocks from school. What per cent of the students live more than five blocks from school?

D1

Jack took a mathematics test that contained 40 questions. He answered 85% of the questions correctly. How many of the 40 questions did he answer correctly?

D2

Last summer Doris saved 54% of her earnings. She saved \$81. How many dollars did Doris earn last summer?

D3

E What number satisfies $54000 = 720x$?

F Tabulate $\{x \mid 540/720 \sim x/100\}$.

G Does the rate pair 75/100 tell you that, out of each 100 students enrolled at Lee School, 75 students live more than five blocks from school? Why is the rate pair 75/100 the same as 75%?

Now you can answer the question asked in the problem.

75% of the students enrolled at Lee School live more than five blocks from school.

H Read the problem in D2. What are you asked to find?

I You know that Jack answered 85% of the 40 questions correctly. This means that if Jack had done as well on a test that contained 100 questions, he would have answered 85 questions correctly.

J Is the rate pair named below at the right the same rate pair as 85%? What does the first component of this rate pair refer to? What does the second component refer to?

85/100

K The test contained 40 questions. How do you know that 40 is the second component of the rate pair whose first component you are to find? This rate pair is expressed at the right. For what is m a variable?

$m/40$

L What does the condition expressed below at the right tell you about the rate pair whose first component you are to find?

$85/100 \sim m/40.$

M Tabulate $\{m \mid 85/100 \sim m/40\}$.

Now you can use the solution of $85/100 \sim m/40$ to get the answer to the problem.

Jack answered 34 of the 40 questions correctly.

N Read the problem in D3. What are you asked to find?

O How do you know that Doris saved 54 dollars out of each 100 dollars she earned?

P Is 54/100 the same rate pair as 54%? To what does the first component of 54/100 refer? To what does the second component refer? What comparison is represented by 54/100?

54/100

Q You know that Doris saved 81 dollars. How do you know that 81 is the first component of the rate pair whose second component you are to find? For what is w a variable?

$81/w$

R What does the condition expressed below tell you about the rate pair whose second component you are to find?

$54/100 \sim 81/w.$

S Tabulate $\{w \mid 54/100 \sim 81/w\}$.

A Harold saves \$6 out of each \$10 that he earns. The money Harold saves is what per cent of the money he earns?

B 6 is what per cent of 10?

D4

6 is $x\%$ of 10.

D5

T Use the solution of $54/100 \sim 81/w$ to get the answer to the problem.

U Could the per cent used to compare the number of dollars saved with the number of dollars earned be greater than 100%? Explain your answer.

Now you will find the answers to other problems that involve per cents.

A Read problem A in D4. If you do not think about dollars, you can think of the question in problem A as it is written in problem B in D4. To find what per cent 6 is of 10, you must find the first component of a rate pair that has a second component of 100 and that is equivalent to 6/10.

B Is $6/10 \sim x/100$ the condition for problem A? Is it also the condition for problem B in D4?

C The condition expressed in D5 is also a condition for both problem A and problem B. How do you know that "6 is $x\%$ of 10" is the same condition as $6/10 \sim x/100$?

D What number satisfies $6/10 \sim x/100$? Does this number also satisfy "6 is $x\%$ of 10"? How do you know?

E Tabulate $\{x \mid 6/10 \sim x/100\}$.

F The money Harold saves is what per cent of the money he earns? 6 is what per cent of 10?

G Read problem C in D6. If you do not think about pages, you can think of the question in problem C as it is written in problem D in D6. To find 30% of 320, you must find the first component of a rate pair that has a second component of 320 and that is equivalent to 30/100.

H Is $30/100 \sim s/320$ the condition for problem C? Is it also the condition for problem D in D6?

I Is "30% of 320 is s" also the condition for ? problem C? For problem D?

J What number satisfies $30/100 \sim s/320$? Explain why this number also satisfies "30% of 320 is s."

K How many pages did Dolores read that evening? 30% of 320 is what number?

L Read problem E in D7. If you do not think about dollars, you can think of the question in problem E as it is written in problem F in D7. To find this number, you must find the second component of a rate pair that has a first component of 270 and is equivalent to 5/100.

M Is $5/100 \sim 270/n$ the condition for problem E? Is it also the condition for problem F in D7?

N Is "270 is 5% of n" the same condition as $5/100 \sim 270/n$?

O What number satisfies both $5/100 \sim 270/n$ and "270 is 5% of n"?

P Last year, Mr. Roberts' take-home pay was how many dollars? 270 is 5% of what number?

Q Read the problem in D8. Is $12/8 \sim x/100$ the condition for the problem?

R Why is 12/8, and not 8/12, used in the con- ? dition?

S Tabulate $\{x \mid 12/8 \sim x/100\}$.

T Answer the question asked in the problem.

U Read the problem in D9. 125 is which component of the rate pair that you are given?

C Dolores was reading a 320-page book. She read 30% of the pages in one evening. How many pages did she read that evening?

D 30% of 320 is what number?

D6

E Last year Mr. Roberts saved 5% of his take-home pay. He saved \$270. What was his take-home pay?

F 270 is 5% of what number?

D7

June sold 8 tickets to the school play, and Martin sold 12 tickets. The number of tickets Martin sold is what per cent of the number of tickets June sold?

D8

125% of 32 is what number?

D9

V 32 is which component of the rate pair you ? are to find?

W Write a sentence that expresses the condition for the problem in D9.

X Tabulate the solution set of the condition.

Y Use the solution of the condition as the answer to the problem.

In this lesson you have learned to use per cents to solve problems.

On your own

For each problem, write a sentence that expresses the condition for the problem. You may use any letter to name the variable. Then tabulate the solution set and answer the question asked in the problem. U = C.

1 A weather bureau reported that 40% of the days in April were cloudy. How many days in April were cloudy?

2 During a basketball game, David made 7 baskets out of 20 tries. The number of baskets David made was what per cent of the number of tries?

3 One year the Toronto Maple Leafs had 16 players on their hockey team. 25% of these players played centre ice. How many centre ice players did the Maple Leafs have that year?

4 20% of all the students at Long School are in the seventh grade. 92 students are enrolled in the seventh grade. How many students in all are enrolled at Long School?

5 Henry worked 15 mathematics problems and had correct answers for 100% of them. How many correct answers did he have?

6 During a fund-raising drive, the students in Cook School raised \$52, and the students in Fisher School raised \$65. The number of dollars raised by the students in Cook School was what per cent of the number of dollars raised by the students in Fisher School?

7 Use the information given in problem 6 to answer the following question: The number of dollars raised by the students in Fisher School was what per cent of the number of dollars raised by the students in Cook School?

8 Bill sold his bicycle for \$39. This was 65% of the price he had paid for it. How many dollars had he paid for the bicycle?

9 During a sale, Marilyn paid \$30 for a coat that was regularly priced at \$40. The sale price of the coat is what per cent of the regular price?

10 In 1940, a British Columbia newspaper estimated that the province's population by 1960 would be 175% of its population in 1940. In 1940, the population was 800,000. What was the estimated population of British Columbia for 1960?

11 Mr. Becker's monthly take-home pay amounts to \$340. His monthly salary amounts to \$425. His monthly take-home pay is what per cent of his monthly salary?

12 5% of the science club members have paid their yearly dues of 50¢. Four members have paid their dues. How many members does the science club have?

13 The land area of Canada is about 3,560,000 square miles. 16% of this land is suitable for agriculture. About how many square miles of land are suitable for agriculture?

14 Mr. White sold his house for \$17,250. The selling price was 138% of the price he originally paid for the house. How many dollars did Mr. White pay for his house?

15 An urban population is defined as the number of persons residing within the boundaries of cities, towns, and villages of 1,000 or more persons. In 1956 the total population of Canada was 16,080,791. The urban population was about 65% of the total population. What was the approximate urban population in 1956?

16 In 1956, the urban population of Manitoba was about 510,000. This was about 60% of the total population of the province. What was the approximate total population of Manitoba in 1956?

17 What number is 20% of 185?

18 150 is what per cent of 30?

19 What number is 16% of 425?

20 42 is 84% of what number?

21 174% of what number is 348?

22 47 is what per cent of 94?

23 What per cent of 47 is 94?

24 What number is 150% of 242?

25 1536 is 32% of what number?

APPLYING MATHEMATICS

In this lesson you will use per cents to solve problems that involve business arithmetic. You may want to refer to "Applying mathematics" on pages 184-185 for the meaning of some of the business terms.

For each problem, first write a sentence that expresses the condition for the problem. You may use any letter to name the variable. Then tabulate the solution set and answer the question asked in the problem. U = C.

1 Mr. Beck sold $2500 worth of merchandise. He received a commission of $200. His commission was what per cent of his sales?

2 In problem 1 you found what per cent the commission was of the total sales. This per cent of the total sales is the *rate of commission*. Mr. Monroe sold $5000 worth of merchandise. He received a commission of $450. What rate of commission did Mr. Monroe receive?

3 Mr. Martin's rate of commission is 4%. One month he sold $9650 worth of merchandise. What was the amount of his commission?

4 Miss Richardson gets a 5% commission on her total sales. One week her commission was $142. How many dollars' worth of merchandise had Miss Richardson sold that week?

5 Judy received a $5 discount on a dress that was regularly priced at $25. The discount was what per cent of the regular price?

6 In problem 5 you found what per cent the discount was of the regular price. This per cent of the regular price is the *rate of discount*. Mrs. Carey received a $45 discount on a television set that was regularly priced at $180. What was the rate of discount?

7 During a sale, Dobson's Music Store gave a discount of 20% on all merchandise. How much discount did Mr. Bailey receive on a phonograph that was regularly priced at $375?

8 A manufacturer gives a 2% discount to any buyer who pays for an order within 30 days. Mr. Jacobs paid for his order immediately and received a discount of $60. How many dollars' worth of merchandise had Mr. Jacobs bought?

9 Mr. Harvey borrowed $500 and paid $30 interest at the end of one year. The amount of money on which interest is paid is the *principal*. The interest that Mr. Harvey paid was what per cent of the principal?

10 In problem 9 you found what per cent the interest was of the principal. This per cent of the principal is the *rate of interest*. Unless stated otherwise, the rate of interest is given for one year. Mr. Evans paid $10 interest on $200 that he had borrowed. What rate of interest did he pay?

11 Mr. Howard borrowed $8500 and agreed to pay 4% interest. How many dollars of interest did he have to pay at the end of one year?

12 The First Federal Bank charged 5% interest on a loan to Mr. Taylor. After one year, Mr. Taylor paid the bank $69 interest. How many dollars had he borrowed?

13 Mr. Hanson's weekly take-home pay is 80% of his salary. His take-home pay amounts to $112. What is his weekly salary?

14 Mr. Adams bought a suit during a sale and received a discount of $9. The regular price of the suit was $75. What was the rate of discount?

15 Mr. Ross sells property for a real-estate company. He receives a 5% commission on all sales. He received $545 for selling a house. What was the selling price of this house?

16 Mr. Allen agreed to pay 4% interest on $600 he borrowed. How many dollars' interest did he owe at the end of one year?

17 Miss Harper's weekly salary is $80. Her take-home pay is $64. Her take-home pay is what per cent of her salary?

18 Mrs. Burton borrowed \$1750 from a bank. At the end of one year, she owed \$105 interest. What rate of interest had she been charged?

19 During a sale, a store advertised "All merchandise reduced 15%." The discount on a certain rug was \$21. What was the price of the rug before the sale?

20 Miss Carter's monthly salary is \$450. Her take-home pay is 78% of her monthly salary. Her monthly take-home pay amounts to how many dollars?

21 Mr. Howe sold a house and lot for \$28,400. He received a commission of \$852. What was his rate of commission?

22 A merchant was given a 32% discount on a coat that was priced at \$175. He was given a discount of how many dollars?

23 Mr. Lund's yearly take-home pay is \$5312. His take-home pay is 83% of his salary. What is his yearly salary?

24 Mr. Peters sold his house at an auction for \$16,700. He paid the auctioneer a 5% commission on the total amount of the sale. How many dollars did he pay the auctioneer?

KEEPING SKILFUL

Tabulate the solution set of each condition expressed in exercises 1 through 24. U = C.

1 $5/3 \sim b/36$.
2 8 is n% of 10.
3 $4938 + 3967 = f$.
4 $21/w \sim 28/8$.
5 275 is 10% of x.
6 $34m = 14144$.
7 $b/45 \sim 32/20$.
8 f is 6% of 300.
9 $18/8 \sim 144/s$.
10 $806(150) = d$.
11 $325 - 178 > n$.
12 300 is 200% of p.
13 $3827 - k = 948$.
14 $50/x \sim 50/100$.
15 d is 16% of 2375.
16 $529 + h < 735$.
17 123 is x% of 82.
18 $138n = 31326$.
19 $h/90 \sim 250/100$.
20 420 is m% of 420.
21 $85/17 \sim g/187$.
22 $h > 42(73)$.
23 390 is d% of 78.
24 $486/324 \sim 12/s$.

4 | 47 Exploring problems

Problems involving compound conditions about rate pairs

You have solved problems that involve simple conditions for equivalence. In this lesson you will learn how to solve problems by using compound conditions that contain rate pairs.

Read the problem in D1. First you will develop a compound condition for the problem. U = C × C.

A You know that Jane has 4 times as many records as Sally. This means that for each 4 records that Jane has, Sally has 1 record. Use 4 as the first component of the rate pair that represents this comparison. What number will you use as the second component of this rate pair? 4/1

B You know one rate pair that represents the comparison. You want to find other rate pairs equivalent to 4/1. Use x as a variable for the number of records Jane can have. Why is x a variable for the first component instead of for the second component of each rate pair? x/y

C Since y is used as a variable for the second component, to what does y refer?

Jane has 4 times as many phonograph records as Sally has. Jane has fewer than 25 phonograph records. How many records can each of the girls have?

D1

D Now you can express one simple condition for the problem. Does the sentence at the right express this simple condition?

$4/1 \sim x/y.$

E Why is the idea of "less than" used in another simple condition for the problem? Does the sentence at the right express this other simple condition? For what is x a variable?

$x < 25.$

F Does the sentence below at the right express a compound condition for the problem?

$4/1 \sim x/y \wedge x < 25.$

Now you can find the solution set of the compound condition.

G Is the proportional relation tabulated in D2 the solution set of $4/1 \sim x/y$? Is the solution set an infinite set?

> REMINDER
>
> $\{4/1, \ldots\}$ is the set whose members are the rate pair 4/1 and all rate pairs equivalent to 4/1.
>
> *See lesson 42, page 174.*

H Name five other rate pairs that are members of the proportional relation tabulated in D2.

I Each solution of the compound condition must satisfy both $4/1 \sim x/y$ and $x < 25$. Which members of $\{4/1, \ldots\}$ have first components that are less than 25? Can you use each of these members as a solution of $4/1 \sim x/y \wedge x < 25$?

J Tabulate $\{(x, y) | 4/1 \sim x/y \wedge x < 25\}$.

You can use each solution of the compound condition to get an answer to the problem.

If Jane has 4 records, Sally has 1 record.
If Jane has 8 records, Sally has 2 records.
If Jane has 12 records, Sally has 3 records.

Jane has 4 times as many phonograph records as Sally has. Jane has fewer than 25 phonograph records. How many records can each of the girls have?

D1

$\{4/1, \ldots\}$

D2

Mr. Taylor borrowed $260 from a bank. At the end of one year, he paid the bank $273. What was the rate of interest charged by the bank?

D3

Jim bought 2 pencils priced at 3 for 15¢ and 3 erasers priced at 4¢ each. How many cents in all did he spend for these articles?

D4

K What are the other answers to the problem in D1?

Read the problem in D3. You will develop the compound condition for this problem. $U = C \times C$.

L The problem asks you to find the rate of interest. To do this, you must find the number of dollars of interest that the bank charged for each $100 that it loaned. Use m as a variable for the number of dollars of interest charged per $100. Does the rate pair named at the right represent the rate of interest charged?

m

$m/100$

M Do you know how many dollars of interest Mr. Taylor paid for the use of \$260? Use n as a variable for the number of dollars of interest that he paid. n

N Why do you use $n/260$, and not $260/n$? Why do you use $n/260$, and not $n/273$? $n/260$

O Does the sentence at the right express a simple condition for the problem? $m/100 \sim n/260.$

P Why is n, and not m, used in another simple condition for the problem? Does the sentence at the right express this other simple condition? $273 - 260 = n.$

Q Does the sentence in red below express the compound condition for the problem?

$$m/100 \sim n/260 \wedge 273 - 260 = n.$$

Now you can find the solution of the compound condition.

R What replacement can you make for n that satisfies $273 - 260 = n$?

S If you replace n by 13 in $m/100 \sim n/260$, do you obtain $m/100 \sim 13/260$?

T What number satisfies $m/100 \sim 13/260$?

You know that (5, 13) satisfies $m/100 \sim n/260 \wedge 273 - 260 = n$. You can use (5, 13) to get the answer to the problem.

Since Mr. Taylor paid \$13 interest on \$260, the rate of interest charged by the bank was \$5 on each \$100, or 5%.

Read the problem in D4. The exercises that follow will help you develop a condition for the problem. The universe for each of the variables is C.

A Do you know how many cents Jim spent for pencils? For erasers? Use a as a variable for the number of cents Jim spent for pencils. Use b as a variable for the number of cents he spent for erasers. Why is $a + b$, and not $a - b$, used in the condition? $a + b$

B Do you know how many cents Jim spent in all? Use n as a variable for the total number of cents Jim spent. n

C Does the sentence at the right express a simple condition for the problem? $a + b = n.$

D You know that 3 pencils cost 15¢. Does the rate pair named below at the right represent this rate? What does the first component of the rate pair refer to? What does the second component refer to? $3/15$

E You must find how many cents Jim spent for 2 pencils. Remember that a refers to the number of cents he spent for pencils. Why do you use $2/a$, and not $a/2$? $2/a$

F Does the sentence at the right express another simple condition for the problem? $3/15 \sim 2/a.$

G You know that each eraser cost 4¢. Does the rate pair named below at the right represent this rate? What does the first component of the rate pair refer to? What does the second component refer to? $1/4$

H You must find how many cents Jim spent for 3 erasers. Why do you use $3/b$, and not $b/3$? $3/b$

I Does the sentence at the right express another simple condition for the problem? $1/4 \sim 3/b.$

J Does the sentence below express a compound condition for the problem in D4?

$$a + b = n \wedge 3/15 \sim 2/a \wedge 1/4 \sim 3/b.$$

Now you can find the answer to the problem. First you find the solutions of the simple conditions for equivalence. Then you use these solutions to find the solution of the condition for equality.

K What number satisfies $3/15 \sim 2/a$? What number satisfies $1/4 \sim 3/b$?

L If you replace a by 10 and b by 12 in $a + b = n$, do you obtain $10 + 12 = n$?

M What number satisfies $10 + 12 = n$?

N How many cents in all did Jim spend for the pencils and erasers?

Now you know how to solve problems by using compound conditions that involve rate pairs.

On your own

For each of problems 1 through 12, write a sentence that expresses a compound condition. Use any letters you wish to express the variables. Tabulate the solution set of the compound condition and use the solutions to get the answers to the problem. $U = C \times C$.

1 During a basketball game, Mike scored 4 points for each 3 points that Paul scored. Paul scored fewer than 14 points during the game. How many points could each of the boys have scored?

2 In a school election, Carl received 2 votes for each 5 votes that George received. If Carl had received 18 more votes than he did, both boys would have received the same number of votes. How many votes did each of the boys receive?

3 The price of an article after the discount has been deducted is the *net price*. Mrs. Mason received a 10% discount on a lamp that was regularly priced at \$20. The net price amounted to how many dollars?

4 A store gave a 15% discount on a clothes drier that was regularly priced at \$220. The net price of this drier amounted to how many dollars?

5 Larry had 274 stamps in his collection. He bought 5 packages of new stamps. Each package contained 24 stamps. How many stamps did Larry have after he bought the 5 packages?

6 Carol bought a loaf of bread priced at 27¢ and 6 oranges priced at 48¢ per dozen. How many cents in all did she spend for bread and oranges?

7 The number of stamps Jay has is 125% of the number of stamps Ed has. If Ed had 128 more stamps, he would have 364. How many stamps does each of the boys have?

8 Mr. Thomas borrowed \$300 from a credit union. He agreed to pay back \$303 at the end of one month. What was the rate of interest for one month on this loan?

9 Mr. Henderson borrowed \$1250 from his bank. At the end of one year, he paid the bank \$1325. What was the rate of interest?

10 Louise bought three 8-ounce bags of mints and a 12-ounce bag of caramels. How many ounces of candy in all did she buy?

11 The regular price of a chair was \$140. The net price of the chair was \$91. What was the rate of discount?

12 For each 4 lawns that Ed mowed last week, Frank mowed 3 lawns. Together, the boys mowed fewer than 15 lawns. How many lawns could each of the boys have mowed?

For problem 13, write a sentence that expresses a compound condition for the problem. Then give the answer to the problem. The universe for each of the variables is C.

13 Tickets for a school fair were priced at 25¢ for adults and 10¢ for children. Mr. Brown bought 3 tickets for adults and 2 tickets for children. How many cents in all did Mr. Brown spend for the tickets?

Abstract problems involving rate pairs

You have been using conditions for equivalence to solve problems about persons and things. In this lesson you will use conditions for equivalence to solve problems that concern numbers only. $U = C \times C$.

A Read the problem in D1. Use m as a variable for the first component of each rate pair you are to find. Use n as a variable for the second component of each rate pair. Is $m/n \sim 5/3$ one of the simple conditions for the problem? Is $n < 12$ the other simple condition?

B What is the compound condition for the problem?

Now you will find the solution set of the compound condition.

C Is the proportional relation tabulated in D2 the solution set of $m/n \sim 5/3$? Is this set an infinite set?

D Explain how you know that both 20/12 and 25/15 are members of the set tabulated in D2.

E You know that each solution of the compound condition must satisfy both $m/n \sim 5/3$ and $n < 12$. How do you know that 20/12 and 25/15 do not satisfy $m/n \sim 5/3 \wedge n < 12$?

F Which members of the set tabulated in D2 satisfy $n < 12$? Do these rate pairs satisfy the compound condition?

G Tabulate $\{(m, n) | m/n \sim 5/3 \wedge n < 12\}$. Is the set you tabulated an infinite set?

H Is each solution of the compound condition an answer to the problem in D1?

Certain rate pairs are equivalent to 5/3. The second component of each of these rate pairs is less than 12. What are the rate pairs?

D1

$\{5/3, \ldots\}$

D2

A certain rate pair is equivalent to 2/8. The sum of the first component and second component of this rate pair is 20. What is the rate pair?

D3

$\{1/4, \ldots\}$

D4

I Read the problem in D3. Use x as a variable for the first component of the rate pair you are to find. Use y as a variable for the second component of this rate pair. Is $x/y \sim 2/8$ one of the simple conditions for the problem? Is $x + y = 20$ the other simple condition?

J What is the compound condition for the problem?

Now you will find the solution set of the compound condition.

K Is the proportional relation tabulated in D4 the solution set of $x/y \sim 2/8$? Is $\{(x, y) | x/y \sim 2/8\}$ an infinite set?

L Is 5/20 a member of the set tabulated in D4? Is 6/24 a member? Is 8/32 a member? How do you know?

M How do you know that 5/20, 6/24, and 8/32 do not satisfy $x + y = 20$? Do any of these rate pairs satisfy the compound condition?

A certain rate pair is equivalent to 2/8. The sum of the first component and second component of this rate pair is 20. What is the rate pair?

D3

$\{1/4, \ldots\}$

D4

Certain rate pairs are equivalent to 6/8. The first component of each of these rate pairs is less than the second component. What are the rate pairs?

D5

$$h/k \sim 6/8 \wedge h < k.$$

D6

N Which member of the set tabulated in D4 satisfies $x + y = 20$? Does this rate pair also satisfy the compound condition?

O Tabulate $\{(x, y) | x/y \sim 2/8 \wedge x + y = 20\}$.

P Is 4/16 the answer to the problem in D3?

Q Read the problem in D5. Use h as a variable for the first component of each rate pair you are to find. Use k as a variable for the second component.

R Does the sentence in D6 express the compound condition for the problem?

S Tabulate $\{(h, k) | h/k \sim 6/8\}$.

T Which members of the set you tabulated for exercise S have a first component that is less than the second component?

U Tabulate $\{(h, k) | h/k \sim 6/8 \wedge h < k\}$. Is the set you tabulated an infinite set?

V Does each rate pair that satisfies $h/k \sim 6/8$ also satisfy the compound condition?

In this lesson you have learned to solve problems that ask questions about rate pairs. The conditions that you used for the problems were compound conditions.

On your own

For each problem, write a sentence that expresses the compound condition for the problem. You may use any letters you wish as names for the variables. Then tabulate the solution set of the compound condition. $U = C \times C$.

1 Certain rate pairs are equivalent to 4/6. The sum of the first component and second component of each of these rate pairs is less than 20. What are the rate pairs?

2 Certain rate pairs are equivalent to 3/7. The first component of each of these rate pairs is less than 25. What are the rate pairs?

3 A certain rate pair is equivalent to 4/9. The first component of this rate pair is twice the first component of 4/9. What is the rate pair?

4 A certain rate pair is equivalent to 15/18. The second component of this rate pair is 1 more than the first component. What is the rate pair?

5 Certain rate pairs are equivalent to 2/10. The second component of each of these rate pairs is less than 10 times the first component. What are the rate pairs?

6 Certain rate pairs are equivalent to 2/2. The sum of the first component and second component of each of these rate pairs is less than 15. What are the rate pairs?

7 A certain rate pair is equivalent to 7/8. The second component of this rate pair is 3 more than the first component. What is the rate pair?

8 Certain rate pairs are equivalent to 9/6. The first component of each of these rate pairs is less than the sum of the second component and 4. What are the rate pairs?

9 Certain rate pairs are equivalent to 2/3. The sum of the first component and second component of each of these rate pairs is less than 5. What are the rate pairs?

10 A certain rate pair is equivalent to 8/5. The sum of the first component and second component of this rate pair is 52. What is the rate pair?

APPLYING MATHEMATICS

In this lesson you will solve problems similar to those you have studied so far in this book. For each problem, first write a sentence that expresses a condition for the problem. Use any letters you wish as names for the variables. Then tabulate the solution set of the condition and give the answer to the problem. The universe is given for each problem.

1 In a recent year, the expenses of the Canadian railways were $37,220,149 less than the earnings. The expenses amounted to $1,232,387,115. The earnings of the railways amounted to how many dollars? U = N.

2 The second United States astronaut traveled at a rate of approximately 337 miles per minute. At this rate, approximately how many miles did he travel in 15 minutes? U = C.

3 Harriet had more than 20 concert tickets to sell. She sold 14 tickets and then had fewer than 9 left to sell. How many tickets could Harriet have had to begin with? U = N.

4 Joe's golf score at the end of nine holes was 54. His score at the end of eighteen holes was more than 113. What is the lowest score he could have had on the second nine holes? U = N.

5 During a sale, a store advertised "15% off on all merchandise." Mrs. Horton bought a fur jacket and received a discount of $72. What was the regular price of the jacket? U = C.

6 For a science project, Donna mounted a total of 6 moths and butterflies. How many moths and how many butterflies could she have mounted? U = C × C.

7 Mr. Carter planted fewer than 12 shrubs and trees. He planted the same number of trees as shrubs. How many trees and how many shrubs could he have planted? U = C × C.

8 During a sale, a dress shop gave a discount of 20% on all merchandise. The regular price of a dress that was on sale was $30. What was the net price of this dress? U = C × C.

9 The melting point of copper is 1083° centigrade, and the melting point of iron is 1533° centigrade. The melting point of iron is how many degrees higher than the melting point of copper? U = N.

10 Mr. Lee receives a 4% commission on his monthly sales. During October, he sold $7475 worth of merchandise. His October commission amounted to how many dollars? U = C.

11 An outfielder had 36 doubles during a recent baseball season. He had 9 doubles for each 47 hits that season. How many hits did he have that season? U = C.

12 Carol did not have enough money to buy a book that cost 57 cents. After her mother gave her 15 cents, she had more than 62 cents. How many cents could Carol have had before her mother gave her the 15 cents? U = N.

13 The regular price of a sofa was $348. During a sale, the net price of this sofa was less than $252. What is the least number of dollars the discount could have been? U = N.

14 Mr. Bates borrowed $750 from the First Federal Savings Bank. At the end of one year, the interest on his loan amounted to $45. What was the rate of interest? U = C.

15 Helen is 9 years older than Anita. In 4 years, Anita will be 17 years old. How old is each of the girls now? U = C × C.

16 The citizens of West Haven had a campaign to raise $7500 for a new playground. By the end of the campaign, they had raised $8625. The amount raised was what per cent of the goal? U = C.

17 Bill has 15 more arrowheads than Ken has. If Ken had 23 more, he would have 50 arrowheads. How many arrowheads does each of the boys have? U = N × N.

18 Tom bought 4 pieces of miniature railroad track for 13 cents each. He gave the clerk 75 cents. How many cents should he have received in change? U = C × C.

19 When Janet went to the store, she had a total of 11 dimes and nickels in her purse. She had 5 more dimes than nickels. How many nickels and how many dimes did she have? U = N × N.

20 36 is what per cent of 225? U = C.

21 The sum of two numbers is less than 15. When the first number is subtracted from the second number, the difference is 9. What can the numbers be? U = N × N.

22 What numbers greater than 386 can be added to 134 so that each sum is greater than 525? U = N.

23 When the first component of each of certain rate pairs equivalent to 8/12 is subtracted from the second component, the difference is less than 8. What are these rate pairs? U = C × C.

24 What number is 68% of 9350? U = C.

25 The sum of two numbers is 15. The second number is less than the quotient of 78 and 13. What can the numbers be? U = N × N.

26 The sum of the first and second components of each of certain rate pairs equivalent to 6/5 is less than 35. What are the rate pairs? U = C × C.

27 15 is 125% of what number? U = C.

28 28 is what per cent of 112? U = C.

29 What number is 11% of 200? U = C.

CHECKING UP

The small numeral within parentheses tells what page to turn to if you need help with an exercise.

Test 46

Write "T" for each sentence below that expresses a true statement. Write "F" for each sentence that expresses a false statement.

1 The second component of 47% is 100. (187)

2 5/7 ~ 45/56. (174)

3 4/3 is a member of {8/6, . . .}. (174)

4 If you multiply each component of (6, 18) by 3, you obtain (18, 36). (170)

5 (3, 8) and (42, 112) are equivalent ordered pairs. (168)

6 A proportional relation is a set of ordered pairs in which each member is equivalent to each of the other members. (170)

7 If you divide each component of (60, 132) by 12, you obtain (5, 11). (170)

8 There is exactly one member in {2/9, . . .}. (174)

9 {3/5, . . .} = {9/15, . . .}. (175)

10 When U = C, the solution set of $16x = 32$ is the same as the solution set of $8/x \sim 4/16$. (177)

Test 47

From the list given below each exercise, choose the expression that correctly completes the exercise.

11 {9/12, . . .} does not contain the rate pair ——. (174)

a 12/15 b 6/8 c 27/36 d 3/4

12 If 8/3 ~ 32/12, then ——. (174)

a 32(8) = 12(3). c 8(12) = 32(3).

b 3(12) = 8(32). d 12(8) = 12(3).

13 When a regular price is reduced, the amount of the reduction is called the ——. (184)

a service charge c net price

b commission d discount

14 If you divide each component of (119, 301) by ~~~, you obtain the ordered pair (17, 43). (170)

a 3 b 7 c 11 d 13

15 A charge for the use of money is called ~~~. (184)

a discount c interest
b commission d principal

16 ~~~ does not express the rate pair 2 to 3. (173)

a 2/3 b (2, 3) c {2, 3} d 2:3

17 (10, 6) is not equivalent to ~~~. (187)

a 5/3 b 20/12 c 10% d (15, 9)

18 ~~~ is a member of {2/3, . . .}, and the sum of its components is 20. (195)

a 6/14 b 8/12 c 10/15 d 4/16

19 ~~~ represents the same comparison as 30%. (188)

a 6/30 b 30/100 c 30/50 d 3/100

Test 48

For exercises 20 through 25, decide for each ordered pair expressed what replacement should be made for m to obtain an ordered pair that is equivalent to (24, 36). U = C. (171)

20 $(12, m)$ 22 $(4, m)$ 24 $(72, m)$
21 $(m, 72)$ 23 $(m, 9)$ 25 $(m, 3)$

For exercises 26 through 29, U = C. For exercises 30, 31, and 32, U = C × C. Tabulate each set described.

26 $\{x \mid 8/10 \sim x/15\}$ (178)

27 $\{x \mid 48/18 \sim x/12\}$ (178)

28 $\{x \mid 16/x \sim 1/16\}$ (178)

29 $\{x \mid 20/x \sim 85/34\}$ (178)

30 $\{(x, y) \mid x/y \sim 3/5 \wedge y - x = 6\}$ (195)

31 $\{(x, y) \mid x/y \sim 4/5 \wedge x + y < 40\}$ (195)

32 $\{(x, y) \mid x < y + 5 \wedge x/y \sim 2/3\}$ (195)

Test 49

For each problem, write a sentence that expresses a condition, tabulate the solution set of the condition, and give the answer to the problem. The universe is given for each problem.

33 Six pencils cost 25¢. What is the cost of 18 of these pencils? U = C. (176)

34 For every 5 correct answers that Joan had on a test, Barbara had 4 correct answers. Joan had 45 correct answers. How many correct answers did Barbara have? U = C. (180)

35 15% of all the students enrolled in Westview School are in the school band. There are 54 students in the band. How many students are enrolled in Westview School? U = C. (190)

36 Mr. Hanson receives a commission of $70 for each $1000 worth of merchandise he sells. What rate of commission does he receive? U = C. (194)

37 During a sale, a clothing store sold all merchandise at a 20% discount. What was the discount on a suit that was regularly priced at $45? U = C. (190)

38 Mr. Bender bought a set of tools. The regular price of the set was $140. Mr. Bender received a 15% discount. How much did he pay for the set of tools? U = C × C. (195)

39 During the baseball season last year, Bob had 3 hits for each 2 hits that Larry had. In all, Bob had 8 more hits than Larry. How many hits did each boy have? U = C × C. (195)

40 What number is 60% of 25? U = C. (192)

41 48 is 200% of what number? U = C. (192)

42 13 is what per cent of 25? U = C. (191)

43 15% of 120 is what number? U = C. (192)

44 105 is what per cent of 75? U = C. (191)

45 A certain rate pair is equivalent to 5/6 and has a second component that is 4 more than the first component. What is the rate pair? U = C × C. (199)

46 Each of certain rate pairs equivalent to 2/3 also has a second component less than 25. What are the rate pairs? U = C × C. (199)

CHECKING UP

The small numeral within parentheses tells what page to turn to for help if you need it.

Test 50

For exercises 1 through 7, write "T" for each sentence that expresses a true statement. Write "F" for each sentence that expresses a false statement.

1 A graph is a set of dots. (52)

2 $\{1, 3, 5, 7, 9\} = \{9, 5, 1, 7, 3\}$. (12)

3 The surface of a ball suggests a plane. (31)

4 The supplement of a right angle is a right angle. (107)

5 Ray MN is the same as ray NM. (105)

6 If set R has 2 members and set S has 7 members, then $R \times S$ has 14 members. (127)

7 $\{(2, 10), (4, 20), (7, 35)\}$ is a proportional relation. (170)

Test 51

From the list below each exercise, choose the expression that correctly completes the exercise.

8 If $U = N$, then $\{2, 3, 4, 5\}$ is the solution set of ——. (92)

a $x > 1 \wedge x > 5$. **c** $x < 2 \wedge x > 6$.
b $x > 2 \wedge x < 6$. **d** $x > 1 \wedge x < 6$.

9 $A = \{0, 1, 2\}$, $B = \{2, 4\}$, and $C = \{0, 4\}$. $A \cap B \cap C =$ ——. (84)

a $\{0, 4\}$ **b** $\{0, 1, 2, 4\}$ **c** $\{\ \}$ **d** $\{0, 1, 2\}$

10 If $D = \{\ \}$, $E = \{0\}$, and $F = \{0, 2, 4\}$, then $D \cup E \cup F =$ ——. (88)

a $\{0\}$ **b** $\{\ \}$ **c** $\{0, 2\}$ **d** $\{0, 2, 4\}$

11 The intersection of two parallel planes ——. (99)

a contains one member **c** is a line
b is the empty set **d** is an angle

12 In D1, the encircled dots form a graph of the solution set of ——. $U = N$. (53)

a $x - 2 > 2$. **c** $x + 1 > 4$.
b $7 > x + 3$. **d** $7 - x > 4$.

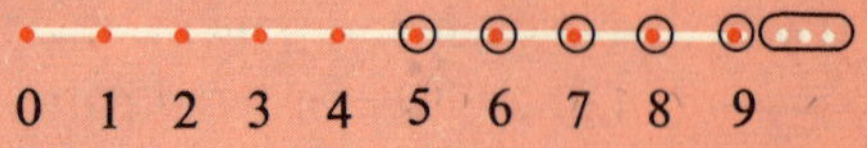

D1

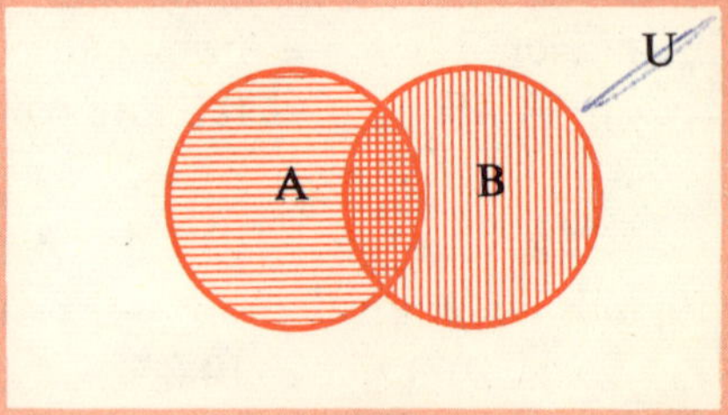

D2

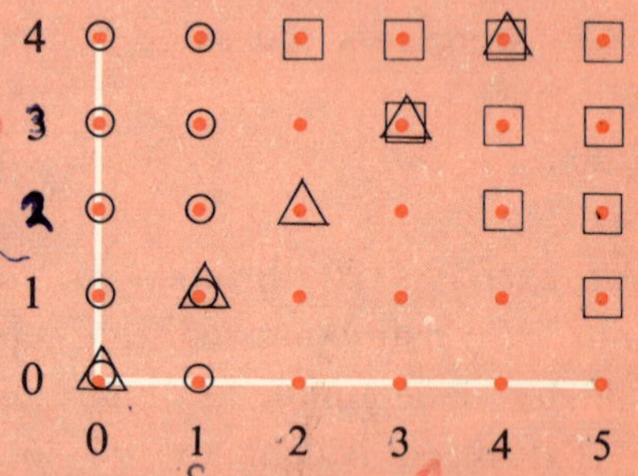

D3

13 Look at D2. The Venn diagram shows you that ——. (85)

a A is a subset of B. **c** A and B are disjoint.
b A and B meet. **d** B is a subset of A.

14 A —— does not separate a plane. (115)

a line **b** ray **c** circle **d** triangle

15 —— represents the same rate as 1 to 5. (174)

a (3, 10) **b** $\{5, 20\}$ **c** 25% **d** 6/30

Test 52

Use the graph in D3 for exercises 16 through 24.

16 The set of dots in D3 is a graph of $R \times S$. $R \times S$ is the universe for (x,y). How many members are in $R \times S$? (131)

17 Tabulate R. (130)

18 Tabulate S. (130)

19 How are the dots in the graph of $\{(x,y) | x < 2\}$ indicated? (135)

20 How are the dots in the graph of the solution set of $x = y$ indicated? (132)

21 How are the dots in the graph of the solution set of $x + y > 5$ indicated? (132)

22 How are the dots in the graph of the solution set of $x < 2 \wedge x = y$ indicated? (147)

23 Tabulate $\{(x,y) | x = y \wedge x + y > 5\}$. (147)

24 Tabulate $\{(x,y) | x + y > 5 \wedge x < 2\}$. (147)

Test 53

For each of the following problems, first write a sentence that expresses a condition. Use any letters you wish as names for the variables. Then tabulate the solution set of the condition and give the answer to the problem. The universe is given for each problem.

25 Sally made 13 aprons. Martha made 5 fewer aprons than Sally. How many aprons did Martha make? U = N. (68)

26 Nancy sold 23 tickets to a school play. Nancy and Ruth sold fewer than 39 tickets in all. How many tickets could Ruth have sold? U = C. (73)

27 The combined score that two teams made during a football game was 18 points. The winning team scored more than 9 points. How many points could the losing team have scored? U = N × N. (153)

28 Carol's school was in session 180 days last year. Carol was absent on 5% of the days. How many days was she absent? U = C. (190)

29 In a volleyball game, Pete's team scored 3 points for every 2 points scored by Harold's team. If Pete's team scored fewer than 16 points, what is the greatest number of points that Harold's team could have scored? U = C × C. (195)

Unit 5

Numeration systems

5 | 49 **Exploring ideas**

Tally, code, and grouping numeration systems

In your study of mathematics you have used many symbols to express ideas. You have used ratios to express rate pairs, for example, and you have used sentences to express statements. You have also learned that a numeral expresses, or names, a number.

In earlier grades you learned how to express the natural numbers and fractions by using a decimal system for naming numbers. The decimal system you used included the symbols 0, 1, 2, and so on. In this unit you will learn more about the decimal numerals for the natural numbers. You will also study other systems for naming the natural numbers. By studying the properties of several different systems for naming numbers, you will better understand the properties of the familiar decimal system.

A Look at D1. When you look at the oval markers, you can think of any objects you wish. For example, you can think of model airplanes or pencils or books. Each stroke in D1 represents one of the objects. Are there as many strokes as there are objects?

The set of strokes is one way to name the number of objects. A numeral that is written as a set of one or more strokes is a *tally numeral.*

B How many different kinds of symbols are used in the tally numeral in D1?

C Think of each stroke in the tally numeral as expressing the number 1. By adding these numbers, you can find the number of objects repre-

D1

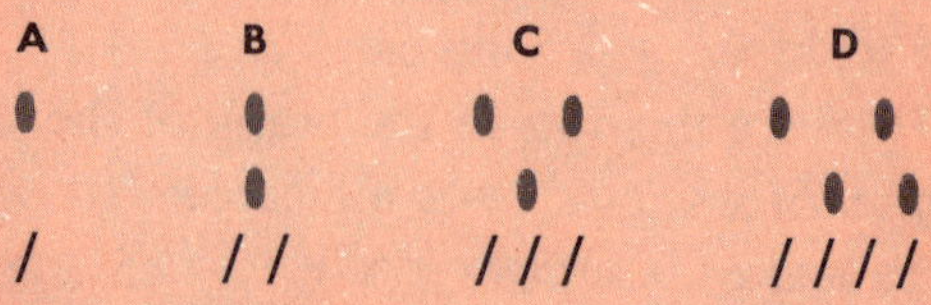

D2

sented in D1. What decimal numeral expresses the number of objects?

Notice that you can write a tally numeral to express a number. However, it is more convenient to use a decimal numeral. You know the words for our decimal numerals. Therefore, unless you are told otherwise, you should use these words or the decimal numerals when you talk about or express numbers. For example, you should use the word "seventeen" or the decimal numeral 17 to express the number of objects represented in D1.

D Look at D2. A tally numeral is shown for each set of objects represented. Does each tally numeral name the number of members in that set of objects?

E How does set B differ from set A? How does the tally numeral for set B differ from the tally numeral for set A?

F How does set C differ from set B? How does the tally numeral for set C differ from the tally numeral for set B?

G How does set D differ from set C? How does the tally numeral for set D differ from the tally numeral for set C?

You have seen how a *tally system* for naming numbers can be developed. A tally numeral for each new number has one more stroke than the tally numeral for the number that immediately precedes it.

H Use a decimal numeral to express the number of members in each set of objects represented in D2.

Give a decimal numeral for each number named below.

I /	**N** //////
J //	**O** ///////
K ///	**P** ////////
L ////	**Q** /////////
M /////	**R** //////////

Since each stroke in a tally numeral expresses the number 1, and the tally numeral expresses the sum of the ones, a tally system has the property of *addition*. A tally system also has the property of *repetition*, because the same symbol, the stroke, may be used more than once in a tally numeral.

Now you will learn about another system for naming numbers.

The sets of objects represented in D3 are the same as the sets represented in D2. A new symbol is used to name the number of members in each set. Each of these symbols is a *code numeral*. You will use these symbols to develop a *code system* for naming numbers.

A In a tally system for naming numbers, each stroke expresses the number 1. What must you know before you can understand the symbols in a code system?

B In D3, what number is named by each of the code numerals?

Use one of the code numerals in D3 to express the number of members in each set tabulated below.

C {river, ocean, lake}

D {Africa, Europe}

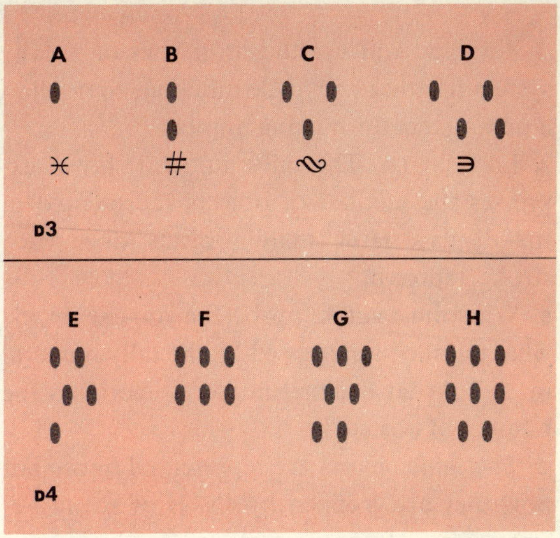

E {green, yellow, blue, red}

F {Montreal}

In a code system for naming numbers, each numeral is made up of just one symbol. Notice that a different symbol must be used for each numeral.

G So far only the symbols shown in D3 have been used as numerals in this code system. Look at D4. Invent a new code numeral to name the number of members in each set of objects represented.

H You have learned that in a code system, no **?** symbol is used more than once. You also have learned that a different symbol is used for each numeral. Does a code system have the property of repetition? Does a code system have the property of addition? Explain your answers.

I Think of a code system for naming the **?** members of {1, 2, 3, . . .}. Do the different symbols used to make the numerals in this code system form an infinite set?

J Does a tally system for naming numbers **?** have any advantage over a code system? Does a code system have any advantage over a tally system? Explain your answers.

Next you will use the properties of a tally system together with code numerals to develop a new system for naming numbers.

A Look at D5. The tally numeral shown expresses the number of objects represented in the display. How many objects does each stroke represent?

B What must you know before you can decide what number is expressed by the tally numeral in D5? What decimal numeral expresses the number of objects?

C The same objects are represented in D6, but now they are grouped by 4's. How many objects were left over after the grouping was completed? In tally numeral A, how many strokes are needed to express the number of objects in each group of 4?

D Now suppose you use a new symbol, a star, in place of each group of four strokes. How many objects does each star represent?

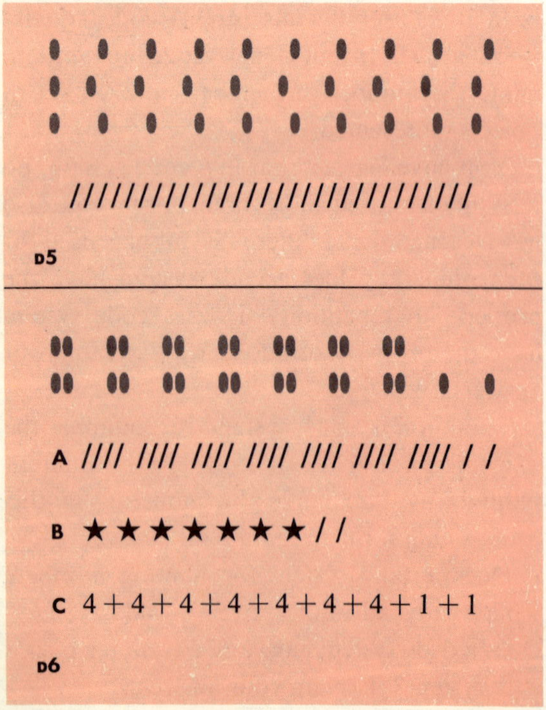

E Why does numeral B in D6 contain seven stars?

F A stroke still represents one object. Why does numeral B also contain two strokes?

G Since each star in numeral B represents a group of four objects, numeral B is a *grouping numeral* for the number of objects represented in D6. You are developing a *grouping system* for naming numbers. Numeral B contains how many stars? How many strokes?

H If you count the number of stars and strokes in numeral B, do you obtain the number of objects represented in D6?

I What is the decimal numeral for the number expressed by the grouping numeral in D6? Use numeral C to help you.

Since a grouping numeral expresses the sum of the numbers expressed by the symbols in the numeral, a grouping system has the property of addition. A grouping system also has the property of repetition because a symbol, such as the star or stroke, may be used more than once in a grouping numeral.

J Study numerals D and E in D7. Each star expresses the number 4, and each stroke expresses the number 1. Do the two numerals name the same number? What is this number?

K Look at D8. It shows the same number of objects as D6, but in D8 four groups of 4 have been put together to form a new group of objects. How many objects are in this group?

L In numeral F in D8, a diamond has been used to represent the group of encircled objects. Does the new symbol express the number 4×4, or 16?

M If you count the number of diamonds, stars, and strokes in numeral F, do you obtain the number of objects represented in D8? How do you obtain this number? What is the number? Remember to use a decimal numeral to express your answer. Numeral G will help you.

N Does numeral F in D8 express the same number as numeral B in D6?

So far in our grouping system we have used a symbol, the star, to name the number 4. We have also used another symbol, the diamond, to name the number 4 × 4, or 16. If we were to continue with this grouping system, we would use a still different symbol to name the number 4 × 4 × 4, or 64. When we group by 4's, we first think of groups of 4, then four groups of 4, then four groups of four groups of 4, and so on. We have used 4 as the *base* of this grouping system.

So far you have studied a tally system, a code system, and a grouping system for naming numbers. Such systems for naming numbers are *numeration systems*.

O One hundred six objects are represented in D9. Numeral H is a base-four grouping numeral that expresses the number of objects. Why are six diamonds used in numeral H? Does this numeral name the number 106?

P Now make a new group out of four of the groups of 16. Why do you use four of these groups of 16? Remember that you are using a base-four grouping system.

D ★★★//

E /★★★/

D7

F ◆★★★//

G 16 + 4 + 4 + 4 + 1 + 1

D8

nu mer a tion sys tem (nü′mər ā′shən sis′-təm). A method or system for naming numbers. A tally system, a code system, and a grouping system are numeration systems.

Q You need a new symbol to express the number 4 × 4 × 4, or 64. Use an arrowhead as this new symbol. How many groups of 4 × 4 × 4 objects are represented in D9?

R What number is expressed by numeral I in D9? Use numeral J to help you obtain the answer.

S Does numeral I express the same number as numeral H? Explain your answer.

H ◆◆◆◆◆◆★★//

I ▶◆◆★★//

J 64 + 16 + 16 + 4 + 4 + 1 + 1

D9

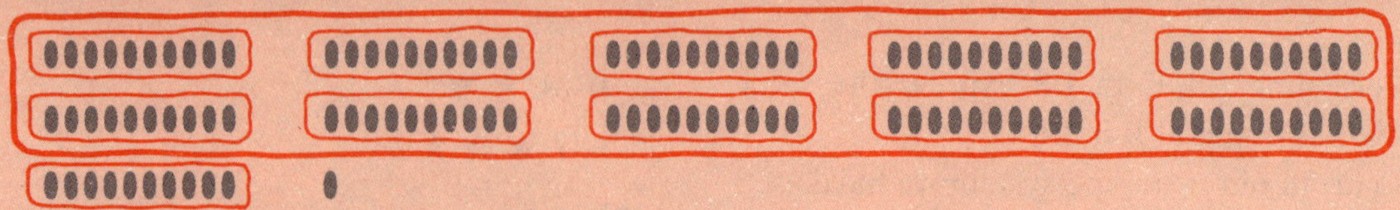

K ◆ ★ /

L 100 + 10 + 1

M ★ / ◆

D10

Any number greater than 1 may be used as a base of a grouping system. You have been using a base-four grouping system. You will use a base-ten grouping system next. In this base-ten grouping system, you will use the stroke for 1, the star for the base, the diamond for the base times the base, and so on.

T Look at D10. How many objects does a stroke represent? How many objects does a star represent?

U Does a diamond represent ten groups of 10 objects? How many objects does a diamond represent?

V Before you can obtain the number expressed **?** by a grouping numeral, what must you know about the symbols in the numeral?

W Does numeral K express the number of objects represented in D10? What is this number? Use numeral L to help you find this number.

X Numeral M is also a base-ten numeral. Does this numeral express the same number as numeral K? In what way do numeral K and numeral M differ?

Now you know how tally, code, and grouping numeration systems can be developed.

On your own

Use grouping numeration systems for all the exercises in this section. For each system use only the symbols given in D11. Study D11 before you begin your work.

/ expresses the number 1.

★ expresses the number of objects equal to the base.

◆ expresses the number of objects equal to the base times the base.

⏵ expresses the number of objects equal to the base times the base times the base.

For example, if the base is 3, then / = 1, ★ = 3, ◆ = 9, and ⏵ = 27.

D11

For each of exercises 1 through 6, write a base-three numeral to express the number of objects represented by markers. For exercise 1 you should write: ★ ★.

1 

2 

3 

4 

5 

6 

For each of exercises 7 through 10, express the number of objects represented by writing a base-eight numeral. For exercise 7 you should write: ★ / / /.

7 

8 

9 

10 

For each of exercises 11 and 12, first express the number of objects represented by writing a base-three numeral. Then express the same number by writing a base-eight numeral.

11 ● ● ● ● ●
● ● ● ●

12 ● ● ● ● ● ● ● ● ●
● ● ● ● ● ● ● ●

For each number named in exercises 13 through 20, express the number by writing a decimal numeral. In each case show how you obtained the numeral. For exercise 13 you should write: $9 + 9 + 3 + 1$, or 22.

13 ◆ ◆ ★ /	(base three)
14 ▶ ◆ ★ /	(base two)
15 ◆ ◆ ★ ★ ★	(base four)
16 ▶ ◆ ◆ ★ / / / /	(base six)
17 ◆ ★ / / / / / / / / /	(base eleven)
18 ▶ ▶ / / /	(base four)
19 ◆ ◆ ◆ ★ ◆ ◆	(base ten)
20 ★ / / / / / / / / /	(base twelve)

KEEPING SKILFUL

Find the sum.

1 3045, 796, 1368, 4201, 579, 607
2 9030, 1132, 475, 8671, 110, 89
3 32347, 98, 56451, 8925, 1003
4 13746, 92086, 47952, 88570, 75
5 273, 9645, 816, 49

Find the difference.

6 2134, 969
7 5000, 4296
8 8765, 6293
9 10073, 295
10 12356, 5974
11 30110, 12943
12 72842, 798
13 43022, 37496

Multiply

14 4862 by 9.
15 38 by 47.
16 105 by 62.
17 993 by 213.
18 800 by 560.
19 307 by 845.
20 864 by 705.

Divide

21 6230 by 63.
22 2886 by 74.
23 36363 by 51.
24 55436 by 134.
25 39123 by 189.
26 22140 by 205.
27 47293 by 65.

5 | 50 **Exploring ideas**

Numeration systems that have place value

In the last lesson you learned that numeration systems can have the properties of repetition, addition, and base. Now you will study another property of numeration systems.

A Look at D1. Each stroke in numeral A expresses the number 1. Each star expresses the number 3. Each diamond expresses the number 3×3, or 9. Each arrowhead expresses the number $3 \times 3 \times 3$, or 27. What is the base of the grouping system in which numeral A is written?

B What is the decimal numeral for the number named by numeral A? Use numeral B to help you obtain your answer.

C How do you know that numeral A has the property of repetition?

When we ask whether a numeral has a certain property, we really want to know whether or not the numeration system to which the numeral belongs has this property.

D How do you know that numeral A has the property of addition? Use numeral B to help you explain your answer.

Now you will learn how to develop a base-three system in which strokes are used in different positions to make the numerals.

A ▶ ◆ ◆ ★ ★ / /

B $1(3 \times 3 \times 3) + 2(3 \times 3) + 2(3) + 2(1)$

D1

E The base-three numeral in D1 is shown again in D2. Numeral C in D2 expresses the same number as numeral A. Notice the two strokes in numeral C that are below the two strokes in numeral A. Each of these strokes also expresses the number 1. In the space below the two stars, each stroke expresses the number 3. Why is it necessary to separate these strokes from the strokes in the space at the right?

F How do you know that the two strokes in the space below the stars express the number 2(3), or 6?

G Each stroke in the space below the diamonds expresses the number 3×3, or 9. Do these two strokes express the number $2(3 \times 3)$, or 2(9), or 18?

H The stroke in the space below the arrowhead expresses the number $1(3 \times 3 \times 3)$. Does this stroke express the number 27?

I What number is expressed by the strokes in numeral C? Use a decimal numeral to express your answer.

J Does numeral C have the property of repetition? Of addition? Explain your answers.

Before you can find the number expressed by the strokes in a grouping numeral like numeral C, you must know what number is expressed by each stroke. By finding the sum of these numbers, you can find the number expressed by the grouping numeral. For numeral C, you know that each stroke in the space farthest to the right expresses the number 1. In the second space from the right, each stroke expresses the number 3. Each stroke in the third space from the right expresses the number 3×3, or 9, and so on.

Notice that in numeral C, the position of a stroke determines the number expressed by the stroke. A numeration system like the one used for numeral C has the property of *place value*. It is called a *place-value numeration system*.

A ➤ ◆ ◆ ★ ★ / /

B $1(3 \times 3 \times 3) + 2(3 \times 3) + 2(3) + 2(1)$

D1

A	➤	◆ ◆	★ ★	/ /
C	/	/ /	/ /	/ /
	$(3 \times 3 \times 3)$	(3×3)	3	1

D2

D	/ /	/	/ /	/
E	/	/ /	/	/ /

D3

F	/ / / /	/ / / / / / /	/ / / / /	/ / / /

D4

G $4(10 \times 10 \times 10) + 7(10 \times 10) + 5(10) + 4(1)$

H $4(1000) + 7(100) + 5(10) + 4(1)$

D5

K Look at D3. Two different numbers are expressed by using a base-three numeration system that has the property of place value. What number is expressed by numeral D? What number is expressed by numeral E?

L Notice that numeral D contains six strokes. Does numeral E also contain six strokes? How is it possible to use six strokes to express two different numbers?

M In the place-value numeration system that we have been discussing, we have used a chart to show the different positions of the strokes. In what other ways might the different positions of the strokes be indicated?

N Look again at numeral A in D1. Does this numeral have the property of place value? How do you know?

Now you will work with other numeration systems that have the property of place value.

A Numeral F in D4 is a base-ten numeral. Each stroke in the space farthest to the right expresses the number 1. Each stroke in the second space from the right expresses the number 10. What number is expressed by each stroke in the third space from the right?

B What number is expressed by each stroke in the fourth space from the right?

C Do numerals G and H in D5 show how to obtain the decimal numeral for the number named in D4? What is the decimal numeral for the number named in D4?

D How does a base-ten system that has the property of place value differ from a base-three system that has the property of place value?

E Four numerals are shown in D6. First think of them as written in a base-three system with place value. Which numerals express the number twenty-five?

F Which of the numerals for the number twenty-five uses fewer strokes? What advantage is there in writing a numeral with as few strokes as possible?

G Now think of the numerals in D6 as written in a base-ten system with place value. Which numerals express the number 234? Which of these numerals requires fewer strokes?

H Look again at numerals I and J in D6. When you write a numeral in a base-three numeration system, why is it never necessary to use more than two strokes in a space?

I When you use a base-ten numeration system, what is the greatest number of strokes needed in a space? Explain your answer.

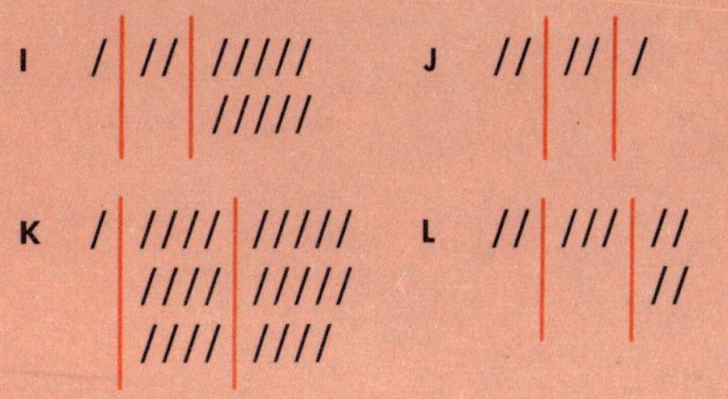

D6

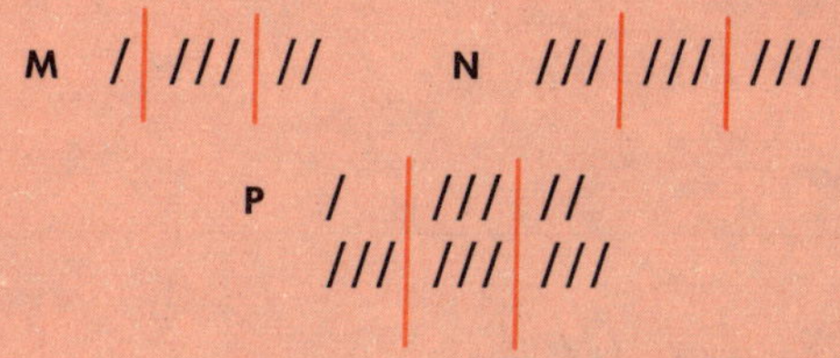

D7

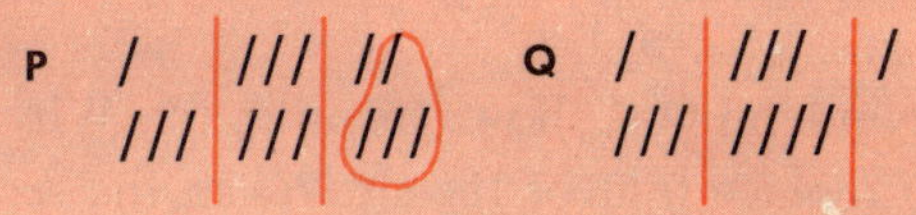

D8

J Each numeral in D7 is a base-four numeral with place value. What number is expressed by numeral M?

K What number is expressed by numeral N?

L Numeral P expresses the sum of the numbers named by numeral M and numeral N. Explain how numeral P was obtained from numerals M and N.

M What number is expressed by numeral P?

N When you are using a base-four numeration system, what is the greatest number of strokes needed in a space?

O Explain how you know that you can regroup the strokes in numeral P. This numeral is shown again in D8. Why should you replace four of the strokes in the space farthest to the right by one stroke in the second space from the right?

P Does numeral Q express the same number as numeral P?

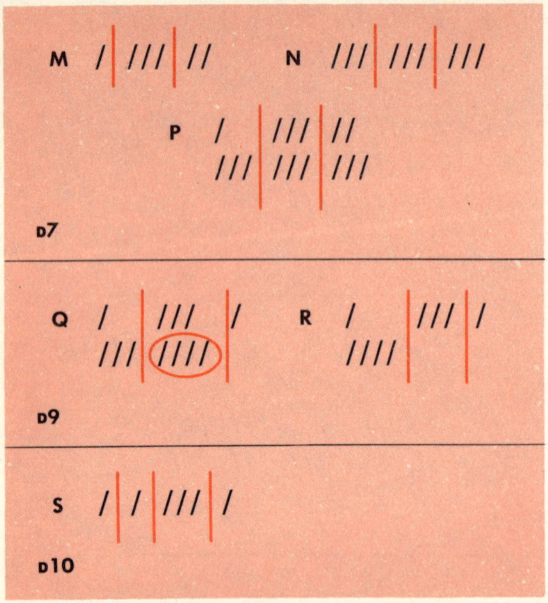

Q Numeral Q is shown again in D9. Why can you replace four of the strokes in the second space from the right by one stroke in the third space from the right? Does numeral R express the same number as numeral Q?

R Explain how the strokes in the farthest space from the right in numeral R can be regrouped.

S The strokes in numeral R have been regrouped in D10. Does the stroke in the fourth space from the right express the number $4 \times 4 \times 4$, or 64?

T What number is expressed by numeral S in D10? Do numeral R and numeral S express the same number? Do numeral S and numeral P in D7 express the same number?

U ? In a place-value numeration system like those you have been using, how can you use the base to determine the greatest number of strokes needed in a space?

In this lesson you studied a few numeration systems that have the property of place value. You learned to use strokes in a numeration system that has place value.

On your own

The numerals in exercises 1 through 5 are written in a base-seven numeration system with the property of place value. Express each number named by writing a decimal numeral. In each case, show how you obtained the numeral. For exercise 1, for example, you should write: $1(7 \times 7) + 4(7) + 3(1)$, or 80.

1		/	////	///
2		///	//////	////
3		/////	///	//////
4	//	////	/////	///
5	/////	//////	////	//

The numerals in exercises 6 through 10 are written in a base-six numeration system that has the property of place value. For each exercise, make a chart that shows how to regroup the strokes. Remember to regroup in such a way that you use the fewest strokes possible in expressing the number in base six.

6		////	//////	////////
7		///	////////	/////
8		////	////	////////
9	//	///////	///////	/////////
10	///	///////	////	///////

11 What number is named by each numeral that you made for exercises 6 through 10?

12 Make a chart and use strokes to express the sum of the numbers named in exercises 6 and 7. Remember that the numerals in these exercises are written in a base-six numeration system with the property of place value. Use as few strokes as possible in your chart.

5 | 51 **Exploring ideas**

Place value and digits in numeration systems

In lessons 49 and 50 you studied numeration systems that have the properties of addition, repetition, base, and place value. You used strokes to write the numerals in these numeration systems. In this lesson you will learn how to use symbols other than the stroke in these numeration systems.

A Numeral A in D1 is written in a base-four system with the property of place value. Do the strokes in the space farthest to the right express the number 3(1), or 3? Why is it necessary to separate these strokes from the other strokes in the numeral?

B What number does numeral A express? Use a decimal numeral to express the number.

C Numeral B in D1 shows how to use the familiar symbols 0, 1, 2, and 3 to write this base-four numeral. What symbol is in the space farthest to the right? Does this symbol tell you how many strokes there are in the space farthest to the right in numeral A? Does this symbol express the number 3(1), or 3?

D Notice the symbol 3 in the second space from the right. Does this symbol tell you how many strokes there are in the second space from the right in numeral A? Does this symbol express the number 3(4), or 12?

E The symbol 0 is used in the third space from the right in numeral B. Does this symbol tell you how many strokes there are in the third space from the right in numeral A? Does this symbol express the number 0(4 × 4), or 0?

	(4×4×4)	(4×4)	4	1
A	/		///	///
B	1	0	3	3

D1

B 1033

C 1(4 × 4 × 4) + 0(4 × 4) + 3(4) + 3(1)

D2

F What number is expressed by the symbol 1 in numeral B?

G Does numeral B express the same number as numeral A?

H In numeral B, the symbol 3 is used instead of three strokes, and the symbol 1 instead of one stroke. For how many strokes is the symbol 0 used?

I For how many strokes would the symbol 2 be used in a numeral similar to numeral B?

The familiar symbols 0, 1, 2, and 3 are code symbols, called *digits*. Notice that a digit is exactly one symbol.

J Numeral B from D1 is shown again in D2. **?** Notice that this time a chart has not been used. How do you know that the digit 1 expresses the number 1(4 × 4 × 4), and not the number 1(4 × 4)?

K Does the position of each digit in numeral B determine the number expressed by that digit?

L Does numeral B have the property of place value?

M What number does numeral B express? Remember to use a decimal numeral to express the number. Use numeral C to help you obtain your answer.

N Is the digit 3 used more than once in numeral B? Does numeral B have the property of repetition?

Using the same digits with each power of the base; properties of a modern numeration system

B 1033

C 1(4 × 4 × 4) + 0(4 × 4) + 3(4) + 3(1)

D2

"one zero three three,

1033_{four}

base four"

D3

D 2031_{four} = 2(64) + 0(16) + 3(4) + 1(1).

E 2301_{four}

F 2310_{four}

G 302_{four}

H 20_{four}

I 301_{four}

J 1000_{four}

D4

	(10×10×10×10)	(10×10×10)	(10×10)	10	1
A	//	/////	////	///// ////	/////
B	2	5	4	9	5

D5

O Does numeral B in D2 have the property of addition? Use numeral C to help you explain your answer.

When you are working with numerals in bases other than ten, you need some way of naming them so that you will not become confused and also so that you can talk about them. D3 shows a good way to read and write numeral B in D2. Notice that the name of the base is written as a word and placed to the right and below the digits. Study D3.

P Look at the numerals in D4. What is the base of these numerals? Which numeral is read "two zero three one, base four"?

Q Read each of the other numerals in D4 in the way suggested in D3.

R Explain how you would obtain the decimal numeral for each of the numbers expressed by the numerals in D4. Then give a decimal numeral for each of the numbers.

You can also use digits in numeration systems that have bases other than four. Now you will study a base-ten numeration system that has place value.

A Numeral A in D5 is a base-ten numeral. What number do the five strokes in the space farthest to the right express?

B Do the strokes in the second space from the right express the number 9(10), or 90? How do you know?

C What number is expressed by the four strokes in the third space from the right? What number is expressed by the five strokes in the fourth space from the right?

D You know that each stroke in the fourth space from the right expresses the number 10 × 10 × 10, or 1000. Since we are grouping by 10's, each stroke in the fifth space from the right expresses the number 10 × 10 × 10 × 10. Does each of these strokes express the number 10,000? What number is expressed by the two strokes?

E What number does numeral A express?

F Now look at numeral B in D5. It is also a base-ten numeral. Does the digit 5 in the space farthest to the right tell you how many strokes there are in the space farthest to the right in numeral A? Does the digit 5 express the number 5(1), or 5?

G For each digit in numeral B, tell what number it expresses.

H Does numeral B express the same number as numeral A?

B 25495

D6

	(12×12×12)	(12×12)	12	1
C	////	////// /////	////	///// /////
D	4	ℰ	4	χ

D7

I Why do you need just ten different digits to ? express any number in a base-ten system with place value? How many different digits do you need to express any number in a base-four numeration system with place value?

J Numeral B is shown again in D6. How do you know that the digit 5 in the fourth place from the right expresses the number 5(1000), and not the number 5(1)?

K Does the position of each digit in numeral B determine the number expressed by that digit?

L How do you know that numeral B has the property of place value? Of repetition? Of addition?

M Why is it not necessary to use a chart in writing numeral B? Why is it more convenient to use numeral B in D6 than to use numeral A in D5?

Since the base of numeral B is not expressed in D6, you know that the base is ten. Decimal numerals are written in a base-ten system with the property of place value. The word *decimal* comes from the Latin word for "ten." Consequently, numeral B is a decimal numeral.

You can read numeral B as "two five four nine five, base ten." But since you know that numeral B belongs to our familiar decimal system, you can say "twenty-five thousand four hundred ninety-five."

The digits from 0 through 9 can also be used in a base-twelve numeration system with place value.

A Numeral C in D7 is a base-twelve numeral. Do the strokes in the space farthest to the right express the number 10(1), or 10? How do you know?

B Do the strokes in the second space from the right express the number 4(12), or 48? How do you know?

C Do the strokes in the third space from the right express the number 11(12 × 12), or 1584? What number is expressed by the strokes in the fourth space from the right?

D How can you determine that numeral C expresses the number eight thousand five hundred fifty-four?

E There are ten strokes in the space farthest ? to the right in numeral C. Can you use a familiar digit instead of the ten strokes? Explain your answer.

Since there is no familiar digit to use instead of the ten strokes, we must use a new digit. In this book, whenever we use the base-twelve numeration system, we will use the digit shown at the right instead of ten strokes. The new digit is read "dek." It was invented by a group of persons interested in the base-twelve system. For any numeration system whose base is greater than ten, we will use this digit for the number ten.

χ

F Look at numeral D in D7. What number does the digit χ express?

G What number is expressed by the digit in the second space from the right in numeral D?

H There are eleven strokes in the third space from the right in numeral C. Do you know of a digit that you can use instead of the eleven strokes?

	(12×12×12)	(12×12)	12	1
C	////	////// /////	////	///// /////
D	4	$\mathcal{E}$	4	$\mathcal{X}$

D7

D $4\mathcal{E}4\mathcal{X}_{twelve}$

D8

/ | / / | / | / / / | / / /

D9

The group of persons who invented the digit $\mathcal{X}$ also invented a digit for the number eleven. We will use this digit, shown at the right, instead of eleven strokes. The digit is read "el." $\mathcal{E}$ For any numeration system whose base is greater than eleven, we will use this digit for the number eleven.

I Look again at numeral D in D7. Does the digit $\mathcal{E}$ express the number $11(12 \times 12)$, or 1584?

J What number does the digit in the fourth space from the right express?

K Does numeral D express the same number as numeral C?

L Numeral D is shown again in D8. Why is it **?** not necessary to use a chart in writing numeral D?

M What words would you say for numeral D?

You have learned that our decimal numeration system has the properties of addition, repetition, base, and place value. You know that decimal numerals are formed from ten digits. You have also seen that bases other than ten can be used to develop numeration systems with the same properties as our decimal system.

On your own

For each of the numeration systems named in exercises 1 through 4, tell what number is expressed by the numeral in D9. Remember to express each number by a decimal numeral.

1 Base four
2 Base six
3 Base seven
4 Base eleven

What number is expressed by each of the numerals below? Your answers should be expressed by decimal numerals.

5 16_{seven}
6 30_{seven}
7 300_{seven}
8 625_{seven}
9 560_{seven}
10 1502_{seven}
11 9_{twelve}
12 90_{twelve}
13 $1\mathcal{X}_{twelve}$
14 $\mathcal{X}1_{twelve}$
15 $\mathcal{E}03_{twelve}$
16 $12\mathcal{X}\mathcal{E}_{twelve}$
17 1111_{two}
18 1011_{two}
19 10111_{two}
20 11100_{two}
21 11001_{two}
22 10001_{two}

Express the first fifteen counting numbers in each of the following numeration systems.

23 Base five
24 Base six
25 Base nine
26 Base eleven

SPECIAL CHALLENGE

Give the answer to each problem.

A Mr. Ames sold 2 used cars for \$528 each. He sold one of the cars for 20% less than he paid for it. He sold the other car for 20% more than he paid for it. Decide whether Mr. Ames made money or lost money on the sale of these 2 cars. Then tell how many dollars he made or lost.

B Jim has three samples of rock. He weighed the rocks two at a time so that each rock was weighed with each of the other rocks. The weights were 14 pounds, 15 pounds, and 19 pounds. How much does each rock weigh?

KEEPING SKILFUL

For each of exercises 1 through 5, first tabulate the solution set described. Then make a graph of each solution set. $U = N \times N$.

1 $\{(x, y) \mid x < 8 \wedge x + y = 7\}$
2 $\{(x, y) \mid y - 2 = 4 \wedge y - x > 1\}$
3 $\{(x, y) \mid x < 5 \wedge y = 4 + x\}$
4 $\{(x, y) \mid x + y = 9 \wedge x + 1 = y\}$
5 $\{(x, y) \mid 7 > 3 + x \wedge 8 - x > y\}$

For each of exercises 6 through 15, tabulate the solution set of the condition. $U = C$.

6 $27/54 \sim m/6$.
7 $r + 7 < 15$.
8 b is 3% of 1700.
9 78 is d% of 65.
10 $x + 6 < 93 \div 3$.
11 $9/7 \sim 207/s$.
12 $146 - t > 129$.
13 162 is 75% of n.
14 $3/4 \sim b/608$.
15 c is 130% of 150.

Make one sketch for exercises 16 through 20. Then use your sketch for exercises 21 through 26. The universe is the plane that includes circle G.

16 Make a sketch of circle G. Make a sketch of radius GH.
17 Make a sketch of chord HJ. Points G, H, and J are noncollinear.
18 Make a sketch of diameter JK.
19 Locate point M in the exterior of circle G. H is between G and M.
20 Locate point B between K and G. Locate C between H and J.
21 Write a standard description of circle G.
22 Write a standard description of the interior of circle G. Of the exterior of circle G.
23 Write a sentence that expresses a true statement comparing $\overline{GK}$ and $\overline{JG}$.
24 Write a sentence that expresses a true statement comparing $\overline{GM}$ and $\overline{GC}$.
25 Write a sentence that expresses a true statement comparing $\overline{HG}$ and $\overline{MG}$.
26 Write a sentence that expresses a true statement comparing $\overline{GH}$ and $\overline{JK}$.

5 | 52 Exploring ideas

Egyptian, Roman, and Babylonian numeration systems

You know that a modern numeration system has the properties of addition, repetition, base, and place value. Many numeration systems of ancient times also had some, or all, of these properties. In fact, a modern numeration system was developed by combining the advantages of these ancient systems. In this lesson you will study the Egyptian, Roman, and Babylonian numeration systems. You will discover how each of these systems was helpful in the development of the numeration system that we use today.

A D1 shows some of the symbols in the numeration system of the ancient Egyptians. The Egyptians used a picture of a vertical staff to express the number 1. They used a symbol sometimes called a "heelbone" to express the number 10. The "heelbone" could be used instead of how many vertical staffs? The symbol for 100 could be used instead of how many "heelbones"?

B Study the symbols shown in D1. What was the base of the Egyptian numeration system?

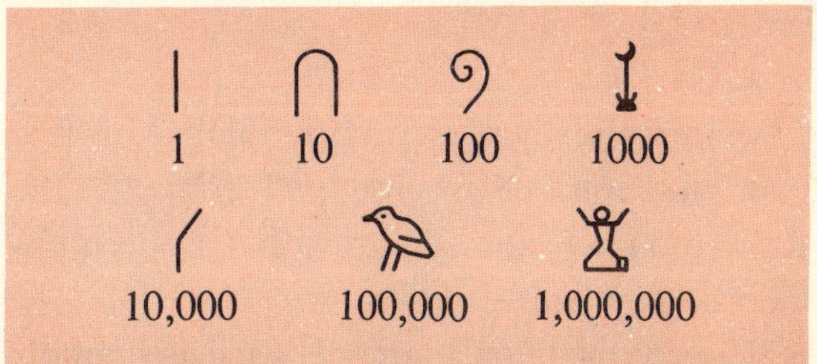

D1

C D2 shows four numerals as the Egyptians might have written them. Numeral A expresses the number 100 + 100 + 10 + 10, or 220. Do you obtain the number named in numeral A by counting the symbols in numeral A? Explain your answer.

D Now look at numeral B in D2. The Egyptian numeration system did not have the property of place value. What number does numeral B express? How did you obtain your answer?

E Are numeral A and numeral B names for the same number?

F What number does numeral C express? What number does numeral D express?

G Did the Egyptian numeration system have the property of addition? Of repetition? Explain your answers.

Next you will use the Egyptian numeration system to find the sum of several numbers.

H What number is expressed by each numeral in D3?

I To find the sum of the numbers expressed in D3, you first collect the symbols in the numerals. Does numeral H in D4 show this collection?

J What number does numeral H express? How did you obtain your answer?

K How was numeral I obtained from numeral H? Does numeral I express the same number as numeral H?

L Why do you think our decimal numeration ? system is more convenient for naming numbers than the ancient Egyptian numeration system?

D2

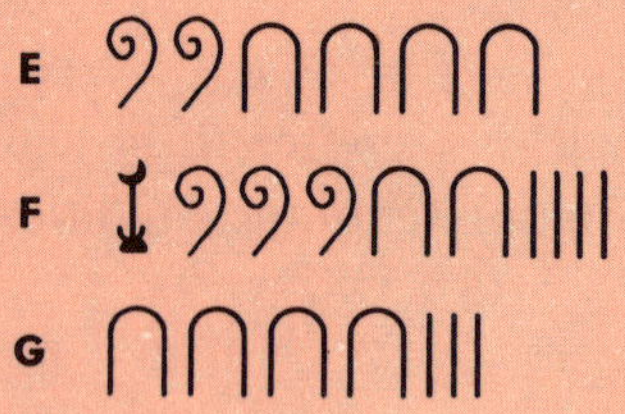

D3

D4

I	V	X	L	C	D	M
1	5	10	50	100	500	1000

D5

You are already somewhat familiar with Roman numerals. Now you will compare the Roman numeration system with a modern numeration system.

A The seven letters commonly used as symbols in the Roman numeration system are shown in D5. The Roman symbol I expresses the number 1. What is the Roman symbol for the number 10? For the number 10×10? For the number $10 \times 10 \times 10$?

B The Roman numeration system also had a special symbol for the number 5(1). What is this symbol?

C What is the Roman symbol for the number 5(10)? For the number $5(10 \times 10)$?

A VI	E XI	G LX	J CX
B IV	F IX	H XL	K XC

D6

N XCIII
P CXIII

D7

Q XX
R LIII
S CXXXVII

D8

The Romans used groups of 10 in their numeration system. However, since there are special Roman symbols for 5 ones, for 5 groups of 10, and for 5 groups of 10×10, the Roman numeration system is really a "mixed" grouping system.

D Look at numeral A in D6. The Roman symbol for the number 1 is to the right of the symbol for the number 5. To find the number expressed by numeral VI, you add 1 to 5. What number does numeral A express?

E What is the Roman numeral for the number 7? For the number 8?

F How is numeral B in D6 like numeral A? How is numeral B different from numeral A?

To find the number expressed by the numeral IV, you subtract the number 1 from the number 5. If a symbol is written at the right of another symbol that expresses a greater number, you add the lesser number to the greater. If a symbol is written at the left of another symbol that expresses a greater number, you subtract the lesser number from the greater.

G To obtain the number expressed by numeral E, which do you do, add 1 to 10 or subtract 1 from 10? What number is expressed by numeral E?

H To obtain the number that numeral F expresses, which do you do, add 1 to 10 or subtract 1 from 10? What number is expressed by numeral F?

I Does the Roman numeration system have the property of addition? Is subtraction also used in the Roman system?

J What number is expressed by each of the numerals in D6?

K For which numbers that you obtained for exercise J did you use addition? For which numbers did you use subtraction?

L Study numerals N and P in D7. What number does each symbol in numeral N express? What number does each symbol in numeral P express?

M What number is expressed by numeral N? By numeral P?

N Does the position of a symbol in a Roman numeral always determine the number expressed by that symbol? Does the Roman numeration system have the property of place value?

O The same symbols are used in numeral N and numeral P. Explain why numeral N and numeral P do not name the same number.

P Does the Roman numeration system have the property of repetition? Explain your answer.

Now you will use the Roman numeration system to find the sum of several numbers.

Q What number is expressed by each numeral in D8?

R To find the sum of the numbers expressed in D8, you first collect the symbols in the numerals. You will have how many I's? You will have how many X's?

S Does numeral T in D9 show the collection of numerals? What Roman symbol can you use instead of the five I's? What Roman symbol can you use instead of the five X's?

T Now look at numeral U in D9. Does it name the same number as numeral T?

U How was numeral W obtained? What number does numeral W express?

V Are numeral T, numeral U, and numeral W names for the same number? Which of these numerals is the most convenient to use?

W ? When you add XCVII and XLV, why should your collection of numerals be XC + XL + VVII, and not CLXXVVII?

X ? Do you think that our decimal system is more convenient for naming numbers than the Roman system? Explain your answer.

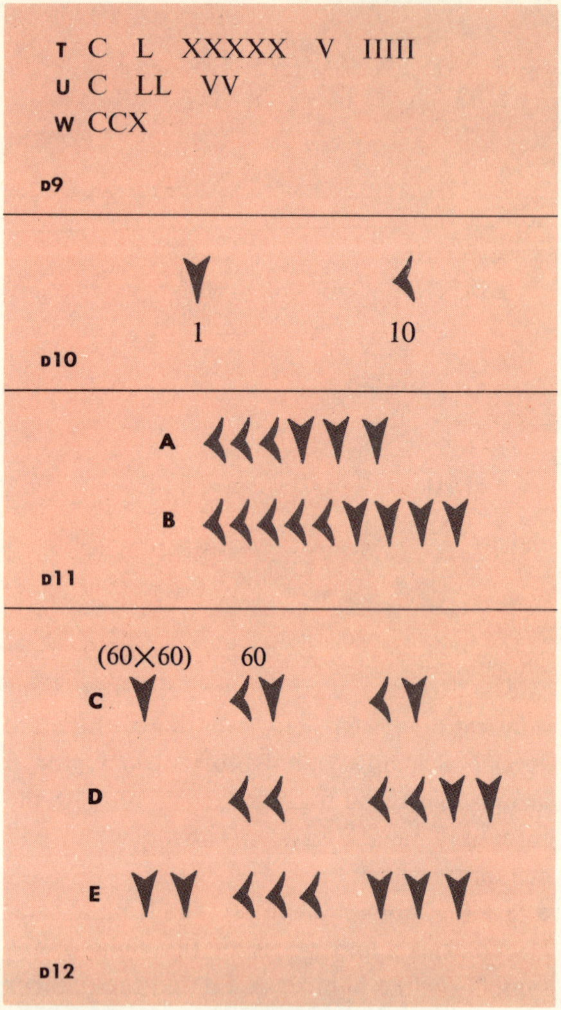

The Babylonian numeration system used only two symbols and a base of sixty.

A D10 shows some Babylonian symbols. What number does each symbol in D10 express?

B Numeral A in D11 expresses the number 10 + 10 + 10 + 1 + 1 + 1, or 33. What number does numeral B express?

C Did the Babylonian numeration system have the property of addition? Of repetition?

D To express numbers greater than sixty, the symbols in Babylonian numerals were arranged in a special way. Look at numeral C in D12. The symbols in the group farthest to the right express the number 10 + 1, or 11. Look at numeral D. What number is expressed by the symbols in the group farthest to the right?

E To find the number expressed by the symbols in the group second from the right, you first find the number expressed by each symbol. Then you find the product of each of these numbers and 60. In numeral C, the symbols in the group second from the right express the number 10(60) + 1(60), or 660. In numeral D, what number is expressed by the symbols in the group second from the right?

F In numeral C, the symbol in the group third from the right expresses the number 1(60 × 60), or 3600. What number does numeral C express?

G To find the number expressed by numeral D, you find the sum of the numbers expressed by the symbols in the groups. What number does numeral D express?

H In numeral E, what number is expressed by the symbols in the group third from the right? What number does numeral E express?

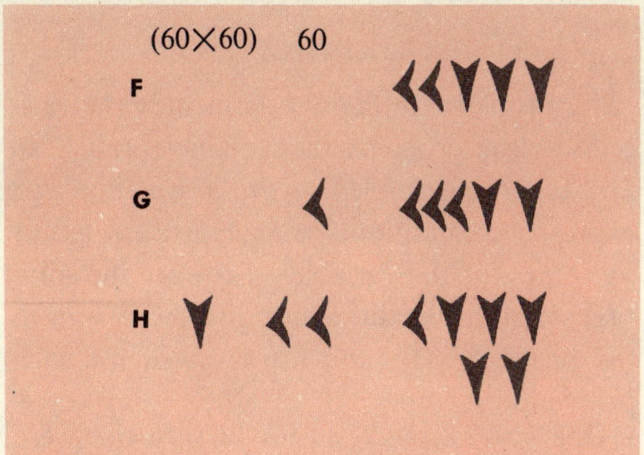

D13

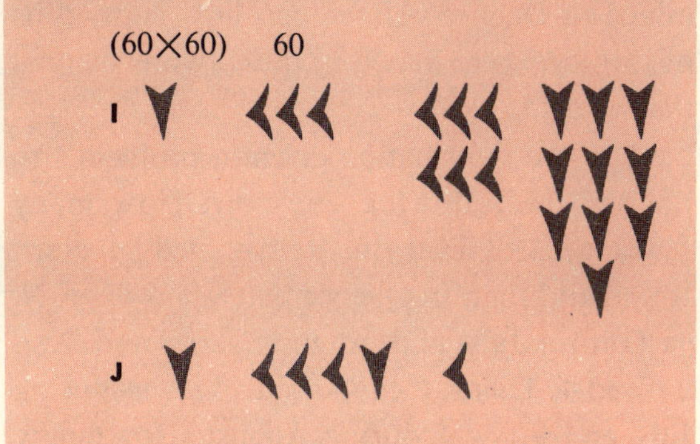

D14

I Did the Babylonian system have the property of place value? Explain your answer.

Now you will use the Babylonian numeration system to find the sum of several numbers.

J Look at D13. What number does each numeral express?

K To find the sum of the numbers expressed in D13, first collect the symbols in the numerals, keeping the groups of symbols separated. Does numeral I in D14 show this collection?

L What number does numeral I express?

M In the group farthest to the right in numeral I, how many times is the symbol for the number 1 used? What Babylonian symbol can you use instead of these ten symbols?

N In the group farthest to the right in numeral I, how many times is the symbol for the number 10 used? Why can you use a symbol for 1 in the group second from the right in place of these symbols for 10?

O Now look at numeral J in D14. Does numeral J express the same number as numeral I? Which of these numerals is more convenient to use?

P Do you think our decimal numeration system is a more convenient system for naming numbers than the Babylonian system? Explain your answer.

In this lesson you have compared the properties of some ancient numeration systems with the properties of a modern numeration system.

On your own

For each of exercises 1 through 9, write the decimal numeral for the number expressed. If you do not remember what numbers the symbols in the numerals express, look at D1 on page 219, D5 on page 220, and D10 on page 222.

1 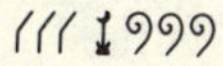

2 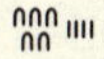

3 

4 MDCCLXXVI

5 DCXLIV

6 XCIX

7 

8 

9 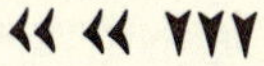

The numerals in exercises 10 through 14 are decimal numerals. For each exercise, first use the Egyptian numeration system to write a numeral for the number named. Then write a Roman numeral for the number.

10 89 **11** 105 **12** 1416 **13** 3244 **14** 928

The numerals in exercises 15 through 20 are Roman numerals. Use the Egyptian numeration system to express each number named.

15 XLII **17** DLXXIV **19** CDL

16 CCCXXVI **18** MDXC **20** CMLVII

CHECKING UP

If you have trouble with these two tests, you can find help in lessons 49 through 52.

Test 54

For each numeration system described in exercises 1, 2, and 3, tell what number is expressed by the numeral in the display below. Give your answer as a decimal numeral.

1 Base six **2** Base nine **3** Base twelve

For each of exercises 4 through 12, what number is expressed by the Roman numeral?

4 VIII	**7** XLVI	**10** XXXIII
5 XIV	**8** XCI	**11** MCMLXIII
6 XIX	**9** CIX	**12** DXX

Test 55

A list of numeration systems is given below. For each of exercises 13 through 16, choose from the list the system that is described in the exercise.

a Tally system

b Grouping system without place value

c Grouping system with place value and digits

d Grouping system with place value and the stroke

e Code system

13 This numeration system does not have the property of repetition.

14 The greatest number of strokes needed in any space in a numeral is one less than the base.

15 The number of symbols needed to form the numerals is equal to the base of the numeration system.

16 The number of times a symbol is used in a numeral is the same number as the number expressed by that numeral.

APPLYING MATHEMATICS

The problems in this lesson include the various kinds of problems that you have studied so far. For each problem, write a sentence that expresses a condition. You may use any letters as names for the variables. Tabulate the solution set of the condition and give the answer to the problem. The universe is given for each problem.

1 One year, 8,174,779 tons of iron ore were mined in Newfoundland, and 8,872,948 were mined in Quebec. Altogether, how many tons of iron ore were mined in these two provinces that year? U = N.

2 Use the information given in problem 1 to answer the following question: How many fewer tons of iron ore were mined in Newfoundland than in Quebec that year? U = N.

3 During July and August, Jerry and Ken mowed 42 lawns. Ken mowed 14 lawns during July and 9 lawns during August. How many lawns did Jerry mow during these two months? U = N × N.

4 In a recent year there were about four times as many factories in Montreal as there were in Vancouver. There were about 1200 in Vancouver. About how many factories were there in Montreal? U = C.

5 Mrs. Brown made more than 35 cupcakes. She sent 24 of them to a bake sale and had fewer than 17 cupcakes left. How many cupcakes could she have made? U = N.

6 Sue is younger than Ann. In 5 years, Ann will be 19 years old. What is Ann's age now? What can Sue's age be now? U = C × C.

7 The Hayes Store for Men had 115 raincoats to sell at a 30% discount. By the end of the first day, there were fewer than 59 raincoats left to sell. How many raincoats could have been sold that day? U = N.

8 Kay bought some chocolate cookies at 5¢ each and some ginger cookies at 3¢ each. She bought fewer chocolate cookies than ginger cookies. She bought 7 cookies in all. How many cookies of each kind could she have bought? U = C × C.

9 Over a five-year period, 39,138,000 tons of raw sugar were produced in the world. Approximately 34% of this total was produced in North America. About how many tons of raw sugar were produced in North America during this five-year period? U = C.

10 There are 71,768,000 telephones in Canada and the United States together. If there were 877,000 more telephones in Canada, the number of telephones in Canada would be 6,000,000. How many telephones are there in each of these two countries? U = N × N.

11 Scientists believe that the Chubb Crater in the province of Quebec, was formed by the impact of a huge meteorite. The depth of this crater is 1800 feet. The comparison of its width to its depth is 64 feet to 10 feet. What is the width of the Chubb Crater? U = C.

12 The rate of interest at a certain bank is 6%. Mr. Horton borrowed $1350 and repaid his loan with interest at the end of one year. How much did he pay the bank at the end of the year? U = C × C.

13 During a basketball game, Ted scored 7 more points than Bill. Together, they scored 21 points. How many points did each boy score during the game? U = N × N.

14 Mrs. Jackson paid $172 for a freezer that was regularly priced at $215. What was the rate of discount? U = C × C.

15 It is said that the earth's temperature rises 1° Fahrenheit for each 60 feet beneath the earth's surface. What is the earth's temperature 18,120 feet beneath the surface, if the surface temperature is 49° Fahrenheit? U = C × C.

KEEPING SKILFUL

For exercises 1 through 8, round each number named to the next lesser thousand, to the next greater hundred, and to the next lesser ten.

1 1926	3 6203	5 35,165	7 2711
2 47,491	4 1999	6 9002	8 95,659

Find the sum.

9 8033, 6945, 9826, 9403

10 6858, 702, 73413, 553

11 14033, 34042, 50823, 41374, 56428

12 29639, 70130, 4775, 86562, 10075

13 711008, 647, 3246, 26054

Find the difference.

14 4938, 654	17 754110, 191786
15 8023, 6042	18 10174, 2942
16 3554, 2718	19 71857, 59759

Multiply	Divide
20 6293 by 82.	26 17784 by 76.
21 145 by 37.	27 14336 by 81.
22 208 by 145.	28 5292 by 106.
23 476 by 319.	29 41648 by 213.
24 194 by 284.	30 50076 by 319.
25 802 by 550.	31 38000 by 125.

For exercises 32 through 46, tabulate each set described. U = C × C.

32 $\{(x, y) | x + y < 6\}$

33 $\{(m, n) | m/n \sim 3/4 \wedge n - m = 4\}$

34 $\{(r, s) | s - r = 3 \wedge r + 8 < 17\}$

35 $\{(c, d) | c/d \sim 15/10 \wedge c > d\}$

36 $\{(x, y) | x + y = 150 \wedge 68 - y = 17\}$

37 $\{(m, n) | 9/15 \sim m/n \wedge n - m < 9\}$

38 $\{(s, t) | s < t \wedge s + t < 9\}$

39 $\{(a, b) | a/b \sim 14/21 \wedge a + b < 30\}$

40 $\{(x, y) | 8/100 \sim 50/x \wedge x - 50 = y\}$

41 $\{(s, t) | t - 18 > s \wedge t = 972 \div 36\}$

42 $\{(m, n) | n/m \sim 5/6 \wedge 33 - m = n\}$

43 $\{(c, d) | c/47 \sim 432/282 \wedge c + d < 80\}$

44 $\{(a, b) | b + a < 25 \wedge b = 3a\}$

45 $\{(m, n) | m/2 \sim n/100 \wedge m = 11 - 8\}$

46 $\{(x, y) | x/y \sim 54/63 \wedge x + y < 13\}$

5 53 Exploring ideas

Factors, powers, and exponential notation

In the preceding lessons of this unit you studied the properties of a modern numeration system. In this lesson you will learn how to write numerals in a form that will make it easier for you to change numerals from one base to another. First you must learn more about products of numbers.

A Does each sentence in D1 express a true statement? Does each sentence suggest a different way of thinking about 16?

B You can think of 16 as the product of 2 and 8. Look at D1 again. Describe other ways to think of 16 as a product.

C The counting numbers used to obtain a product are *factors* of that product. Are 2 and 8 factors of 16? Are 16 and 1 factors of 16? Is 4 a factor of 16? Is 6 a factor of 16?

D Some numbers may be used as a factor more than once to obtain a product. 4 may be used twice as a factor to obtain 16. How many times may 2 be used as a factor to obtain 16?

E You know that $3 \times 4 = 12$ is a true statement. Is 3 a factor of 12? Is 4 a factor of 12?

F Is $6 \times 2 = 12$? Is 6 a factor of 12? Is 2 a factor of 12?

G Is $3 \times 2 \times 2 = 12$? Which factor is used more than once in $3 \times 2 \times 2 = 12$?

H The six statements expressed in D2 were obtained from $a \times b = c$. Is each statement true?

I What replacements were made for the variables in $a \times b = c$ to obtain $12 \times 1 = 12$? Are 12 and 1 factors of 12? Explain your answer.

J Are 7 and 2 factors of 14? Are 8 and 3 factors of 24?

K Which factors of 45 are expressed in D2?

If $a \times b = c$, then the replacements for a and b are both factors of the replacement for c. U = C.

L Is 1 a factor of 15? Is 1 a factor of 60?

M Is 15 a factor of 15? Is 60 a factor of 60?

N ? Suppose that b in $1 \times b = b$ is replaced by any member of {1, 2, 3, . . .}. Will the statement obtained be true?

O ? Think of any member of {1, 2, 3, . . .}. Is 1 a factor of the number? Is the number a factor of itself?

You know that the decimal numeration system has the property of place value. You know, for example, that the digit 3 in the decimal numeral 347 expresses the number $3(10 \times 10)$. Notice that 10 is used twice as a factor. There

A $2 \times 8 = 16.$	C $4 \times 4 = 16.$
B $16 \times 1 = 16.$	D $2 \times 2 \times 2 \times 2 = 16.$

D1

U = C.

$a \times b = c.$

E $12 \times 1 = 12.$	H $3 \times 15 = 45.$
F $7 \times 2 = 14.$	I $5 \times 9 = 45.$
G $8 \times 3 = 24.$	J $45 \times 1 = 45.$

D2

fac tor (fak′tər). One of the numbers used to form a product. In $a \times b = c$, suppose that a, b, and c are replaced by members of {1, 2, 3, . . .}. If a true statement is obtained from $a \times b = c$, then the replacement for a is a factor of the replacement for c. The replacement for b is also a factor of the replacement for c.

is a shorter way to show how many times you are using the same number as a factor.

A D3 shows how to write and read a numeral that expresses the number obtained when 10 is used twice as a factor. Study D3.

B You can also read the numeral 10^2 as "ten squared." Is $10^2 = 10 \times 10$? How do you know that 10^2 and 100 are the same number?

C You say "the third power of 10" or "ten cubed" for the numeral 10^3. The numeral 10^3 expresses the number obtained when 10 is used three times as a factor. Is $10^3 = 10 \times 10 \times 10$? Are 10^3 and 1000 the same number?

When you write the numeral 10^2 to express the number 100 or the numeral 10^3 to express the number 1000, you are using *exponential notation* (eks′pō nen′shəl no tā′shən).

D Use exponential notation to express the number obtained when you use 10 as a factor four times. What is this number?

E The numeral 10^1 expresses the number 10. What number is expressed by the numeral 5^1?

F Numbers like 10^1, 10^2, 10^3, and 10^4 are *powers* of 10. The number 10^1 is the first power of 10. The number 10^2 is the second power of 10. What power of 10 is 10^4?

The number 10 is the *base* of the powers 10^1, 10^2, 10^3, and 10^4. The base of a power is the number that is used as a factor one or more times. The number 4 is the *exponent* of 10^4. The exponent is the number that tells how many times the base is used as a factor.

G What number is the exponent of 10^2? Of 10^3? Of 10^7? How many times is 10 used as a factor in 10^2? In 10^3? In 10^7?

H Look at D4. Exponential notation is used to express five numbers. Each of these numbers was obtained by replacing each variable in a^n by a member of {1, 2, 3, . . .}. What replacements were made in a^n to obtain 3^6? To obtain 7^1? To obtain 5^4?

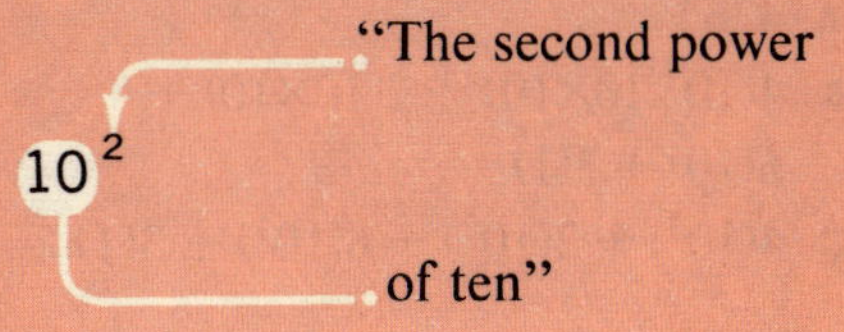

D3

U = C.

a^n $\quad 3^6 \quad 7^1 \quad 5^4 \quad 11^2 \quad 10^7$

D4

pow er (pou′ər). A number that is obtained by using the same factor one or more times. Suppose that, in a^n, a and n are both replaced by members of {1, 2, 3, . . .}. The number obtained from a^n is called the nth power of a. The replacement for the variable a is the **base** of a^n. The replacement for the variable n is the **exponent** (eks pō′nənt) of a^n.

I Is 3^6 a power of 3?

J What is the base of 3^6? What is the exponent of 3^6? How many times is 3 used as a factor in 3^6?

K For each of the other powers named in D4, name the number that is the base. Name the number that is the exponent.

L Express each number named in D4 without using exponential notation.

M Is $3^1 = 3$? Is $20^1 = 20$?

N Suppose that you replace a in $a^1 = a$ by any member of {1, 2, 3, . . .}. Will the statement you obtain be true? Is the first power of each counting number the same as that counting number?

What number is expressed by each of the numerals in exercises O through S?

O 1^1 **P** 1^3 **Q** 1^7 **R** 1^{25} **S** 1^{100}

T Suppose that you replace n in $1^n = 1$ by any member of {1, 2, 3, . . .}. Will the statement you obtain be true? Explain your answer.

A 4263

B $4(10 \times 10 \times 10) + 2(10 \times 10) + 6(10) + 3(1)$

C $4(10^3) + 2(10^2) + 6(10^1) + 3(1)$

D5

You have learned how to obtain the number expressed by a numeral written in exponential notation. Now you will learn to write numerals by using exponential notation.

A You can think of the number 16 as the product 4×4 or the product $2 \times 2 \times 2 \times 2$. Is $4^2 = 4 \times 4$? Is $2^4 = 2 \times 2 \times 2 \times 2$? Can 16 be expressed by either 4^2 or 2^4?

Each number named below is a power of 10. Use exponential notation to express each of these powers.

B 100 C 10,000 D 1000 E 100,000

F Look at D5. Numeral A is a base-ten, or decimal, numeral. Does numeral B show how the number 4263 was obtained?

G How was numeral C obtained? Does numeral C also show how the number 4263 was obtained? Numeral C is the *expanded form* of the decimal numeral 4263.

In the decimal numeral 4263, the digit 3 is associated with (1). The digit 3 expresses the number 3(1), or 3. The digit 6 is associated with the first power of ten. The digit 6 expresses the number $6(10^1)$, or 60.

H Which digit in the numeral 4263 is associated with the second power of ten? Which digit in the numeral is associated with the third power of ten?

I Which of the following is the expanded form of the decimal numeral 35,927?

$3(10^5) + 5(10^4) + 9(10^3) + 2(10^2) + 7(10^1)$

$3(10^4) + 5(10^3) + 9(10^2) + 2(10^1) + 7(1)$

Write each decimal numeral below in expanded form.

J 185 K 7330 L 29,537 M 663,501

In this lesson you have learned about factors, powers, exponents, and exponential notation. You also know how to write decimal numerals in expanded form.

On your own

Use set A, tabulated below, as you answer exercises 1 through 4.

A = {1, 2, 3, 5, 12, 18, 30, 36, 45, 54, 85, 99}.

1 List the names of the members of A that have 2 as a factor.

2 List the names of the members of A that have 3 as a factor.

3 List the names of the members that have 5 as a factor.

4 List the names of the members that have 7 as a factor.

Tabulate the set of all possible factors of each number expressed in exercises 5 through 10. For exercise 5 you should write: {1, 2, 4, 8}.

5 8 6 19 7 14 8 11 9 35 10 60

11 Is 1 a factor of each number expressed in exercises 5 through 10? Is each of these numbers a factor of itself?

For each of the powers expressed below, name the number that is the base. Name the number that is the exponent.

12 10^4 13 15^3 14 7^7 15 9^{10}

For each of exercises 16 through 27, express each number named without using exponential notation.

16 2^1 19 2^5 22 1^9 25 10^5

17 2^2 20 9^1 23 5^3 26 4^1

18 2^4 21 9^2 24 3^5 27 12^2

28 Use exponential notation to express 81 as a power of 3.

29 Use exponential notation to express 64 as a power of 2.

30 Use exponential notation to express 121 as a power of 11.

31 Use exponential notation to express 1,000,000 as a power of 10.

For each of sentences 32, 33, and 34, tell whether it expresses a true or a false statement.

32 $10^3 < 3^{10}$. **33** $1^7 = 7^1$. **34** $3^4 > 3^3$.

Each numeral in exercises 35 through 39 is a decimal numeral. Write each numeral in expanded form.

35 16 **36** 58 **37** 749 **38** 1007 **39** 262,844

KEEPING SKILFUL

For each of exercises 1, 2, and 3, first tabulate sets S and T. Next tabulate $S \cup T$. Then tabulate $S \cap T$. $U = N \times N$.

1 $S = \{(m, n) \mid m + n < 10 \wedge m + 1 = n\}$.
$T = \{(m, n) \mid 4 > n \wedge n > m\}$.

2 $S = \{(r, s) \mid r < 6 \wedge 7 - r = s\}$.
$T = \{(r, s) \mid s > r \wedge s + 19 = 25\}$.

3 $S = \{(g, h) \mid g + 5 < 11 \wedge h + 2 = 9\}$.
$T = \{(g, h) \mid g + h = 9 \wedge h + 1 < 8\}$.

Use one sketch for exercises 4 through 11.

4 Show $\triangle ABC$.

5 Show circle B that intersects $\overline{BC}$ in point G and $\overline{AB}$ in point F.

6 Locate point J in the interior of circle B and in the exterior of $\triangle ABC$.

7 Locate point K in the interior of $\triangle ABC$ and in the interior of circle B.

8 Locate point M in the interior of $\angle CBA$ and in the exterior of $\angle CAB$.

9 Which points named are in the intersection of $\triangle ABC$ and the interior of circle B?

10 Which points named are in the union of circle B and the exterior of $\triangle ABC$?

11 Which points named are in the intersection of $\triangle ABC$ and the exterior of circle B?

5 54 Exploring ideas

Converting numerals from one base to another

In the last lesson you learned to write decimal numerals in expanded form. In this lesson you will learn to use the expanded form for numerals with bases other than ten. You will also learn more about changing numerals from one base to another.

A Suppose that 5623 is a decimal numeral. Which digit in the numeral expresses the number of ones?

B Which digit in the numeral 5623 is associated with the first power of ten? With the second power of ten? With the third power of ten?

C Write the decimal numeral 5623 in expanded form.

D Look at D1. What is the base of numeral A? Does numeral B show how to obtain the number expressed by numeral A?

REMINDER

Numerals that have bases other than ten are read and written in a special way.

See lesson 51, page 216.

A 5623_{seven}

B $5(7 \times 7 \times 7) + 6(7 \times 7) + 2(7) + 3(1)$

C $5(7^3) + 6(7^2) + 2(7^1) + 3(1)$

D1

You know that the digit 7 is not used in a base-seven system. Since the digit 7 is a decimal symbol for the number seven, numeral B in D1 is a decimal numeral.

E Explain how numeral C was obtained from numeral B.

F Does numeral C also show how to obtain the number expressed by numeral A?

Numeral C is the expanded form of the numeral 5623_{seven} Numeral C is also a decimal numeral. All of the expanded forms of numerals that you will work with in this book will be decimal numerals.

G Numeral C shows you that the digit 3 in numeral A expresses the number of ones. Is the digit 2 in numeral A associated with the first power of seven?

H Which digit in the numeral 5623_{seven} is associated with the second power of seven? With the third power of seven?

In lesson 49 you learned about the base of a grouping system. Now you will use what you know about powers to learn more about the base of a numeration system.

For exercise C, you wrote the decimal numeral 5623 in expanded form. Ten is the *base* of the numeration system to which the numeral 5623 belongs. The digits in the numeral 5623 are associated with powers of ten. D1 shows how to write the numeral 5623_{seven} in expanded form. In this case, seven is the base of the numeration system to which the numeral 5623_{seven} belongs. This time the digits in the numeral are associated with powers of seven.

I Look at D2. What is the base of numeral D?

J Numeral E in D2 is the expanded form of numeral D. Use numeral E to answer the following question: What is the number whose powers are associated with the digits in numeral D?

A 5623_{seven}

B $5(7 \times 7 \times 7) + 6(7 \times 7) + 2(7) + 3(1)$

C $5(7^3) + 6(7^2) + 2(7^1) + 3(1)$

D1

D 4817_{nine}

E $4(9^3) + 8(9^2) + 1(9^1) + 7(1)$

D2

A 310_{four}	$3(4^2) + 1(4^1) + 0(1)$
B 101_{two}	$1(2^2) + 0(2^1) + 1(1)$
C 452_{six}	$4(6^2) + 5(6^1) + 2(1)$
D $5£9_{twelve}$	$5(12^2) + 11(12^1) + 9(1)$

D3

base of a place-value numeration system. The number whose powers are associated with the digits in the numerals in a place-value numeration system.

K Which digit in numeral D expresses the number of ones? With what power of the base is each of the other digits associated?

Read each of the numerals below. Then write each numeral in expanded form.

L 1302_{four} **M** 3542_{six} **N** 3277_{eight}

In previous lessons you changed, or converted, numerals with bases other than ten to base-ten numerals. Now you will use what you have learned about writing numerals in expanded form to convert numerals from one base to another.

A Look at D3. Read each numeral in the first column. What is the base of each of these numerals?

B In numeral A, how many ones does the digit 0 express? With what power of 4 is the digit 1 associated? With what power of 4 is the digit 3 associated?

C In numeral B, with what power of 2 is the digit 0 associated? In numeral C, with what power of 6 is the digit 4 associated? In numeral D, with what power of 12 is the digit £ associated?

D In the second column in D3, numerals A, B, C, and D have been written in expanded form. Does each expanded form show how to obtain the number expressed by the numeral in the first column?

E What number is expressed by each numeral in the first column?

Write each of the following numerals in expanded form:

F 30_{seven}	**H** 210_{three}	**J** 1314_{five}
G 25_{eight}	**I** 435_{six}	**K** 10101_{two}

L Tell what number is expressed by each numeral in exercises F through K. Remember to use a decimal numeral to express each number.

You know how to convert a numeral with a base other than ten to a decimal numeral. In the following exercises you will learn to convert a decimal numeral to a numeral with a base other than ten.

A Suppose that you want to convert the decimal numeral 97 to a base-five numeral. To find a base-five numeral that expresses the number 97, first decide for what powers of 5 the numeral will have digits. If there is to be a digit for 5^2, for example, then 97 must be equal to or greater than 5^2. What number is the second power of 5? Will there be a digit for 5^2?

B If there is to be a digit for 5^3, then 97 must be equal to or greater than 5^3. Will there be a digit for 5^3? How do you know?

C Since there is to be a digit for 5^2, must there also be digits for 5^1 and 1? How many digits will there be in the base-five numeral for 97?

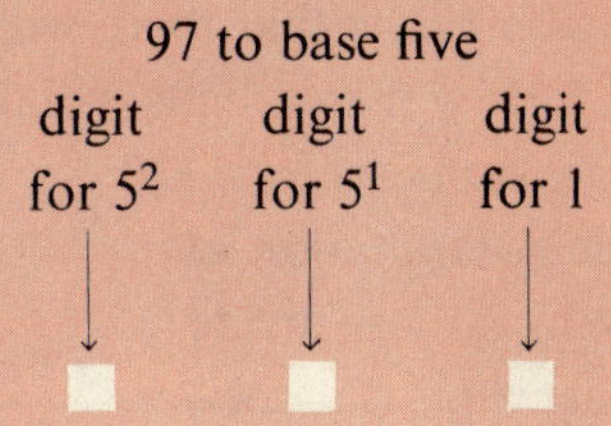

D4

D Study D4. To find the digit that belongs in the space associated with 5^2, you divide 97 by 5^2. Is this the same as dividing by 25?

E Study the computation at the right. How does it show that the digit 3 is associated with 5^2? In which space in D4 does the digit 3 belong?

```
25)97 | 3
   75 |
   22 |
```

F When 97 is divided by 25, the remainder is 22. Divide the 22 by 5^1. Look at the computation. What digit is associated with 5^1? In which space in D4 does the digit 4 belong?

```
5)22 | 4
  20 |
   2 |
```

G How many ones remain? In which space does the digit 2 belong?

H The numeral at the right expresses the same number as the numeral 97. Which digit in the numeral 342_{five} expresses the number of ones? With which power of 5 is each of the other digits in the numeral 342_{five} associated?

342_{five}

I Convert the numeral 342_{five} to a decimal numeral. Is $97 = 342_{five}$?

J Next you will convert the decimal numeral 132 to a base-eight numeral. In a base-eight numeral, the digits are associated with powers of what number?

K If there is to be a digit for 8^2, the number 132 must be equal to or greater than 8^2. What number is the second power of 8? Will there be a digit for 8^2?

L How do you know that there will not be a digit for 8^3? How many digits will there be in the base-eight numeral for 132?

M Study the computation at the right. Why do you divide by 64? What digit is associated with 8^2? What is the remainder?

$$\begin{array}{r|l} 64\overline{)132} & 2 \\ 128 & \\ \hline 4 & \end{array}$$

N Now divide the remainder, 4, by 8^1. How do you know that the digit associated with 8^1 is 0?

$$\begin{array}{r|l} 8\overline{)4} & 0 \\ 0 & \\ \hline 4 & \end{array}$$

O How many ones remain?

P The numeral at the right expresses the same number as the numeral 132. Which digit in the numeral 204_{eight} expresses the number of ones? With which power of 8 is each of the other digits associated?

204_{eight}

Q Convert the numeral 204_{eight} to a decimal numeral. Is $132 = 204_{eight}$?

Each numeral below is a decimal numeral. You are to convert each numeral to a numeral in another numeration system. The base of the other numeration system is expressed by the word within parentheses.

R 85 (six) **S** 123 (twelve) **T** 31 (two)

We can also convert a numeral that does not have ten as a base to another numeral that also does not have ten as a base. For example, let us convert the numeral 346_{nine} to a base-twelve numeral.

U First convert the numeral 346_{nine} to a decimal numeral. What is the decimal numeral for 346_{nine}?

V Now convert the decimal numeral you obtained for exercise U to a base-twelve numeral. What is the base-twelve numeral?

W Do the numeral 346_{nine} and the base-twelve numeral you obtained for exercise V express the same number?

In this lesson you have learned to use the expanded form for numerals with bases other than ten. You also have learned how to convert a numeral with any given base to a numeral with a different base.

On your own

Each numeral in exercises 1 through 4 is written in expanded form. First write the numeral from which each expanded form was obtained. Be sure to express the base of this number. Then write the decimal numeral for the number expressed.

1 $3(5^3) + 1(5^2) + 2(5^1) + 3(1)$

2 $6(7^2) + 4(7^1) + 5(1)$

3 $5(8^3) + 7(8^2) + 0(8^1) + 0(1)$

4 $2(12^2) + 11(12^1) + 8(1)$

For each of exercises 5 through 13, convert the numeral to a decimal numeral.

5 635_{seven}	**8** 3405_{six}	**11** 1211021_{three}
6 1001_{two}	**9** 1042_{five}	**12** 495_{eleven}
7 972_{twelve}	**10** 31022_{four}	**13** 2377_{eight}

For exercises 14 through 21, convert each decimal numeral to a numeral in the numeration system whose base is expressed within parentheses.

14 104 (base five)	**18** 3257 (base seven)
15 64 (base twelve)	**19** 43 (base three)
16 87 (base two)	**20** 72961 (base eight)
17 648 (base five)	**21** 213 (base nine)

For each of exercises 22 through 25, express the first fourteen counting numbers in the numeration system indicated in the exercise.

22 Base ten	**24** Base twelve
23 Base two	**25** Base eight

For exercises 26 through 33 convert each numeral to a base-twelve numeral.

26 346_{seven}	**30** 2102_{three}
27 1011_{two}	**31** 5641_{seven}
28 437_{eight}	**32** 156
29 106	**33** 43122_{five}

Computing in numeration systems other than the decimal system

Now that you have learned to express numbers using different numeration systems, you are prepared to compute in different systems. This practice in computation will help you to understand better the properties of the decimal numeration system.

A Look at D1. The first ten natural numbers are expressed as both decimal numerals and base-four numerals. Write decimal numerals for the next five natural numbers. Then write base-four numerals for the same five natural numbers.

B How many different digits are needed for a decimal numeration system? For a base-four numeration system?

When used alone, the ten digits of a decimal system express the natural numbers from zero through nine. You already know how to add any two of these natural numbers. You also know how to use a decimal numeral to express their sum.

When used alone, the four digits of a base-four system express the natural numbers from zero through three. The work that follows shows how to add any two of these numbers and how to use a base-four numeral to express the sum.

The table in D2 is part of an addition table for a base-four numeration system. When completed, the table will show how the sum of any two of the first four natural numbers can be expressed as a base-four numeral.

Decimal	0	1	2	3	4	5	6	7	8	9
Base four	0	1	2	3	10	11	12	13	20	21

D1

+	0	1	2	3
0	0	1	2	3
1	1	2	3	
2	2	3		
3	3	10	11	12

D2

C Study the table in D2. To find the numeral that expresses the sum of 1 and 3, first find the red numeral 1 in the top row. Then look down the column until you find the numeral that is opposite the red numeral 3. Notice that the numeral 10 ("one zero") is used to express the sum of 1 and 3. Why are no digits other than 0, 1, 2, and 3 used in a base-four numeration system?

D Suppose that you want to express the sum of 2 and 3 as a base-four numeral. Which should you use, the numeral 11 or the numeral 5? Explain your answer.

E What base-four numeral should you use to express the sum of 3 and 3? The sum of 2 and 2?

F Copy and complete the table in D2.

Next you will review how to express the sum of twenty-five and thirty-nine as a decimal numeral. Then you will learn how you can do the same computation with base-four numerals.

G Look at the work below. Add the ones in 25 and 39. Should you think of 14 as 1 ten and 4 ones? Where should you write a digit to express the 4 ones? You should remember the 1 ten to add to the other tens.

```
 25
 39
 --
  4
```

H Add the tens in 25 and 39. Do not forget to include the 1 ten you obtained from adding the ones. How many tens in all are there? Where should you write a digit to express the total number of tens? What decimal numeral expresses the sum of 25 and 39?

$$\begin{array}{r} {\scriptstyle 1} \\ 25 \\ 39 \\ \hline 64 \end{array}$$

I To add 25 and 39 using base-four numerals, first convert each base-ten numeral to a base-four numeral. What number is expressed by the base-four numeral 121? What number does the base-four numeral 213 express?

121_{four}

213_{four}

J Add the ones first. From the addition table in D2, you see that $1 + 3 = 10$. (Read 10 as "one zero" and not as "ten.") Does the base-four numeral 10 express 1 four? Why should you write the digit 0 in ones' place? Remember 1 four to add to the other fours.

$$\begin{array}{r} {\scriptstyle 1} \\ 121 \\ 213 \\ \hline 0 \end{array}$$

K In the base-four numeral 121, how many fours does the digit 2 express? In the base-four numeral 213, how many fours does the digit 1 express? Add the fours. Remember to include the 1 four you obtained from adding the ones. How many fours are there in all? Why should you think of this sum as 10 fours or 1 sixteen? Why do you write the digit 0 in fours' place? What number do you remember?

$$\begin{array}{r} {\scriptstyle 1\,1} \\ 121 \\ 213 \\ \hline 00 \end{array}$$

L In the base-four numeral 121, the digit 1 at the left expresses $1(4^2)$, or $1(16)$. What does the digit 2 in the base-four numeral 213 express? Add the sixteens. Remember to include the 1 sixteen you obtained from adding the fours. Is 10 the sum of the fours? Think of the 10 sixteens as 1 sixty-four. Why do you write the digit 0 in sixteens' place? Why do you write the digit 1 in sixty-fours' place?

$$\begin{array}{r} {\scriptstyle 1\,1} \\ 121 \\ 213 \\ \hline 1000 \end{array}$$

+	0	1	2	3
0	0	1	2	3
1	1	2	3	
2	2	3		
3	3	10	11	12

D2

Base four

$$\begin{array}{r} {\scriptstyle 1\,1} \\ 233 \\ 212 \\ \hline 1111 \end{array}$$

D3

M Does the base-four numeral 1000 express the same number as the decimal numeral 64?

N Study D3. The numbers added are expressed as base-four numerals. So is their sum. You can verify the base-four computation by using the decimal system. Convert 233_{four} and 212_{four} to decimal numerals and add.

O Is $47 + 38 = 85$? Is $1111_{four} = 85$? Is the computation shown in D3 correct?

P Using the base-four system, add the numbers expressed by 203_{four} and 123_{four}. Verify your answer by using the decimal system.

In the following exercises you will use the base-twelve system to express numbers and their sums.

Q Make an addition table for the base-twelve numeration system. Your table should show how to express the sum of any two of the first twelve natural numbers in a base-twelve system. What digits will you use to express the numbers ten and eleven?

R D4 shows base-twelve numerals for two numbers and their sum. Is the sum correct? Use the addition table you made to help you.

Base twelve

$$\begin{array}{r} {\scriptstyle 1\,1} \\ 1\,9\,\mathcal{E}\,9 \\ \underline{\chi\,0\,\mathcal{E}\,\chi} \\ \mathcal{E}\,\chi\,\mathcal{E}\,7 \end{array}$$

D4

×	0	1	2	3
0	0	0		0
1	0	1	2	
2		2	10	
3	0		12	21

D5

S Use the decimal system to verify the computation shown in D4.

Using the base-twelve numeration system, add each pair of numbers expressed by the numerals below. Verify your answers by using the decimal system.

T $2\mathcal{E}\chi_{\text{twelve}}$, 504_{twelve} U 137_{twelve}, $\chi 89_{\text{twelve}}$

Now you will learn to use various numeration systems to express the product of two numbers. The first numeration system you will use will be a base-four numeration system.

The table shown in D5 is part of a multiplication table for the base-four system. This table, when completed, will show how the product of any two of the first four natural numbers can be expressed as a base-four numeral.

A Which should you use, the numeral 10 or the numeral 4, to express the product of 2 and 2 as a base-four numeral? Why should you use the numeral 12, and not the numeral 6, to express the product of 2 and 3? Why should you use the numeral 21 to express the product of 3 and 3?

B Copy and complete the table in D5.

Now you are prepared to find the product of the two numbers expressed by the base-four numerals 1321 and 3. Use the base-four multiplication table you completed for exercise B.

C From your table, you see that $3 \times 1 = 3$. Why do you write the digit 3 in ones' place?

$$\begin{array}{r} 1321 \\ \underline{3} \\ 3 \end{array}$$

D Next you multiply the fours. Why can you think of the 2 in 1321 as 2 fours, or 20? $3 \times 20 = 120$. Why should you think of 120 as 1 sixteen and 2 fours? You write the digit 2 in fours' place and remember the 1 sixteen to add to the other sixteens.

$$\begin{array}{r} 1321 \\ \underline{3} \\ 23 \end{array}$$

E Now multiply the sixteens. Why can you think of the 3 sixteens as 300? $3 \times 300 = 2100$. Why should you think of 2100 as 2 sixty-fours and 1 sixteen? Why do you write the digit 2, and not the digit 1, in sixteens' place? Remember the 2 sixty-fours to add to the other sixty-fours.

$$\begin{array}{r} 1321 \\ \underline{3} \\ 223 \end{array}$$

F Finally, multiply the sixty-fours. How many sixty-fours are there? $3 \times 1000 = 3000$. How do you know that there are 11 ("one one") sixty-fours in all? Why should you write the digit 1 in sixty-fours' place? What digit is written in two hundred fifty-sixes' place?

$$\begin{array}{r} 1321 \\ \underline{3} \\ 11223 \end{array}$$

G To verify the base-four computation, convert 3_{four} and 1321_{four} to decimal numerals and multiply. Does the numeral 363 name the product you obtain? Then convert 11223_{four} to a decimal numeral. Your two products should be the same. Is $11223_{\text{four}} = 363$ a true statement?

Base four

3232
3
―――――
23022

D6

Base twelve

31£
4
―――――
1078

D7

H Look at D6. Two numbers and their product are expressed as base-four numerals. Verify the computation shown in D6. Is it correct?

I Next you will see how the base-twelve system can be used to express numbers and their products. Make a multiplication table for the base-twelve system.

J Look at D7. Two numbers and their product are expressed as base-twelve numerals. Why is the digit 8 written in ones' place? Why is the digit 7 written in twelves' place? In what place is the digit 0 written? The digit 1?

K Verify the computation shown in D7.

L 603 and 8 are base-twelve numerals. Using base-twelve numerals, show how you compute to find the product of the numbers expressed by these numerals. Verify your answer.

Now you will learn to compute with base-two numerals.

D8 shows an addition table and a multiplication table for a base-two numeration system.

M Why are the digits 0 and 1 the only digits
? used in the tables?

N To express the sum of 1 and 1 as a base-two numeral, why should you use the numeral 10, and not the numeral 2?

O Look at example A in D9. Two numbers and their sum are expressed as base-two numerals. Is the computation correct? Use the addition table in D8 to help you.

P Look at example B in D9. Two numbers and their product are expressed as base-two numerals. Is the computation correct? Use the multiplication table in D8 to help you.

Q Now use the decimal system to verify the computation shown in example A and example B in D9.

R Look at D10. The numerals are base-two numerals. Is the product correct? Verify the computation.

Now you know how to add and multiply using numeration systems other than the decimal system.

+	0	1
0	0	1
1	1	10

×	0	1
0	0	0
1	0	1

D8

Base two

A

101
111
―――――
1100

B

101
1
―――――
101

D9

Base two

111
11
―――――
111
1110
―――――
10101

D10

On your own

For each of exercises 1 through 8, find the sum of the numbers expressed. Express your answer as a numeral in the same numeration system as the numerals in the exercise. Then verify your computation by using decimal numerals.

1 10_{four}, 10_{four}
2 21_{four}, 30_{four}
3 3303_{four}, 2032_{four}
4 1120_{four}, 1301_{four}, 3002_{four}
5 $15\mathcal{E}_{twelve}$, 32_{twelve}
6 19_{twelve}, χ_{twelve}
7 $1\chi_{twelve}$, 13_{twelve}
8 23_{twelve}, $\mathcal{E}8_{twelve}$, 50_{twelve}

For each of exercises 9 through 16, find the product of the numbers expressed. Express your answer as a numeral in the same numeration system as the numerals in the exercise. Then verify the answer by using decimal numerals.

9 30_{four}, 2_{four}
10 22_{four}, 3_{four}
11 13_{four}, 2_{four}
12 1100_{four}, 3_{four}
13 592_{twelve}, 2_{twelve}
14 6301_{twelve}, 8_{twelve}
15 1550_{twelve}, $\mathcal{E}_{twelve}$
16 1008_{twelve}, χ_{twelve}

17 Make an addition table for a base-seven numeration system. Make your table so that it shows how to express the sum of any two of the first seven natural numbers as base-seven numerals.

18 Make a multiplication table for a base-seven numeration system. Your table should show how to express the product of any two of the first seven natural numbers as base-seven numerals.

For each of exercises 19 through 28, find the sum or product as directed and express the answer as a base-seven numeral.

Find the sum.

19 10_{seven}, 23_{seven}
20 236_{seven}, 25_{seven}
21 66_{seven}, 56_{seven}
22 606_{seven}, 536_{seven}
23 64_{seven}, 10_{seven}, 5_{seven}
24 64_{seven}, 43_{seven}, 21_{seven}

Find the product.

25 12_{seven}, 5_{seven}
26 303_{seven}, 4_{seven}
27 135_{seven}, 6_{seven}
28 546_{seven}, 3_{seven}

For each of exercises 29 through 36, find the sum or product as directed and express the answer as a base-two numeral.

Find the sum.

29 10_{two}, 1_{two}
30 11_{two}, 101_{two}
31 11_{two}, 10_{two}, 11_{two}
32 1001_{two}, 1101_{two}

Find the product.

33 110_{two}, 1_{two}
34 111_{two}, 101_{two}
35 1010_{two}, 11_{two}
36 1001_{two}, 11_{two}

SPECIAL CHALLENGE

A sports writer gave his editor an article about Babe Ruth. The editor was confused for awhile but then smiled because he understood what the writer had done. The article is given below. Rewrite the article so that anyone can read it without confusion. Do not change the words or the order of the words.

"Babe Ruth was one of the greatest players in the history of baseball. He was born February 10, 12435, and died August 24, 13004, at the age of 125. He played on a major league baseball team from 12510 through 12550. He played with the New York Yankees from 12520 through 12542. Babe Ruth set many records during his lifetime of baseball. Some of these records are: 10054 strikeouts, 13304 bases on balls, 14121 runs batted in, and 10140 extra-base hits.

"Perhaps his most impressive record was set in 12531. In that year, Babe Ruth set a record for the number of home runs hit during one season in the major leagues. He hit 140 home runs in 414 games. This record has stood for 54 years!"

5 56 **Exploring ideas**

Decimal numerals for numbers greater than one thousand

In earlier grades you learned to use decimal numerals to express numbers greater than one thousand. In this lesson you will learn more about these decimal numerals.

Look at D1. Notice that the digits in the decimal numeral are written in groups. Counting from the right, each group contains three digits. Each group of digits in the numeral is called a *period.*

A Each period in a decimal numeral, except for the period farthest to the right, has a special name. These names are shown above the numeral in D1. Which digits are in the thousands' period? Which digits are in the millions' period? Which digits are in the billions' period?

The words you use to read the name of each period are shown in D2. You read the digits in each period in the same way that you read the digits in the period farthest to the right, and then you say or think the name of the period.

B How do you read the digits in the fourth period from the right?

C How do you read the digits in the third period from the right?

D How do you read the digits in the second period from the right?

E How do you read the digits in the period farthest to the right? Remember that there is no special name for this period.

F Now read the numeral below.
69,840,020,002.

billions	millions	thousands	
256,	193,	462,	109

D1

256, 193, 462, 109

"256 billion
193 million
462 thousand
109"

D2

G Look at the numerals in exercises H through M. How are the periods in each numeral indicated?

H 721,635,599,483 **K** 660,030,900,002
I 20,840,500,080 **L** 1,005,000
J 87,692,110 **M** 2,470,000,002

Notice that the period farthest to the left is the only period that sometimes has only one or two digits in it.

N Read each of the numerals in exercises H through M.

O Which numeral in exercises H through M expresses the greatest number? Which numeral expresses the least number?

Sometimes you will use numerals for numbers greater than billions. The name of the next period after the billions' period is *trillions.* The name of the next period after the trillions' period is *quadrillions.* If you are curious to know the names of other periods, look up the word "numeration" in a dictionary or encyclopedia.

Read each of the numerals in exercises P through S.

P 4,672,792,844,631 **R** 61,334,492,766,900
Q 25,985,234,096,741 **S** 500,370,004,019

T Look at D3. Does the position of each digit in the numeral tell you the number expressed by that digit? Your answer depends upon what property of a decimal numeration system?

U What do the names above the periods in the numeral in D3 tell you?

Each of the positions within a period in a decimal numeral also has a special name. The names of the positions, or places, are shown below the digits in D3.

A Which digits form the thousands' period in the numeral in D3? Notice that in this period the digit 3 expresses the number three hundred thousand. The digit 1 expresses what number?

B Which digits form the millions' period? In this period, what number is expressed by the digit 7? By the digit 5? By the digit 4?

C Which digit is in ten thousands' place? In tens' place? In billions' place?

Many times it is convenient to express a number by using exponential notation.

D Look at D4. Are 10^2 and 100 the same number? What number is the same as 10^3? What number is the same as 10^4? Does each sentence in D4 express a true statement?

REMINDER

10^2, 10^3, and 10^4 are powers of 10.
A power is a number that is obtained
by using the same factor
one or more times.

See lesson 53, page 227.

E Numeral D in D5 expresses the product of two numbers, 7 and 10^6. Is 7 a number less than 10? Is 10^6 a power of 10? Are 7×10^6 and 7,000,000 the same number?

Notice that 7 is one of the factors of the number 7×10^6. Notice also that 7 is one of the numbers from 1 to 10. The other factor, 10^6, is a power of 10. Any numeral that expresses the product of a number from 1 to 10 (but not including 10) and a power of 10 is in *scientific notation*. Numeral D is the scientific notation for the number 7,000,000.

F Numeral E is the scientific notation for what number? Numeral F is the scientific notation for what number?

billions			millions			thousands					
2	8	6	4	5	7	3	0	1	2	9	8
hundred billions	ten billions	billions	hundred millions	ten millions	millions	hundred thousands	ten thousands	thousands	hundreds	tens	ones

D3

A $10^2 = 10 \times 10.$

B $10^3 = 10 \times 10 \times 10.$

C $10^4 = 10 \times 10 \times 10 \times 10.$

D4

D 7×10^6

E 5×10^5

F 4×10^3

D5

sci en tif ic no ta tion (sī′ən tif′ik nō tā′shən). A method of expressing a number as the product of a number from 1 to 10 and a power of 10.

The numeral 5×10^2 is the scientific notation for 500. The number 800,000,000 is expressed in scientific notation by the numeral 8×10^8.

G What number is expressed by the numeral **?** 30×10^2? By the numeral 3×10^3? Which of these numerals is in scientific notation? How do you know?

Use scientific notation to express each of the numbers named below.

H 600	**K** 400,000,000
I 70,000	**L** 100,000
J 3,000,000	**M** 8,000,000,000

In this lesson you have learned more about reading and writing names for numbers greater than one thousand. You have also learned how to express some numbers by using scientific notation.

On your own

For each of exercises 1 through 6, write the words that you would say in reading the numeral. For exercise 1 you should write "eighty-five million ninety thousand eighty."

1 85,090,080	**4** 674,982,315
2 59,073	**5** 765,100,200
3 356,521	**6** 2,965,461,332

For each of exercises 7 through 16, use digits to write the numeral.

7 seventy thousand four

8 nine hundred thousand six

9 four hundred thousand seven hundred thirty

10 six hundred twenty-three thousand forty

11 seven million seven thousand seventy

12 forty-five million six hundred thousand

13 fifty-two million eighty-nine thousand fourteen

14 one billion twenty-four thousand three hundred nineteen

15 five hundred eighty million seven hundred thousand sixteen

16 three trillion four hundred million

For each of exercises 17 through 22, write the decimal numeral for the number expressed.

17 4×10^3	**19** 9×10^2	**21** 5×10^6
18 2×10^5	**20** 8×10^4	**22** 7×10^{10}

For each of exercises 23 through 32, use scientific notation to express the number named.

23 8000	**28** 50,000,000
24 200	**29** 400,000,000
25 700,000	**30** 600,000,000
26 40,000	**31** 80,000,000
27 3000	**32** 200,000,000

APPLYING MATHEMATICS

In this lesson you will solve problems similar to the ones that you have studied so far in this book. For each problem, first write a sentence that expresses a condition. Use any letters you wish as names for the variables. Then tabulate the solution set of the condition and give the answer to the problem. The universe is given for each problem.

1 Terry had 110 newspapers to sell. He sold all but 25 of them. How many newspapers did he sell? U = N.

2 A road crew can build 5 miles of road in 3 months. At this rate, how many months will it take the crew to build a road that is to be 115 miles long? U = C.

3 The area of the Pacific Ocean is 63,801,668 square miles. The area of the Atlantic Ocean is 31,839,306 square miles. What is the total area of the Atlantic and Pacific Oceans? U = N.

4 After Mrs. Smith bought 13 yards of drapery material, she had more than 41 yards. What is the least number of yards she could have had before she bought the 13 yards of material? U = N.

5 The citizens of Foster raised $9213 for park equipment. The amount they raised was $758 more than their goal. What was their goal? U = N.

6 Ken has 18 travel posters, and Dick has 13 travel posters. Carl has fewer posters than Ken and Dick have together, but more posters than Dick has. How many posters can Carl have? U = N.

7 Mr. Fisher borrowed \$950 from a local bank. At the end of one year, he paid \$57 interest. What rate of interest was he charged? U = C.

8 In Canada, there are over 30 national parks and at least 300 provincial parks. There are how many times as many provincial parks as national parks? U = C.

9 On May 1, Mr. Roberts had more than 63 cars to sell. During the month, he sold 17 of these cars and then had fewer than 54 cars left to sell. How many cars could Mr. Roberts have had to sell on May 1? U = N.

10 For each game played in some leagues, the home team is required to supply 48 baseballs. At the end of a certain game, there were fewer than 19 baseballs left. How many baseballs could have been used during this game? U = N.

11 Last year, Mr. Lang's take-home pay was \$7395. He saved \$2 out of each \$17 of his take-home pay. How much money did he save last year? U = C.

12 The Second National Bank charges 6% interest on the money it lends. Miss Wilson borrowed \$750 from this bank. She agreed to repay her loan with interest at the end of one year. How much did Miss Wilson owe the bank at the end of one year? U = C × C.

13 The area of Canada is 3,851,809 square miles. The area of Canada is about 17 times the area of France. The area of France is about how many square miles? U = C.

14 One day an appliance salesman sold more electric fans than steam irons. He sold fewer than 6 fans and irons in all. How many appliances of each kind could he have sold? U = C × C.

15 Mr. Davis received a commission of \$260 for the month of April. He said that his March commission had been 125% of his April commission. How much commission did Mr. Davis receive for the month of March? U = C.

16 During a sale, Mrs. Jones paid \$273 for a dresser that was regularly priced at \$350. What rate of discount did she receive? U = C × C.

17 Certain rate pairs are equivalent to 2/3. The product of the first and second components of each of these rate pairs is less than 100. What are the rate pairs? U = C × C.

18 51 is 34% of what number? U = C.

19 What number is 96% of 7625? U = C.

20 660 is what per cent of 528? U = C.

SPECIAL CHALLENGE

Captain Nemo discovered a strange country where the inhabitants used a base-seven system of numeration with the property of place value. When the inhabitants counted, they used the words *re*, *mi*, *fa*, *sol*, *la*, *ti*, *re-do*, *re-re*, and so on. Use the word names of the numbers in this system of numeration for exercises A, B, and C.

A Write the names of the natural numbers from 1 through 25.

B Write the names of the natural numbers from 45 through 60.

C Write the names of the natural numbers from 340 through 354.

D Captain Nemo also discovered another country where the inhabitants used a base-nine place-value numeration system. Invent names for the numbers in this system of numeration. Then write the names of the natural numbers from 1 through 27, from 60 through 70, and from 510 through 521.

CHECKING UP

The small numeral within parentheses tells you what page to turn to for help if you have trouble with an exercise.

Test 56

Write "T" for each sentence below that expresses a true statement. Write "F" for each sentence that expresses a false statement.

1 A code numeration system has the property of addition. (207)

2 In the numeral 427,216, the first three digits are in the thousands' period. (239)

3 A tally numeration system has the property of repetition. (207)

4 The decimal numeral 60,000,000 is read "sixty billion." (238)

5 One billion is greater than one trillion. (238)

6 A place-value numeration system has the property of repetition. (218)

7 The digit 3 in the decimal numeral 34756 is associated with the fifth power of 10. (230)

8 $121_{three} = 21_{five}$ is a true statement. (232)

9 The decimal numeration system has the property of place value. (217)

10 The sum of the numbers expressed by the Roman numerals XVI and XIX is the number expressed by the numeral XXXV. (222)

Test 57

From the list given below each exercise, choose the expression that correctly completes the exercise.

11 The numbers 3^2, 3^3, and 3^4 are ~~~~ of 3. (227)

a exponents **b** factors **c** powers **d** bases

12 The ~~~~ of the numeral 742 is the numeral $7(10^2) + 4(10^1) + 2(1)$. (228)

a exponential notation **c** factored form
b expanded form **d** product

13 The decimal numeral 407,000,000,000 is read "~~~~." (238)

a four hundred seven trillion
b forty million seven
c four hundred seven billion
d four hundred seven quadrillion
e forty-seven billion

14 The decimal numeral ~~~~ names the same number as the numeral 25_{seven}. (215)

a 19 **b** 25 **c** 25(7) **d** 7

15 The set of factors of 48 does not contain ~~~~. (226)

a 1 **b** 7 **c** 12 **d** 16

16 ~~~~ is not a factor of 30. (226)

a 30 **b** 1 **c** 12 **d** 6

17 A ~~~~ numeration system uses nine different digits. (217)

a base-twelve **c** base-nine
b base-ten **d** base-eight

18 The numeral 42031 cannot be a ~~~~ numeral. (217)

a base-four **c** base-eight
b base-six **d** base-twelve

19 The numeral 10_{seven} expresses the ~~~~ of the numeration system. (216)

a exponent **c** base
b sum **d** power

Test 58

20 What is the exponent of 5^3? (227)

21 What number is expressed by the numeral 1^{1000}? (227)

22 What base-two numeral expresses the sum of 111_{two} and 1101_{two}? (236)

23 What base-two numeral expresses the product of 1011_{two} and 111_{two}? (236)

24 What base-eight numeral expresses the sum of 476_{eight} and 1555_{eight}? (234)

25 What base-twelve numeral expresses the sum of $\mathcal{X}\mathcal{E}9_{twelve}$ and $3\mathcal{X}_{twelve}$? (234)

26 What base-twelve numeral expresses the product of $3\mathcal{E}_{twelve}$ and 5_{twelve}? (236)

A	/	///	/	//
B	///	///////	////	//////

Use the display for exercises 27 through 30.

27 Think of numeral A as a base-four numeral. What number is named by this numeral? (213)

28 Think of numeral A as a base-eight numeral. What number is named by this numeral? (213)

29 Think of numeral A as a base-ten numeral. What number is named by this numeral? (213)

30 Think of numeral B as a base-five numeral. Using a chart and strokes, write a base-five numeral that expresses the same number as numeral B. Use as few strokes as possible. (213)

Test 59

Write a decimal numeral for each number named in exercises 31 through 36. (215)

31 1011_{two}

32 340_{five}

33 592_{twelve}

34 555_{nine}

35 $6\chi32_{eleven}$

36 110101_{two}

37 Convert the numeral 133 to a base-four numeral. (231)

38 Convert the numeral 29 to a base-two numeral. (231)

39 Convert the numeral 2000 to a base-twelve numeral. (231)

40 Convert the numeral 365_{seven} to a base-five numeral. (232)

Test 60

Write a decimal numeral for each number named in exercises 41 through 44. Do not use exponential notation. (239)

41 7×10^4

42 1×10^7

43 8×10^6

44 9×10^9

Use scientific notation to express each number named in exercises 45 through 48. (239)

45 2000

46 60,000

47 5,000,000

48 40,000,000

CHECKING UP

The small numeral within parentheses tells what page to turn to for help if you need it.

Test 61

Write "T" for each sentence below that expresses a true statement. Write "F" for each sentence that expresses a false statement.

1 A numeral is the same as a number. (5)

2 The quotient of 1200 and 150 is the same as the quotient of 40 and 5. (57)

3 The solution set of a condition in two variables is a subset of the universe for the variables. (129)

4 The sentence $x - 7 < y$ expresses an inequality. (21)

5 $\{x \mid 1/x \sim 2/8\} = \{x \mid 8/2 \sim x/1\}$. (178)

6 The exponent of the power 3^8 is the number 8. (227)

7 Infinitely many lines contain two given points. (33)

8 The numeral 651_{seven} expresses the same number as the numeral 2310_{five}. (232)

9 There is at least one point between any two different points. (37)

10 If ℓ_1 separates plane ABC into two half-planes, and the intersection of $\overline{BC}$ and ℓ_1 is the empty set, then point B and point C are in different half-planes. (41)

Test 62

What words or symbols best complete exercises 11 through 19?

11 The amount of money on which interest is paid is the ~~~. (194)

12 The price of an article after the discount has been deducted from the regular price is the ~~~. (198)

13 Each member of the solution set of a condition is a ~~~ of the condition. (24)

14 A ~~~ is the boundary of a half-space. (41)

15 The union of set A and set A is ___. (89)

16 If the union of two sets is ___, then each set is the empty set. (89)

17 $\{0, 1, 2\} \cap \{0, 3, 6\} \cap \{0, 5, 10\} =$ ___. (84)

18 The intersection of set B and set C is a ___ of the union of sets B and C. (88)

19 A ratio is a name of a ___. (173)

Test 63

From the list given below each exercise, choose the expression that correctly completes the exercise.

20 The two axes used to make a graph of a Cartesian set are ___. (130)

a parallel c horizontal
b perpendicular d vertical

21 The interior of an angle is the intersection of two ___. (114)

a rays c planes
b half-planes d half-lines

22 If $U = C$, the union of $\{x \mid x/17 \sim 8/34\}$ and $\{x \mid 34x = 8(17)\}$ contains ___. (177)

a no members c two members
b one member d infinitely many members

23 The set of counting numbers is ___. (73)

a $\{1, 3, 5, \ldots\}$ c $\{0, 2, 4, \ldots\}$
b $\{0, 1, 2, \ldots\}$ d $\{1, 2, 3, \ldots\}$

24 To change the numeral 392 to a base-seven numeral, you first divide the number 392 by ___. (231)

a seven c three hundred forty-three
b twenty-one d forty-nine

25 If $U = C$, the solution set of $x/y \sim 9/6 \wedge x + y < 22$ contains ___. (199)

a two members c four members
b no members d infinitely many members

26 A given line is included in ___. (35)

a exactly one plane
b exactly two planes
c exactly three planes
d infinitely many planes

27 Three noncollinear points are contained in ___. (35)

a exactly one plane
b exactly two planes
c exactly three planes
d infinitely many planes

28 The intersection of two disjoint sets is ___. (85)

a not a set c the universe
b a set with one member d the empty set

Test 64

For each problem, write a sentence that expresses a condition. Tabulate the solution set of the condition, and give the answer to the problem. The universe is given for each problem.

29 The regular price of a subscription to a certain magazine is \$4. Fred was able to get this subscription for \$3. What per cent of the regular price did Fred pay for the subscription? $U = C$. (190)

30 The basic price of one model of a car is \$2450. The basic price of a different model is 90% of the price of the first model. What is the price of the cheaper model if it includes a heater that costs \$69 extra? $U = C \times C$. (195)

31 There are 231 more students enrolled in Scott School than in Brown School. If 78 more students enroll in Scott, the total enrollment will be 550. How many students are enrolled in each school? $U = N \times N$. (153)

32 Mr. Lucas fills the radiator of his car with antifreeze at the rate of 1 quart of antifreeze to 2 quarts of water. If the radiator holds 21 quarts, how much antifreeze and how much water should he use? $U = C \times C$. (195)

33 42 is what per cent of 70? $U = C$. (191)

34 65% of 180 is what number? $U = C$. (192)

35 24 is 30% of what number? $U = C$. (192)

36 391 is what per cent of 230? $U = C$. (191)

37 57 is 150% of what number? $U = C$. (192)

Symbols
and how to read them

These displays show you how to read the mathematical symbols used in this book. They are arranged in the order in which they were introduced. Whenever, in your work, you come to a symbol that you have forgotten how to read, look for one like it among those on this page and the next page. If you need more information about the symbol, turn to the page of the book whose numeral is given above the symbol. There you will find a complete explanation of the meaning of the symbol.

page 11

{ Michigan, Huron, Superior, Erie, Ontario }

"The set whose members are Michigan, Huron, Superior, Erie, Ontario"

page 16

$x + 6 = 9.$

"x plus six equals nine."

page 19

K = { 5, 6, 7, 8, 9, 10 }.

"K equals the set whose members are five, six, seven, eight, nine, ten."

page 20

$x + 2 > 6.$

"x plus two is greater than six."

page 20

$2n < 9.$

"Two times n is less than nine."

page 22

{ 0, 1, 2, . . ., 1000 }

"The set whose members are the natural numbers from 0 through 1000"

page 23

{ 0, 1, 2, . . . }

"The set whose members are the natural numbers"

page 27

$\{ x \mid x < 6 \}$

"The set whose members are all x that satisfy the condition that x is less than six"

page 33

$\overleftrightarrow{RS}$

"Line RS"

page 38

$\overline{XZ}$

"Segment XZ"

page 39

$\overline{AB} \cong \overline{CD}.$

"Segment AB is congruent to segment CD."

page 83

$\{1, 2, 3, 4\} \cap \{2, 4, 6\}$

"The intersection of the set whose members are one, two, three, four and the set whose members are two, four, six"

page 83

$C \cap D = \{2, 4\}.$

"The intersection of C and D equals the set whose members are two, four."

page 87

$\{5, 10\} \cup \{6, 8, 10\}$

"The union of the set whose members are five, ten and the set whose members are six, eight, ten"

page 87

$C \cup D = \{5, 6, 8, 10\}.$

"The union of C and D equals the set whose members are five, six, eight, ten."

page 91

$x + 3 > 7 \wedge 6 + x < 14.$

"x plus three is greater than seven and six plus x is less than fourteen."

page 91

$\{x \mid x+3>7\} \cap \{x \mid 6+x<14\}$

"The intersection of
the solution set of
$x+3>7$ and
the solution set of
$6+x<14$"

page 104

$\overleftrightarrow{AB}$

"Ray
AB"

page 105

$\angle ABC$

"Angle
ABC"

page 109

$\triangle ABC$

"Triangle
ABC"

page 123

(Paris, Spain)

"The ordered pair
whose first component
is Paris and
whose second component
is Spain"

page 124

(1, 2)

"The ordered pair
one, two"

page 127

$A \times B$

"A
cross
B"

page 128

(a, b)

"The ordered pair
a, b"

page 138

$\{(x, y) \mid x > y\}$

"The set whose
members are
all ordered pairs
x, y
that satisfy the
condition that
x is greater
than y"

page 139

point (1, 4)

"Point
1, 4"

page 169

$(2, 7) \sim (4, 14).$

"The ordered pair
two, seven
is equivalent to
the ordered pair
four, fourteen."

page 174

$1/15 \sim 2/30.$

"One to
fifteen
is equivalent to
two to thirty."

page 174

{ 4/7, . . . }

"The set whose members
are
the rate pair 4/7 and
all rate pairs equivalent
to 4/7"

page 175

$\{(x, y) \mid x/y \sim 4/7\}$

"The set whose
members are
the ordered
pairs x, y
that satisfy
the condition that
x to y
is equivalent to
four to seven"

page 187

88 %

"Eighty-eight
per cent"

page 216

1033_{four}

"one zero three three,
base four"

page 227

10^2

"The second power
of ten"

page 238

256, 193, 462, 109

"256 billion
193 million
462 thousand
109"

Answers to ? exercises

Answers to ? exercises are keyed to your book by page number and exercise letter. For example, the answer for exercise O on page 6 is labelled **6 O**. When an exercise includes two or more questions, the answers to these questions are separated by an asterisk (*).

6 O No * The sentence in D3 does not tell you who has a birthday in September. Sentence A in D4 tells you that Richard has a birthday in September.

7 F No. You obtain a different sentence that expresses the same false idea.

11 B The set of odd numbers from 1 through 9

13 E There are many sentences that express the same idea as each of the sentences in D1. Examples are: "Three is less than 4" and "III is less than four."

14 G The idea expressed by a closed sentence is either true or false. The idea expressed by an open sentence is a requirement that is neither true nor false.

17 H No * $3y = 12$ is a condition, not a statement, and therefore cannot be an equation. * Yes * $3(4) = 12$ is a true statement that includes the idea of equality and therefore is an equation.

18 P Yes * Since only members of the universe are used as replacements for the variable in a condition, each member of the solution set must also be a member of the universe.

19 E Yes. {7, 9, 11} and {9, 11, 7} have exactly the same members. * Yes. R and T are different names for the same set.

19 F Yes * S and T are different names for the same set. In the tabulation {13, 14, 15, 13}, a name for the number thirteen is listed twice but the members of {13, 14, 15, 13} are exactly the same as the members of {13, 14, 15}.

21 M Nine * No. None of the statements obtained includes the idea of equality. * No. The condition does not include the idea of equality.

23 I 2,000,000

23 L No. For any natural number that you name, you can name another natural number that is greater. * There is no end to the list of names of the members in the set of natural numbers.

23 P No * If you could, there would be a greatest natural number, but you know that there is no greatest natural number. There are more members in the set of natural numbers than any natural number you can name.

25 D Yes * Yes. When each member of one set is also a member of a second set, the first set is a subset of the second set.

25 E Yes * Yes * Yes When one set is a subset of a second set and the second set is also a subset of the first set, the two sets are the same set.

29 C If your pencil is sharp enough, you can place many dots between any two dots. There would be even more points between any two points represented by the dots you make.

29 D Think of the set of points between two given points. Picture E represents such a set. There is no end to the number of points in this set. Therefore picture E represents an infinite set of points.

30 N Space is an infinite set of points because you cannot use a natural number to tell how many points there are in space.

31 H No * Since a line extends endlessly in opposite directions you cannot say one line is longer than another line. * Line b contains different points from line c.

32 M Yes * You can picture as many lines as you want included in a plane.

32 N Yes. Even with a pencil having the sharpest tip possible, you cannot represent all the lines included in a plane.

33 D Yes * Think of making sketches of lines that contain C. You can make sketches of lines as close together as possible and there are still many lines containing C that you have not represented.

33 E No * There are many planes that contain C, so all the lines that contain C would not be included in one plane.

33 H Yes. D3 represents only 4 of the geometric figures, each of which contains E and F. It is impossible to make sketches of all the geometric figures that contain E and F.

34 P Yes * Since any two points determine a line, you know that two points are always contained in the same line.

34 D Yes. If the stick is straight, it will touch the board all along its length.

34 F Yes. Since each point in $\overleftrightarrow{AC}$ is also in the plane, $\overleftrightarrow{AC}$ is a subset of the plane. * Yes. $\overleftrightarrow{CB}$ is the same line as $\overleftrightarrow{AC}$.

35 B Yes * Points A and B are in the plane suggested by the surface of the book cover. Since $\overleftrightarrow{AB}$ contains two points of this plane, $\overleftrightarrow{AB}$ is included in the plane.

35 D No * The book could have more leaves to suggest other planes that include $\overleftrightarrow{AB}$.

35 E Yes * No matter how many leaves the book had, they could not suggest all the planes that include $\overleftrightarrow{AB}$.

35 K Yes * Points A, B, and D are noncollinear points. Two of these points determine a line and the third point is not in the line. There is exactly one plane that includes a given line and contains a point not in the line. * Yes * Points A, B, and E are also noncollinear and are contained in exactly one plane.

35 L Yes * Two of the points determine a line that does not contain the third point. Only one plane includes this line and contains the third point. * No

38 T The property that for any two points, there is at least one point between them. Suppose that the two given points are A and B. The property states that there is at least one point between A and B. You can name this point C. Now you can locate at least two more points between A and B. One of these points is between A and C and the other point is between C and B. You can keep on locating points between A and B in this same way.

39 G Yes * Each member of $\overline{XW}$ is also a member of $\overleftrightarrow{XW}$.

39 C No * No * $\overline{AB}$ and $\overline{GH}$ do not contain the same points and therefore are not the same. Since equality means "the same as," $\overline{AB} = \overline{GH}$ is not a true statement.

41 F Yes. Since every plane extends endlessly, each plane separates space into two sets of points, or half-spaces.

42 M Yes. Since every line extends endlessly in opposite directions, each line included in a plane separates the plane into two half-planes.

42 S Yes * Yes * Yes * Yes. Each point in a line is the boundary of two half-lines.

42 T Yes * H is not between I and J.

43 J No * No * If a segment is less than another segment, the first segment cannot also be the same size or greater than the second segment.

46 J No * Any point that satisfies $\overline{AX} < \overline{AB}$ determines a segment that is less than $\overline{AB}$, while any point that satisfies $\overline{AX} \cong \overline{AB}$ determines a segment that is the same size as $\overline{AB}$. * No * Any point that satisfies $\overline{AX} > \overline{AB}$ determines a segment that is greater than $\overline{AB}$, and this point cannot also determine a segment that is the same size as $\overline{AB}$.

46 N Yes * Point B * Yes. B satisfies $\overline{AX} \cong \overline{AB}$.

46 P Yes. Each point in a circle together with the centre of the circle determines a radius of the circle. * Since a circle contains infinitely many points and each of these points together with the centre determines a radius, a circle has infinitely many radii.

47 K Both endpoints of a chord are in the circle and only one endpoint of a radius is in the circle.

47 N A sphere. There would be infinitely many radii in infinitely many planes. The endpoints of all these radii in all the planes would determine a sphere.

47 A Yes * Three points must be either collinear or noncollinear. You already know that three noncollinear points determine a plane. You also know that if three points are collinear, they are contained in the same line, and that a plane that contains two of the points must contain the third point. Since the three points are in the same plane, they are coplanar points.

47 B In your sketch, one of the dots should not be in the picture of the plane. Your sketch should be similar to the one below.

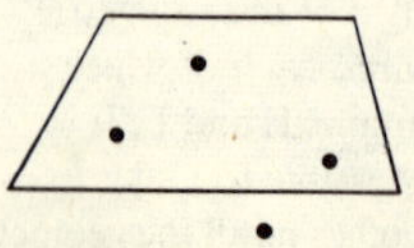

48 I Circle R is the solution set of $\overline{RX} \cong \overline{RS}$ and the interior of circle R is the solution set of $\overline{RX} < \overline{RS}$.

48 M Circle R is the solution set of $\overline{RX} \cong \overline{RS}$ and the exterior of circle R is the solution set of $\overline{RX} > \overline{RS}$.

51 M No. Points to the right of point 26 are associated with natural numbers that are greater than 26. The condition $x < 26$ requires that each member of $\{x \mid x < 26\}$ be less than 26. * Yes. Points to the left of point 26 are associated with natural numbers that are less than 26.

53 Q The graph shown in D14 could be the graph of the solution set of infinitely many conditions. Some examples of these conditions are: $x > 3$, $x + 1 > 4$, and $x + 16 > 19$.

57 L No

57 Q No

62 B Because both $15 - n$ and 9 are equal to the number of quarters Sue had left.

62 D Because both $x + 5$ and 39 are equal to the number of coins George had after Joe gave him the 5 coins.

66 C Conditions for inequality * In lesson 17 you made conditions for equality for the problems.

69 F An example of a problem that can be solved by using the condition $15 + n = 27$ is: Bill had 15 model cars. After he made some more, he had 27 model cars. How many more model cars did Bill make?

70 K An example of a problem that can be solved by using the condition $x + 8 = 17$ is: After Mrs. Morgan bought 8 more hamburger buns, she had 17 hamburger buns in all. How many hamburger buns did she have before she bought the 8?

70 Q An example of a problem that can be solved by using the condition $n - 9 = 15$ is: Dick spent 9 cents of his money and then had 15 cents left. How much money did Dick have before he spent the 9 cents?

71 V An example of a problem that can be solved by using the condition $32 - n = 13$ is: Helen had 32 magazines. She gave some of these magazines to her sister and then had 13 magazines left. How many magazines did Helen give to her sister?

71 I An example of a problem that can be solved by using $18 + 24 = w$ is: Jane made 18 cupcakes in the morning and 24 cupcakes in the afternoon. How many cupcakes did she make altogether?

72 P An example of a problem that can be solved using $237 - 49 = n$ is: Mary is reading a book that has 237 pages. She has read 49 pages. How many pages does she have left to read before she finishes the book?

75 S The additional information given for problem C is different from the additional information given for problem D.

82 F Sets A and B were used to find members for the set {Peru, Chile}. The members of {Peru, Chile} are the only countries that belong to both set A and set B.

83 L Yes * The intersection of D and C is {2, 4} because 2 and 4 are the only objects that belong to both D and C. You already know that the intersection of C and D is {2, 4}. * Yes * Since $D \cap C$ and $C \cap D$ have the same members, they are equal sets, and $C \cap D = D \cap C$ is a true statement.

83 N No * No * 5 is a member of F but not E. 10 is a member of E but not F. The intersection of E and F contains those objects, and only those objects, that are members of both set E and set F.

85 I Their intersection is the empty set because disjoint sets have no common members.

85 O Their intersection is not the empty set because sets that meet have some common members.

86 V If one set is a subset of a second set, the intersection of the two sets is the first set.

86 W The intersection of a set with itself is the set itself. * The common members of a set and itself are all the members of the set.

86 X Yes * Since each member of the intersection of two sets is also a member of each of the two sets, you know that the intersection of two sets is a subset of each of the two sets. If the intersection of two sets is the empty set, however, the intersection is also a subset of both sets, since the empty set is a subset of every set.

86 Y The empty set * A set and the empty set have no common members and therefore have no members in their intersection.

86 E Sets S and M were used to furnish the members for this set. Each teacher who is a member of either S or M, or of both S and M, is a member of {Mr. Adams, Miss Evans, Mr. Wilson, Mr. Cox}.

87 N Yes * The union of D and C is {5, 6, 8, 10}. You already know that the union of C and D is {5, 6, 8, 10}. * Yes * Since $D \cup C$ and $C \cup D$ have the same members, they are equal sets. Therefore, $C \cup D = D \cup C$ is a true statement.

88 Q No * 6 does not belong to either E or F. * Yes * 0 belongs to E. * Yes * 11 belongs to F. The union of E and F contains those objects, and only those, that belong to either set E or set F or to both set E and set F.

88 Z $K \cap L = \{4, 5, 6, \ldots, 10\}$. * Yes * You know that $K \cup L = \{0, 1, 2, \ldots\}$. Therefore, each member of $K \cap L$ is also a member of $K \cup L$.

89 O Yes * Set A contains all the cities that are in either A or B, or in both A and B. A does not contain any other members, so set A is the union of sets A and B.

89 R Their union is the second set.

89 S Yes * Since each member of A is also a member of $A \cup B$, A is a subset of $A \cup B$. * Yes * Since each member of B is also a member of $A \cup B$, B is a subset of $A \cup B$. * Yes * Since each member of $A \cap B$ is also a member of $A \cup B$, $A \cap B$ is a subset of $A \cup B$.

89 T The given set * The given set contains all the members that are in the given set or the empty set, or both the given set and the empty set.

89 U The set itself * You know that the union of two sets contains only those members that are in either set, or in both sets. You also know that the union of two sets must contain all the members of each set. Therefore, the union of a set with itself must be the set itself.

89 V Each of the sets must be the empty set. If one of the sets had at least one member, the union of the two sets would have at least one member.

89 W The two sets are the same set. Both the union and the intersection of a set with itself are the set itself. So, if the union of two sets is the same as the intersection of these two sets, they must be the same set.

91 H Yes * $\{x \mid x+3>7\} = \{5, 6, 7, \ldots\}$. $\{x \mid 6+x<14\} = \{0, 1, 2, \ldots, 7\}$. 5, 6, and 7 are the only numbers that belong to both $\{x \mid x+3>7\}$ and $\{x \mid 6+x<14\}$. Therefore, {5, 6, 7} is the intersection of $\{x \mid x+3>7\}$ and $\{x \mid 6+x<14\}$.

92 I Yes * They contain exactly the same members.

92 P The intersection of the solution sets of two simple conditions contains those members, and only those members, that satisfy both simple conditions. You know that the solution set of a compound condition that includes "and" also contains those

Answers to ? page 100

members, and only those members, that satisfy both simple conditions. Therefore, the solution set of the compound condition and the intersection of the solution sets of the simple conditions are the same.

93 G In D11, the dots in the graph of $\{x \mid x<9\}$ are encircled. The dots in the graph $\{x \mid x<9 \wedge x+2<8\}$ are some of these encircled dots. In the Venn diagram you made for exercise E, the picture of a circle that represents $\{x \mid x<9 \wedge x+2<8\}$ should be in the interior of the picture of a circle that represents $\{x \mid x<9\}$. * In D11, all the dots that are enclosed by squares are also encircled. In the Venn diagram, the picture of a circle that represents $\{x \mid x+2<8\}$ also represents $\{x \mid x<9 \wedge x+2<8\}$.

95 F No * Each member of $\{x \mid x+6>12\}$ does not satisfy the other simple condition for the problem.

95 I The intersection, since it contains only those members that belong to both sets.

100 L One. There is exactly one plane that contains three noncollinear points. * If E were a member of both plane ABD and plane ABC, then two planes would contain the three noncollinear points A, B, and E.

100 M Since the two planes have common members, the planes must intersect. Two planes are parallel only if they have no common members. *

Answers to ? page 100

You know that the intersection of two planes that meet is a line. Since three points are in the intersection of the two planes, the points must be members of the same line.

100 N Since planes FGH and EGH have points G and H in common, points G and H are in the intersection of planes FGH and EGH. Therefore, the intersection of plane FGH and plane EGH is line GH.

101 C Points L and N are contained in ℓ_3. Since ℓ_3 contains two points of plane LMN it is included in the plane * ℓ_3

101 G No * You do not know whether or not $\overleftrightarrow{AB}$ and $\overleftrightarrow{CD}$ are included in the same plane. $\overleftrightarrow{AB}$ and $\overleftrightarrow{CD}$ are parallel only if they are included in the same plane.

102 I ℓ_4 and ℓ_5 are not included in one plane and are skew lines. Their intersection is the empty set.

102 J ℓ_6 and ℓ_7 are included in the same plane and are parallel.

102 P One. If two lines intersect, the lines are included in the same plane.

104 C The set of points that contains A and all the points in the line to the left of A

105 I $\overrightarrow{QP}$ is the set of points consisting of Q and all points in ℓ_1 to the left of Q.

105 K No * They have different endpoints and extend in opposite directions.

105 E Yes. The vertex of an angle together with a point in each side of the angle are three noncollinear points. Any three noncollinear points are contained in the same plane. * Yes

105 F No * The sides of an angle are rays, and a ray extends endlessly in one direction, so you cannot say that one side of an angle is longer than the other side. No * For the same reason, it is not sensible to say that one angle has longer sides than another angle.

107 G ∠GHI ≅ ∠MNO is a true statement because congruent angles are the same size. If two angles are the same size as a third angle, then the two angles must also be the same size.

107 J The sketches below illustrate how the picture of either one of the sides of ∠MNO may be extended to make a sketch of the supplement of ∠MNO. * Yes. A right angle is congruent to its supplement.

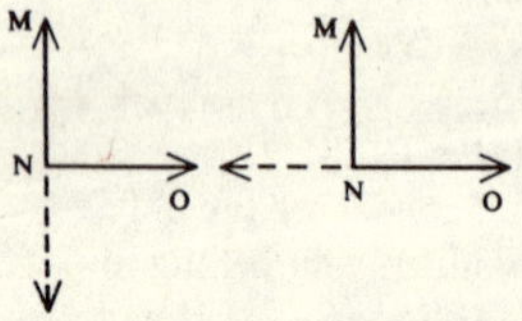

109 B Yes * The union of these three sets contains all the points that belong to each of the three sets.

109 E No * There is exactly one plane that contains three noncollinear points. Therefore, the vertices of a triangle are contained in one plane. Since a line that contains two points of a plane is included in that plane, the sides of a triangle are included in the plane determined by the vertices.

109 G No * The sides of ∠ABC contain points that are not members of the sides of △ABC.

110 G Yes * A triangle that has three congruent sides must have two congruent sides.

110 H Yes * Since each member of the set of equilateral triangles is also a member of the set of isosceles triangles, the set of all equilateral triangles is a subset of the set of all isosceles triangles.

110 I No * Isosceles triangles have only two congruent sides and are not members of the set of all equilateral triangles.

110 N Any figure that has more than one right angle cannot be a triangle.

111 O A right triangle may be an isosceles triangle. * A right triangle cannot be an equilateral triangle.

111 P See the diagram below that is to be made for both this exercise and for exercise Q. * A ∩ B is the set of all equilateral triangles and is a subset of set A.

111 Q See the diagram below. * B ∩ C is the empty set.

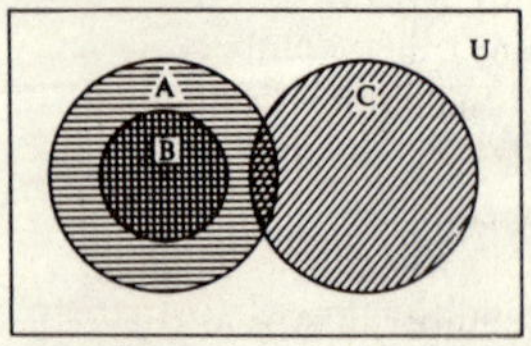

111 R C ∩ D is the set of all scalene triangles having one right angle. Sets C and D meet.

111 F The drawing below may be used to illustrate that the three sides of one triangle need not be congruent to the three sides of the other even though three angles of one are congruent to three angles of the other.

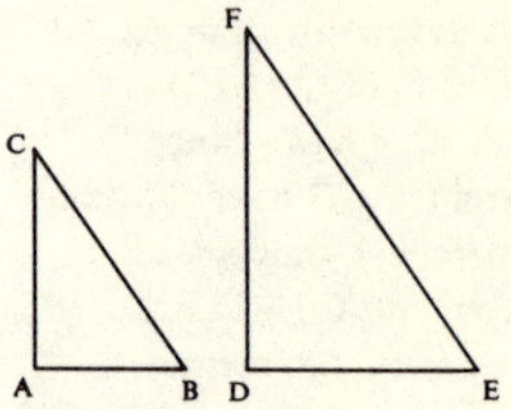

∠ABC ≅ ∠DEF.
∠ACB ≅ ∠DFE.
∠CAB ≅ ∠FDE.

111 G The three angles of one triangle would be congruent to the three angles of the other triangle if three sides of one are congruent to three sides of the other.

113 K By the portion of the sketch that has pictures of both horizontal and vertical lines

114 M The intersection contains one point since there is a point in one of the sides of the angle that is between C and D.

114 R The intersection contains one point since there is a point in one of the sides of the triangle that is between M and N.

115 D Two. The simple closed curve is the boundary of each of these regions.

115 E It is not a simple closed curve or an angle, because each of these figures separates the plane into two regions.

115 F The intersection contains at least one point since there is at least one point in the simple closed curve that is between the two points.

122 C No * The sentence in D2 is an open sentence. An open sentence expresses

a condition, not a statement. A condition is neither true nor false.

123 R The symbol (Paris, Norway) is read "The ordered pair whose first component is Paris and whose second component is Norway." The symbol {Paris, Norway} is read "The set whose members are Paris, Norway." * (Paris, Norway) is an ordered pair while {Paris, Norway} is a set having two members.

124 H $x + x = 4$ has one variable. $x + y = 4$ has two variables. * $x + x = 4$ requires you to find a number which added to itself equals 4. $x + y = 4$ requires you to find any two numbers whose sum is 4.

127 F By finding the product of the number of members in set M and the number of members in set N

127 G No * The first component of (June, Thanksgiving) is a member of B and the second component is a member of A. * Yes * (June, Thanksgiving) is a member of $B \times A$, not of $A \times B$. No * Since A and B are different sets, the first components of the members of $A \times B$ are different from the first components of the members of $B \times A$. The same is true for the second components.

128 L Yes * Each member of the solution set of "a is a holiday in b" is also a member of the universe for (a, b).

129 Q The members of set S. Since y is the first component of (y, x), you must use the first components of members of $S \times T$ as replacements for y. * The members of set T. Since x is the second component of (y, x), you must use the second components of members of $S \times T$ as replacements for x.

129 A One possible diagram is shown below.

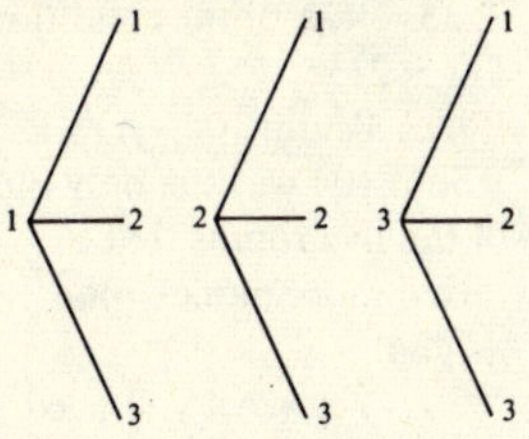

129 E The universe is given for (m, n). m is the first component of (m, n) and must be replaced by the first component of (1, 3). n is the second component of (m, n) and must be replaced by the second component of (1, 3).

131 G Yes * Yes * (1, 0)

132 N Yes * Each dot in the graph of the solution set of $x + 2 < y$ is also in the graph of $A \times B$.

133 L Yes * The solution set of $y + 3 = x$ is {(3, 0)}. The encircled dot in the graph in D8 represents the point that is associated with (3, 0).

134 C The universe is a set of numbers, not a set of ordered pairs of numbers.

134 G The universe, $A \times A$, is given for (x, y), so the first components of the members of $A \times A$ may be used as replacements for x.

136 C No * Since no member of the set tabulated in exercise A satisfies $x < y$, the set cannot be the solution set of $x < y$. * Yes * The set tabulated in exercise A contains all the members of the universe that satisfy $x > y$, so this set is the solution set of $x > y$.

136 F There are many conditions that have {(0, 2), (1, 3), (2, 4), (3, 5)} as a solution set. Some examples of these conditions are $x + 2 = y$, $x + 3 = y + 1$, $y - 2 = x$.

138 C The condition $x > y$ * $\{(x, y) | x > y\}$ contains all the members of the universe, and only those members of the universe, that satisfy $x > y$.

139 C Yes * Both components of each member of $N \times N$ are natural numbers. Each ordered pair whose components are natural numbers is a member of $N \times N$.

139 D Yes * Since N is an infinite set, then the Cartesian set of N must also be infinite.

140 B Yes * Since the graph of the solution set is a subset of the universe, the graph of the universe includes a graph of the solution set.

141 P To make a graph of the solution set of $x + y < 4$, use all the dots below those in the solution set of $x + y = 4$. * To make a graph of the solution set of $x + y > 4$, use all the dots above or to the right of the dots in the graph of the solution set of $x + y = 4$.

144 L If you replaced x by 5, you would obtain the condition $5 + y = 4$. There is no member of B that satisfies this condition. If you replaced x by 6, you would obtain the condition $6 + y = 4$. There is no member of B that satisfies this condition.

Answers to ? page 148

144 C If a number greater than 3 is used as a replacement for x in $x + y < 4$, no member of B will satisfy the condition obtained.

145 F No * For each replacement of r by a natural number, there is a replacement for s that satisfies the condition obtained. Therefore, the solution set of $s = 2r + 1$ is an infinite set.

145 L $s > 2r + 1$. * One possible chart is shown below.

r	0	1	2	3	4
s	2	4	6	8	10
	3	5	7	9	
	4	6	8	10	
	5	7	9		
	6	8	10		
	7	9			
	8	10			
	9				
	10				

147 C The universe is a set of ordered pairs.

148 J Yes. $\{(x, y) | x + y = 6 \wedge y = 2x\}$ contains all the members of the universe that satisfy both $x + y = 6$ and $y = 2x$. The intersection of $\{(x, y) | x + y = 6\}$ and $\{(x, y) | y = 2x\}$ also contains all the members of the universe that satisfy both $x + y = 6$ and $y = 2x$.

148 Q $\{(x,y) | x + y < 7\} \cap \{(x,y) | y > x\}$ contains only those members of the universe that belong to both $\{(x,y) | x + y < 7\}$ and $\{(x,y) | y > x\}$. These are the same members of the universe that belong to $\{(x,y) | x + y < 7 \wedge y > x\}$.

Answers to ? page 149

149 C Yes. The condition $x + 1 = 4$ makes no requirement about the second component of an ordered pair. * Yes

149 J Yes. The condition $y + 1 < 7$ makes no requirement about the first component of an ordered pair.

159 K Each solution of the compound condition must satisfy both of the simple conditions. If a number less than 5 is used to replace a in $a - 5 = b$, the condition obtained cannot be satisfied by a member of N. For example, if a is replaced by 4, the condition obtained is $4 - 5 = b$. There is no member of N that satisfies $4 - 5 = b$.

168 J No * There are infinitely many ordered pairs that represent the rate at which the pencils are sold. Examples of other ordered pairs that represent this rate are (5, 20), (10, 40), (20, 80).

169 A No * To decide if (a,b) and (c,d) are equivalent ordered pairs, you must know what the replacements for the variables are.

170 Q Yes * Any ordered pair is equivalent, as well as equal, to itself. For example: you know that (2, 4) is equivalent to (2, 4) because $2 \times 4 = 2 \times 4$.

171 O Yes. The product of 6 and the second component of each ordered pair will be equal to the product of the first component of the ordered pair and 8.

174 G Each member of a proportional relation is equivalent to each of the other members. If you know one member, you can tell which rate pairs are members of the proportional relation and which are not members.

175 I Yes * 4/7 is a member of the proportional relation {8/14, . . .}, and each member of a proportional relation is equivalent to each of the other members. * Yes * Since 8/14 and 4/7 are equivalent rate pairs, {8/14, . . .} and {4/7, . . .} are the same proportional relation. * Yes * Since 100/175 and 4/7 are equivalent rate pairs, {100/175, . . .} and {4/7, . . .} are the same proportional relation.

175 M Yes. Since 8/14 and 4/7 are equivalent rate pairs, $\{(x,y) \mid x/y \sim 8/14\}$ and $\{(x,y) \mid x/y \sim 4/7\}$ are the same proportional relation.

176 B The first component of 16/8 refers to the number of plants. Since 4 is the number of plants for which you want to find the cost, 4 must be the first component of the rate pair you are to find.

178 O {2} * {2} * Yes. The two sets contain the same member.

178 G 10/32 * $10/32 \sim 15/48$.

182 L Both of the rate pairs 20/60 and 60/20 represent the rate at which cars can be washed. If you think of the rate pair 20/60, then $20/60 \sim w/15$ is the condition for the problem. If you think of the rate pair 60/20, then $60/20 \sim 15/w$ is the condition for the problem.

183 M Both of the rate pairs 35/2 and 2/35 represent the rate. If you think of the rate pair 35/2, then you will use either the condition $s/4 \sim 35/2$, or the condition $35/2 \sim s/4$. If you think of the rate pair 2/35, then you will use either the condition $2/35 \sim 4/s$, or the condition $4/s \sim 2/35$.

186 C Room 104 * Yes * Room 104 was the only one of the five rooms that raised more money than its goal.

187 J Yes * All you need to do is compare the first components of the rate pairs that have second components of 100.

188 D No * No * To receive a grade greater than 100%, the first component of the rate pair representing the comparison would have to be greater than the second component. This means that Susan would have had to answer more questions correctly than were on the test, which is impossible.

191 C You know that $x\%$ is the same as $x/100$. Therefore, both "6 is $x\%$ of 10" and $6/10 \sim x/100$ require you to find the first component of a rate pair that has a second component of 100 and that is equivalent to 6/10.

192 I Yes * Yes. "30% of 320 is s" is the same condition as $30/100 \sim s/320$ since both conditions require you to find the first component of a rate pair that has a second component of 320 and that is equivalent to 30/100.

192 R You want to compare the number of tickets Martin sold with the number of tickets June sold. 12/8, not 8/12, represents this comparison.

192 V The second component. The problem asks you to find the first component of a rate pair that has a second component of 32 and that is equivalent to 125/100.

207 H No * Since the same symbol cannot be used more than once in a code numeral, the code system does not have the property of repetition. * No * Since each numeral in a code system consists of just one symbol, addition cannot be used to find the number expressed. Therefore, the code system does not have the property of addition.

207 I Yes. In a code system, a different symbol is used to name each member of {1, 2, 3, . . .}. Since {1, 2, 3, . . .} is an infinite set, an infinite set of symbols must be used to name the members of {1, 2, 3, . . .}.

207 J Yes * A tally system is easier to learn because it has only one symbol which is used again and again. * Yes * In a code system, each number is expressed with just one symbol. A number like 5000 is easier to express in a code system than in a tally system.

208 H No. There are only 9 stars and strokes in all but there are 30 objects in all.

208 J Yes * 14. Since each numeral contains 3 stars and 2 strokes, they name the same number. The arrangement of the

stars and strokes in the numeral does not matter.
209 P Since you are using a base of four, you must group by 4's. The new group contains 4 groups of 4 groups of 4.
210 V You must know what number is expressed by each symbol.
212 E You must be able to tell which strokes express the number 1 and which strokes express the number 3.
212 L Yes * By distributing the six strokes in the four spaces in two different ways
212 M You could leave an open space to separate the strokes in one position from those in another position. Numeral E in D3 could be written / // / //.
213 N No * The symbols in the numeral could be rearranged in any order, but the numeral would still express the same number.
213 D The numbers expressed by the symbols in the numeral are different. For example, a stroke in the second space from the right in a base-ten numeral expresses the number 10, while a stroke in the same position in a base-three numeral expresses the number 3.
213 H Three strokes in any space may be replaced by one stroke in the next space to the left.
213 I 9 * Ten strokes in any space may be replaced by one stroke in the next space to the left.
214 U The greatest number of strokes needed in a space is one less than the base.
215 J 1 is the fourth digit from the right, not the third digit from the right.
217 I Think of a base-ten numeration system that uses strokes. The most strokes you need in any space is 9. This means that you need 10 different digits to express the numbers 0 through 9. * In a base-four system, you need 4 different digits to express the numbers 0 through 3.
217 E No * Ordinarily, you use only the digits from 0 through 9. There is no single digit that expresses the number 10.
218 L Since there is exactly one digit in each position in numeral D, you can determine what position a digit is in without using a chart.
220 L The decimal numeration system requires fewer symbols to name most numbers than the Egyptian numeration system requires. For example, the decimal numeral 1607 has four symbols, while numeral I in D3 has 14 symbols. There are some exceptions, of course. The Egyptian numeral for 1,000,000, for example, has only one symbol, while the decimal numeral has seven.
221 N No. It is true that XC and CX express different numbers, so position makes some difference; but in most cases, the symbols can be in any order. * No. For example, in the numeral XXX, each of the X's expresses the number 10.
221 O If a symbol that expresses a lesser number is written to the left of a symbol that expresses a greater number, you subtract the lesser number from the greater. If a symbol that expresses a lesser number is written to the right of a symbol that expresses a greater number, you add the lesser number to the greater. To find the number expressed by XCIII, you subtract 10 from 100 and then add 3 to the difference. To find the number expressed by CXIII, you add 100, 10, and 3.
222 W The arrangement of the symbols is important in XCVII and XLV. The symbol X must remain on the left of C to show that 10 is subtracted from 100. Similarly, the symbol X must remain on the left of L to show that 10 is subtracted from 50.
222 X The decimal system is more convenient than the Roman system. * Fewer symbols are necessary to express most numbers in the decimal system than in the Roman system. The use of subtraction and a mixed base makes Roman numerals more difficult to understand than decimal numerals.
223 I Yes * In the Babylonian numeration system, the position of each symbol in a numeral determined the number expressed by the symbol.
223 O Yes * Numeral J, because fewer symbols are used than in numeral I.
223 P The decimal numeration system is more convenient because it has only one base and more code symbols. For example to express each of the numbers from 2 through 9 in the decimal system, you use only one symbol while in the Babylonian system you would use more than one symbol for each of the numbers from 2 through 9.
226 N Yes. You know that if you choose any member of {1, 2, 3, . . .} and multiply this number by 1, the product will be the number you chose.
226 O Yes * Yes. Since the product of 1 and the number you chose is the number, both 1 and the number are factors of the number.
227 N Yes * Yes
227 T Yes * If you replace *n* by 1, a true statement is obtained because the first power of any number is the number. If you replace *n* by any other counting number, a true statement is obtained because, no matter how many times 1 is used as a factor, the product is always 1.
232 V $285 \div 144 = 1$, remainder 141. $141 \div 12 = 11$, remainder 9. $285 = 1£9_{twelve}$.
232 W Yes. You know that both the numerals 346_{nine} and $1£9_{twelve}$ express the number 285.
236 M 0 and 1 are the only digits used in the base-two numeration system.
240 G 3000 * 3000 * 3×10^3 * 3 is a number from 1 to 10, and 10^3 is a power of 10. 30×10^3 is not in scientific notation because 30 is not a number from 1 to 10.

Index

In this index, the numerals in heavy type refer to your glossary of mathematical terms. The glossary includes the dictionary-type definitions expressed in red boxes throughout the text.

2 3 4 5 6 7 8 9 10 11 12 13 14 15 16 17 18 19 20 21 22 23 24 25 R 70 69 68 67 66 65 64 63